SYMMETRY AND MAGNETISM

SERIES OF MONOGRAPHS ON SELECTED TOPICS IN SOLID STATE PHYSICS

Editor: E. P. WOHLFARTH

Symmetry and Magnetism

BY

ROBERT R. BIRSS

Senior Lecturer in Physics
University of Sussex, Brighton

Second Edition

1966

NORTH-HOLLAND PUBLISHING COMPANY – AMSTERDAM

First edition 1964

Second edition 1966

PUBLISHERS:

NORTH-HOLLAND PUBLISHING CO. – AMSTERDAM

SOLE DISTRIBUTORS FOR U.S.A. AND CANADA:

INTERSCIENCE PUBLISHERS, a division of

JOHN WILEY & SONS, INC. – NEW YORK

PRINTED IN THE NETHERLANDS

EDITOR'S PREFACE

The third volume of this series is concerned with a subject that appears at first sight rather abstract but which has, in fact, exceedingly wide practical applications when the properties of magnetic crystals are being considered. Here the presence of spin ordering introduces symmetry additional to that specified by the usual geometrical description of non-magnetic substances provided by classical crystallography. Dr. R. R. Birss develops the concepts of symmetry from first principles and discusses the connection between symmetry and magnetism on a fully rigorous basis. The book cannot in any sense be regarded as 'easy', but a careful study of this branch of mathematical physics will prove to be rewarding for all those interested in magnetism or solid state physics in general.

Most of the mathematical development of this subject was pioneered by Soviet theoretical physicists, and many of their publications are referred to throughout this book. It seems appropriate, therefore, to pay tribute to their initial and continuing endeavours by the publication, in English, of a monograph devoted to a subject in which Soviet science has been so eminent.

E. P. WOHLFARTH

PREFACE TO THE FIRST EDITION

All scientists use symmetry arguments in one form or another, often without feeling any pressing need to formalize them. A useful measure of simplification can often be achieved merely by recognizing that two aspects are identical, that a situation looks exactly the same when viewed from two different directions. However, in dealing with crystals – and the majority of solids are crystalline – it is important to formulate the physical properties of crystals in a systematic tensor notation, if the maximum amount of simplification is to be obtained by the use of symmetry arguments.

The purpose of this book is to explain how the symmetry of magnetic and non-magnetic crystals is specified and how such specifications can be used to simplify the forms of tensors characterizing the (steady-state) macroscopic physical properties of crystals: the book is not concerned with the explanation of these properties in terms of microscopic structure. The application of symmetry arguments to non-magnetic crystals is, of course, not new (there is an excellent account in J. F. Nye's textbook 'Physical Properties of Crystals') but the emphasis in the present work is on magnetic properties and magnetic crystals, and much of the material presented here derives from recent work – mainly in the U.S.S.R. – on magnetic symmetry groups.

Throughout the book, the term 'magnetic crystals' is understood to mean crystals that exhibit ordered arrays of (spin) magnetic moments. It therefore includes, as an important class, antiferromagnetic crystals, as well as the more obviously magnetic materials such as the ferromagnetic metals iron and nickel or the ferrimagnetic ferrites and garnets.

Because physical crystals possess planes, axes and centres of symmetry, they may be allocated to one of 32 crystal classes. Further sub-divisions of these classes are obtained, however, when translational symmetry is taken into account (by including the possibility of screw axes and glide planes). The total number of possible spatial symmetries so obtained is 230, since only 230 distinguishable patterns may be formed in three dimensions by the periodic repetition of an – asymmetric – object as a motif. Because the 230 spatial symmetries are derived from 230 three-dimensional patterns, the statement that a crystal may be allocated to one of them is essentially a geometrical description – it is a statement about the geometry of the crystal when its component parts are considered to be not in motion but at rest in average positions. For many crystals such a statement is a satisfactory description of the symmetry of the crystal, that is of the mutual relation of its constituent atoms in respect of type and position. However, a ferromagnetic, ferrimagnetic or antiferromagnetic crystal exhibits, in addition, an orderly distribution of (spin) magnetic moments and the directions assumed by these moments constitute a repetitive feature that is not included in a geometrical description of the crystal.

It is in this respect that the geometrical description afforded by classical crystallography may be inadequate in providing a faithful representation of the physical crystal, and the physical properties of these magnetic crystals are therefore not necessarily characterized completely by allocating them to one of the 230 spatial symmetries. For example, X-ray or electron diffraction may reveal that a certain rotation of the crystal will bring similar atoms into coincidence, but, when the distribution of spins has been established (e.g. by neutron diffraction), it may transpire that this rotation does not bring the spins into coincidence. The classical 230 spatial symmetries give rise to 230 non-magnetic symmetries that are sufficient to describe diamagnetic and paramagnetic crystals, which do not exhibit ordered arrays of magnetic moments, but it is to be expected that further magnetic symmetries will be needed to describe magnetic crystals.

It is only comparatively recently that these magnetic symmetries were discovered by pursuing the analogy with patterns in three dimensions in a manner pioneered by A. V. Shubnikov in his book 'The Symmetry and Antisymmetry of Finite Figures', published (in Russian) in 1951. Although only 230 three-dimensional patterns can be produced by the periodic repetition of a single object, this number can be greatly increased if the object can exist in two forms which are geometrically equivalent but which may be distinguished from each other on some other basis. If, for example, objects that are coloured black or white but are otherwise identical are used as motifs, the number of distinguishable patterns in three dimensions is increased to 1191. To these 1191 bi-coloured patterns must be added the 230 mono-coloured (black *or* white) patterns, giving a total of 1421 coloured patterns. Just as the 230 uncoloured patterns correspond to the 230 non-magnetic symmetries so the 1421 coloured patterns correspond to 1421 magnetic symmetries. The corresponding numbers of crystallographic classes are 32 non-magnetic classes and $32 + 58 = 90$ magnetic classes. These ideas are developed more fully in the first three chapters of the book. The operation of interchanging black and white motifs represents a change in direction of magnetic moment which, it is shown in Chapter 3, § 1, corresponds to the operation of time-inversion. The appropriate magnetic symmetry is therefore found not solely by a consideration of spatial symmetry but rather by inspecting the symmetry of a crystal in space-time. The following table exhibits the various correspondences between the coloured and uncoloured patterns, the magnetic and non-magnetic symmetries and the magnetic and non-magnetic crystal classes: it also contains some additional information and may usefully be referred to as a summary table at appropriate points in the book.

The extension of the concept of spatial symmetry, considered in the first two chapters, to that of symmetry in space-time is discussed in detail in Ch. 3. The rest of the book is devoted to explaining how, once a classification by space-time symmetry has been achieved, this information may be used to simplify the forms

230 Uncoloured patterns	230 Non-magnetic space groups	32 Non-magnetic point groups, $\mathscr{G}'$, that contain R (the time-inversion operation) as a member. Bold-face type is not used for the Hermann–Mauguin symbols appropriate to these groups	Groups appropriate to diamagnetic and para-magnetic crystals and to some non-pyromagnetic antiferromagnetic crystals
230 Mono-coloured patterns	230 Magnetic space groups (the classical space groups)	32 Magnetic point groups, $\mathscr{G}$, that do not contain R at all (the classical point groups). Bold-face type is used for the Hermann–Mauguin symbols appropriate to these groups	Groups appropriate to ferromagnetic and ferri-magnetic crystals, to pyro-magnetic antiferromag-netic crystals (i.e. those that can exhibit parasitic ferromagnetism) and to some non-pyromagnetic antiferromagnetic crystals
1191 Bi-coloured patterns	1191 Additional magnetic space groups	58 Additional magnetic point groups, $\mathscr{M}$, that contain R only in combination with other symmetry opera-tions. Bold-face type is used for the Hermann–Mauguin symbols appropriate to these groups	

of tensors that represent the magnetic properties of crystals. Macroscopic steady-state properties are considered – not only static properties but dynamic properties, such as transport pheno-mena, where a system is permanently in non-equilibrium but has reached a steady state. Not all magnetic properties are considered in detail. Those that do receive attention are included as illustrative examples of the simplifications imposed by symmetry: it is thought that they are reasonably representative of the various *types* of macroscopic steady-state properties but it must be confessed that the selection has been considerably influenced by the author's previous research interests. In an effort to secure reasonable completeness, some of the sections in Ch. 5 have, perhaps, been made longer than might be thought necessary. However, it is hoped that those who are interested in magnetocrystalline and magnetomechanical properties will find them useful, whilst those who are not will regard them merely as examples that have been treated in more detail, with a consequent increase in the complexity of the formulation.

The author wishes to express his gratitude to many colleagues, particularly Professor M. Blackman, Dr. T. W. B. Kibble and Dr. E. P. Wohlfarth, who have been of considerable assistance in preparing this book, and to thank his father, Mr. R. R. Birss, who was good enough to read the manuscript critically and whose comments and advice have been most helpful. This opportunity is taken of gratefully acknowledging permission being given to quote and reproduce tables and illustrations by many authors and by The Royal Society, The Institute of Physics and The Physical Society, The American Institute of Physics and Messrs. John Wiley and Sons Limited.

ROBERT R. BIRSS

PREFACE TO THE SECOND EDITION

The second edition is occasioned by the rapid disposal of the first and no substantial alterations have been made to the original. However, a number of errors have been eliminated from textual and tabular material and the author wishes to thank those who have been kind enough to suggest amendments or to proffer constructive criticisms.

ROBERT R. BIRSS

CONTENTS

CONTENTS

xiii

CRYSTALLOGRAPHIC REFERENCE TABLES

LIST OF MOST IMPORTANT SYMBOLS

The following list of symbols does not include those used in immediate context with a statement defining them, nor does it include conventional mathematical symbols. When used as superscripts or subscripts the symbols n and m represent integers; the suffixes α and β can assume the values 1 and 2; the suffixes i, j, k, l and p can assume the values 1, 2 and 3 (and 4 in Ch. 3, § 4); the suffix A can assume the values 1, 2, 3, 4, 5 and 6.

B_i	Magnetic induction (or its components) relative to coordinate axes Ox_i
B_n	Fourth-order magnetostriction constants for cubic crystals
B	Magnetic induction (vector, i.e. tensor of first rank)
c	Velocity of electromagnetic waves in vacuo
C_3	Anticlockwise rotation through 120°
C_3^2	Anticlockwise rotation through 240°
C_n	Anticlockwise rotation through $2\pi/n$; second-order magnetostriction constants for cubic crystals
C_{ijkl}	Elastic stiffness constants (tensor of fourth rank)
C_{AB}	Contracted matrix form of the tensor C_{ijkl}
d, d'	General tensor of zero rank, i.e. a scalar
d_i	General tensor of first rank, i.e. a vector, (or its components) relative to coordinate axes Ox_i

d'_i	General tensor of first rank, i.e. a vector, (or its components) relative to coordinate axes Ox'_i
d_{ij}	General tensor of second rank (or its components) relative to coordinate axes Ox_i
d'_{ij}	General tensor of second rank (or its components) relative to coordinate axes Ox'_i
d_{ijkl}	General tensor of fourth rank (or its components) relative to coordinate axes Ox_i
$d_{ijk...n}$	General tensor of arbitrary rank (or its components) relative to coordinate axes Ox_i
$d'_{ijk...n}$	General tensor of arbitrary rank (or its components) relative to coordinate axes Ox'_i
$d_{i_1 i_2...i_m j_1 j_2...j_n}$	General tensor of rank $n + m$ (or its components) representing, relative to coordinate axes Ox_i, a physical property of a crystal
D_i	Dielectric displacement (or its components) relative to coordinate axes Ox_i
D	Dielectric displacement (vector, i.e. tensor of first rank)
e_{ij}	Strain tensor (or its components) relative to the axes Ox_i
e^*_{ij}	e_{ij} appropriate to equilibrium state
$e_{i_1 i_2...i_m}$	General tensor of rank m (or its components) representing, relative to coordinate axes Ox_i, a physical effect produced in a crystal
$E = C_1$	Identity operation
E_i	Electric field intensity (or its components) relative to coordinate axes Ox_i
E'_i	Electric field intensity (or its components) relative to coordinate axes Ox'_i
E_{ij}	Symmetrical strain tensor (or its components) relative to coordinate axes Ox_i

E_{ij}^{*}	E_{ij} appropriate to equilibrium state
E_A	Contracted matrix form of the tensor E_{ij}
E_A^{*}	E_A appropriate to equilibrium state
E	Electric field intensity (vector, i.e. tensor of first rank)
g_{ijkl}	Elastic compliance moduli with signs changed (tensor of fourth rank)
$\mathscr{G}$	Magnetic (classical) point group of symmetry operations
$\mathscr{G}'$	Non-magnetic point group of symmetry operations
$\hbar$	Dirac's constant (Planck's constant divided by 2π)
H_i	Magnetic field intensity (or its components) relative to coordinate axes Ox_i
$\mathscr{H}$	Sub-group of the group $\mathscr{G}$
H	Magnetic field intensity (vector, i.e. tensor of first rank)
i	$\sqrt{(-1)}$
$i_{j_1 j_2 \ldots j_n}$	General tensor of rank n (or its components) representing, relative to coordinate axes Ox_i, a physical influence applied to a crystal
$I_s(T)$	Spontaneous magnetization at temperature T
$I_s(0)$	Spontaneous magnetization at absolute zero
$I_{2n+\frac{1}{2}}(a)$	Bessel function of imaginary argument
I_i	Magnetization (or its components) relative to coordinate axes Ox_i
J_i	Electrical current density (or its components) relative to coordinate axes Ox_i
J_i'	Electrical current density (or its components) relative to coordinate axes Ox_i'
J	Electrical current density (vector, i.e. tensor of first rank)
$k_n, k_{n,m}$	Anisotropy coefficients

K_n	Anisotropy constants
l_{ip}	Cosine of the angle between Ox_i' and Ox_p
$\lvert l \rvert = \lvert l_{ip} \rvert$	Determinant of the coefficients l_{ip}
$L(a)$	Langevin function, i.e. $\coth a - 1/a$
L_n	Magnetoelastic coupling constants
M_n	Magnetoelastic coupling constants
$\mathscr{M}$	Additional magnetic point group of symmetry operations
$\mathscr{M}'$	Magnetic point group of symmetry operations in general
n	n-fold axis of rotation
$\tilde{n}$	n-fold rotation–reflection axis
$\bar{n}$	n-fold rotation–inversion axis
N_n, N_n', N_n''	Magnetoelastic coupling constants
Ox_i	Rectangular cartesian coordinate axes
Ox_i'	Rectangular cartesian coordinate axes identical to Ox_i, with a common origin O, but differing in orientation
$O'x_i'$	Rectangular cartesian coordinate axes identical to Ox_i, the origin, O', of which moves at velocity v relative to O so as to keep $O'x_3'$ parallel to Ox_3
$P_n(\alpha_3) = P_n(\cos \theta)$	Legendre polynomial of degree n
$P_n^m(\cos \theta)$	Associated Legendre function of the first kind of degree n
Q_n	Fourth-order magnetostriction constants for cubic crystals
Q_i	Pyromagnetic tensor, i.e. vector, (or its components) relative to coordinate axes Ox_i
Q_i^*	Pyroelectric tensor, i.e. vector, (or its components) relative to coordinate axes Ox_i
Q_{ij}	Magnetoelectric tensor (or its components) relative to coordinate axes Ox_i

Q_{ijk} — Piezomagnetic tensor (or its components) relative to coordinate axes Ox_l

Q_{iA} — Contracted matrix form of the tensor Q_{ijk}

R — Time-inversion operator

R_n — Second-order magnetostriction constants for hexagonal crystals

$S(\ )$ — Operator denoting the sum of the three quantities obtained by a cyclic permutation of suffixes on the expression within the brackets

S_3 — Rotation through 120° about the axis Ox_3 followed by reflection in a plane normal to that axis

S_3' — Rotation through 240° about the axis Oxo followed by reflection in a plane normal t_3 that axis

S_{ijkl} — Elastic compliance moduli (tensor of fourth rank)

S_{AB} — Contracted matrix form of the tensor $S_{ijk:}$

t — Time

T — Absolute temperature

T_{ij} — Symmetrical stress tensor (or its components) relative to coordinate axes Ox_l

T_A — Contracted matrix form of the tensor T_{ij}

u_i — Components of displacement of arbitrary point defined in undeformed lattice by the coordinates x_l

U — Elastic energy density

U_2^a — Rotation through 180° about axis Oa

U_2^b — Rotation through 180° about axis Ob

U_2^c — Rotation through 180° about axis Oc

V — Magnetic energy density; magnetocrystalline anisotropy energy density

x_i — Rectangular cartesian coordinates for axes Ox_l

x'_i	Rectangular cartesian coordinates for axes Ox'_i or $O'x'_i$
$Y_{n,m}(\theta, \phi)$	Surface spherical harmonics of degree n
z	Suffix indicating direction parallel to axis Ox_3
α_i	Direction cosines of magnetization vector relative to coordinate axes Ox_i
α	Unit vector parallel to magnetization direction
β_i	Direction cosines of measuring direction relative to coordinate axes Ox_i
β	Unit vector parallel to measuring direction
$\bar{\delta}$	Strain associated with appearance of spontaneous magnetization
δ_{ip}	Kronecker delta
ε_{ij}	Dielectric permittivity tensor (or its components) relative to coordinate axes Ox_i
$\zeta = \zeta(T)$	Reduced magnetization $I_s(T)/I_s(0)$
η	Ratio of intensity of bulk magnetization to its saturation value
θ, ϕ, ψ	Euler angles
λ	Spontaneous magnetostriction
$\lambda_{\alpha\beta}$	Components of transformation matrix representing, for spinors, a particular rotation of the spatial coordinate axes
$[\lambda_{\alpha\beta}]$	Matrix with components $\lambda_{\alpha\beta}$
μ_{ij}	Magnetic permeability tensor (or its components) relative to coordinate axes Ox_i
ϱ	Resistivity; electrical charge density
ϱ_{ij}	Resistivity tensor (or its components) relative to coordinate axes Ox_i
ϱ'_{ij}	Resistivity tensor (or its components) relative to coordinate axes Ox'_i
$[\varrho_{ij}]$	Matrix representation of the tensor ϱ_{ij}
σ	Symmetry matrix

$\sigma^{(n)}$	Particular symmetry matrix
σ^a	Reflection through line Oa, fixed in space
σ^b	Reflection through line Ob, fixed in space
σ^c	Reflection through line Oc, fixed in space
σ_v^a	Reflection in plane containing line Oa and axis Ox_3
σ_v^b	Reflection in plane containing line Ob and axis Ox_3
σ_v^c	Reflection in plane containing line Oc and axis Ox_3
σ_h	Reflection in a plane normal to axis Ox_3
σ_{lp}	Components of symmetry matrix
$|\sigma|$	Determinant of symmetry matrix
$|\sigma^{(n)}|$	Determinant of particular symmetry matrix
ψ	Wave function, or state function, of an electron
ψ_α	Spinor of first rank (or its components) representing ψ
$\omega = \omega(T)$	Isotropic volume strain at temperature T
$\perp$	Suffix indicating direction perpendicular to axis Ox_3

CHAPTER 1

INTRODUCTION

§ 1. SINGLE CRYSTALS

A considerable proportion of the research activity in solid state physics is devoted to understanding the properties of single crystals. This is because the crystalline state is the natural one for most solids, an orderly disposition of atoms being energetically more favourable than an irregular atomic arrangement – indeed the one thing that the majority of solids have in common is that they are crystalline. There is, of course, also the added incentive that a single crystal is more amenable to detailed theoretical treatment than, for example, a piece of glass or rubber.

Single crystals are of considerable practical importance (e.g. piezoelectric crystals) but in most practical applications of solids the materials involved are polycrystalline aggregates of crystalline grains. In a polycrystal, the ordered arrangement of atoms, which extends throughout the whole material in a single crystal, is interrupted at the grain boundaries. The size of the individual grains can vary from macroscopic dimensions to distances of several Ångstroms: the alignment of the crystallites is also variable and it is only in a perfect polycrystal that the crystallographic axes of the individual grains are distributed uniformly over all angular orientations in space. However, in spite of the more frequent occurrence of polycrystalline materials, any explanation of why solids behave as they do must ultimately be dependent on an understanding of the properties of single crystals. In fact, the study of single crystals provides a basis from which, by suitable averaging

1

processes or otherwise, the properties of polycrystals may be interpreted.

The geometrically regular external form, or morphology, of some naturally-occurring mineral single crystals is a reflection of a high degree of symmetry associated with the ordered arrangement of atoms comprising the crystalline lattice. In a polycrystal this inherent symmetry is partly or wholly suppressed by the division of the material into individual crystalline grains with various mutual orientations. However, a completely random distribution of the alignments of the grains ensures that macroscopic physical properties do not depend on direction, and a perfect polycrystal approximates to an isotropic material, that is one for which physical properties are the same in all directions. The isotropy of polycrystalline substances is so readily incorporated into any description of their physical properties that the role played by symmetry is usually taken for granted. For single crystals, on the other hand, it is more difficult to include the consequences of the presence of symmetry in a formulation of the physical properties of the material.

Because a single crystal is inherently symmetrical, it presents the same aspect from a limited number of different directions, although the number of directions from which it appears different is unlimited. Hence it is to be expected that the properties of single crystals will depend on the direction in which they are measured, and all physical properties of single crystals must therefore be regarded as anisotropic, or at least potentially anisotropic. It is nevertheless important to ensure that the inherent symmetry of the crystal is exploited to the full in any macroscopic formulation of its (in general, anisotropic) properties, thereby facilitating subsequent theoretical interpretations of these properties in more fundamental microscopic terms.

§ 2. THE ANISOTROPY OF PHYSICAL PROPERTIES OF CRYSTALS

Not all properties of crystals are anisotropic: a property which inter-relates two scalars, such as mass, volume or temperature, can itself be characterized by a scalar (e.g. density or specific heat). Most properties of crystals, however, cannot be described without reference to direction and all crystals are anisotropic for some of their properties. A simple example of an anisotropic property of crystals is provided by their electrical resistivities.

In an isotropic medium, the relationship between the applied electric field E and the resulting electrical current of density J is of the form

$$E = \varrho J, \tag{1.1}$$

where the scalar ϱ is called the resistivity of the medium. If the conductor is a crystal, the vectors E and J are not always parallel and the resistivity cannot, therefore, be represented by a scalar. Usually, however, E and J are still linearly related so that (1.1) may be replaced by

$$E_1 = \varrho_{11}J_1 + \varrho_{12}J_2 + \varrho_{13}J_3,$$

$$E_2 = \varrho_{21}J_1 + \varrho_{22}J_2 + \varrho_{23}J_3, \tag{1.2a}$$

$$E_3 = \varrho_{31}J_1 + \varrho_{32}J_2 + \varrho_{33}J_3,$$

where E_1, E_2, E_3 and J_1, J_2, J_3 are the components of the vectors E and J in a rectangular cartesian system of coordinate axes Ox_1, Ox_2, Ox_3. Equations (1.2a) may also be expressed in matrix notation thus

$$\begin{bmatrix} E_1 \\ E_2 \\ E_3 \end{bmatrix} = \begin{bmatrix} \varrho_{11} & \varrho_{12} & \varrho_{13} \\ \varrho_{21} & \varrho_{22} & \varrho_{23} \\ \varrho_{31} & \varrho_{32} & \varrho_{33} \end{bmatrix} \begin{bmatrix} J_1 \\ J_2 \\ J_3 \end{bmatrix} \tag{1.2b}$$

for the rules of matrix multiplication impose the same relationships as do (1.2a) viz.

$$E_i = \sum_{j=1}^{3} \varrho_{ij}J_j. \tag{1.2c}$$

Another formulation of these relationships is provided by the dummy suffix notation which permits (1.2c) to be expressed in the form

$$E_i = \varrho_{ij} J_j. \tag{1.2d}$$

Here, as throughout the rest of the book, the Einstein summation convention has been employed, namely that when a letter occurs as a suffix twice in the same term, summation with respect to that suffix is to be automatically understood. Such a suffix is called a dummy or umbral suffix since it is obviously immaterial what symbol is used for this purpose. The range of values of all suffixes is 1, 2, 3, unless some other range is specified.

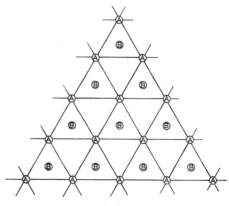

Fig. 1.1a

The resistivity of a crystal is thus described by the resistivity matrix

$$[\varrho_{ij}] = \begin{bmatrix} \varrho_{11} & \varrho_{12} & \varrho_{13} \\ \varrho_{21} & \varrho_{22} & \varrho_{23} \\ \varrho_{31} & \varrho_{32} & \varrho_{33} \end{bmatrix}, \tag{1.3}$$

and it is, perhaps, intuitively obvious that the form of this matrix will be simplified for crystals of high symmetry, the culmination of this simplification being its reduction to a scalar for an isotropic medium. However, it is of some importance to investigate exactly why a simplification in the form of the resistivity matrix is imposed by the presence of crystal symmetry. The simple example which follows brings out some useful points.

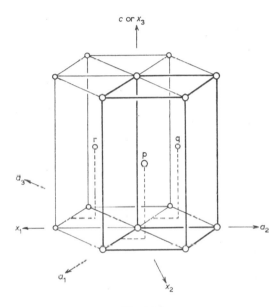

Fig. 1.1 b

Consider a single crystal of a non-magnetic metal such as beryllium or cadmium which exhibits a hexagonal close-packed structure. This crystal structure is represented schematically in Fig. 1.1a, which shows two adjacent layers of atoms which have been labelled A and B. The centres of the A atoms can be made to coincide with the centres of spheres that have been arranged in a single closest-packed layer in which each sphere is in contact with six others. The centres of the B atoms correspond to the centres of a second similar layer of spheres that is packed adjacent to the first so that each sphere in the second layer is in contact with three spheres in the first layer. If further layers are arranged to repeat the sequence ABAB... indefinitely then a hexagonal close-packed lattice is formed, part of which is illustrated in Fig. 1.1b.

The resistivity of such a crystal may be conveniently described with reference to a set of rectangular cartesian coordinates Ox_1, Ox_2, Ox_3 disposed with reference to the hexagonal axes c, a_1, a_2, a_3 as shown in Fig. 1.1b. If an electric current with density of unit magnitude flows in the crystal parallel to the direction a_1 then, from (1.2), the component of the electric field parallel to the hexagonal axis, Ox_3, will be

$$E_3 = \varrho_{31} \cos 60° + \varrho_{32} \sin 60° = \tfrac{1}{2}\varrho_{31} + \tfrac{1}{2}\sqrt{3}\,\varrho_{32}. \quad (1.4a)$$

Similarly, for unit current density parallel to a_2,

$$E_3 = -\varrho_{31}, \quad (1.4b)$$

whilst, for unit current density parallel to a_3,

$$E_3 = \tfrac{1}{2}\varrho_{31} - \tfrac{1}{2}\sqrt{3}\,\varrho_{32}. \quad (1.4c)$$

But it may be seen from a consideration of the crystal structure that the three directions a_1, a_2 and a_3 are entirely equivalent, so that the same value of E_3 must be obtained when a current of unit density is established in any one of these directions. This means that equations (1.4) must all be satisfied simultaneously, and that ϱ_{31} and ϱ_{32} must therefore be identically zero.

This example illustrates how the crystal symmetry imposes certain limitations on the resistivity matrix, and indicates the desirability of relating the coordinate axes to the crystallographic axes in some simple way. It does not, however, exhaust all the possible limitations appropriate to the hexagonal close-packed structure, partly because only one component (E_3) of E has been considered. A more systematic method is to consider the matrix $[\varrho_{ij}]$ itself and to ascertain how this is altered by a rotation of the coordinate axes of 120° about the hexagonal axis. This is discussed in § 6 and in § 3, where it is shown that the coefficients ϱ_{ij} are actually the coefficients of a tensor of the second rank rather than merely the coefficients of a 3×3 matrix.

§3. TRANSFORMATIONS OF AXES

Consider two sets of otherwise identical rectangular cartesian coordinate axes Ox_1, Ox_2, Ox_3 and Ox'_1, Ox'_2, Ox'_3 which have a common origin O but differ in orientation, the angle between Ox'_i and Ox_p being $\cos^{-1} l_{ip}$. The nine coefficients l_{ip} specify the angular relationships between the two sets of axes: thus the direction cosines of a particular axis Ox'_i with respect to x_1, x_2, x_3 are l_{i1}, l_{i2}, l_{i3} whilst the direction cosines of Ox_p with respect to x'_1, x'_2, x'_3 are l_{1p}, l_{2p}, l_{3p}. Of course, the coefficients l_{ip} are not all independent since the mutual orientation of the two sets of axes can be specified by only three parameters (e.g. the Euler angles) and, in fact (NYE [1960]),

$$l_{ik} l_{pk} = \delta_{ip}, \qquad (1.5a)$$

where δ_{ip} is the Kronecker delta,

$$\delta_{ip} \begin{cases} = 1 \quad \text{when} \quad i = p, \\ = 0 \quad \text{when} \quad i \neq p. \end{cases} \qquad (1.5b)$$

Now a vector E representing a physical quantity such as electric field strength will have components E_i relative to Ox_i and E'_i relative to Ox'_i. The relationship between the two sets of components may readily be found by thinking of E_1, E_2, E_3 as vectors directed along Ox_1, Ox_2, Ox_3 respectively and then resolving them along a direction x'_i to give E'_i. Thus

$$E'_i = E_1 \cos \widehat{x_1 O x'_i} + E_2 \cos \widehat{x_2 O x'_i} + E_3 \cos \widehat{x_3 O x'_i}$$

$$= l_{i1} E_1 + l_{i2} E_2 + l_{i3} E_3$$

$$= l_{ip} E_p. \qquad (1.6a)$$

The corresponding inverse transformation is

$$E_i = l_{pi}E'_p. \qquad (1.6b)$$

Similarly the current density vector J transforms as

$$J'_i = l_{ip}J_p, \qquad (1.7a)$$

$$J_i = l_{pi}J'_p, \qquad (1.7b)$$

and, since the position of a point may also be specified by a vector (r), the coordinates of a point transform as

$$x'_i = l_{ip}x_p, \qquad (1.8a)$$

$$x_i = l_{pi}x'_p. \qquad (1.8b)$$

Relative to the axes Ox'_i, the components of the electric field and current density vectors will be connected by a relationship of the form

$$E'_i = \varrho'_{ij}J'_j, \qquad (1.9)$$

the coefficients ϱ'_{ij} being related to the ϱ_{ij} of (1.2d) through (1.6) and (1.7). If it is remembered that any letter may be used as a dummy suffix, then successive application of equations (1.6a), (1.2d) and (1.7b) yields

$$E'_i = l_{ip}E_p$$

$$= l_{ip}\varrho_{pq}J_q$$

$$= l_{ip}\varrho_{pq}l_{jq}J'_j, \qquad (1.10)$$

and comparison of (1.9) with (1.10) gives†

$$\varrho'_{ij} = l_{ip}l_{jq}\varrho_{pq}. \qquad (1.11)$$

The existence of a relationship of this form illustrates an important difference between the ϱ_{ij} and the l_{ip}: it would be meaningless

† It may be noted that equation (1.11) is similar to the transformation law for a product of two coordinates of a point, namely $x'_i x'_j = l_{ip}l_{jq}x_p x_q$.

to enquire how the l_{ip} transform upon a rotation of the coordinate axes, whereas the ϱ_{ij} always transform according to (1.11). The l_{ip} may, like the ϱ_{ij}, be displayed as a matrix, thus

$$[l_{ip}] = \begin{bmatrix} l_{11} & l_{12} & l_{13} \\ l_{21} & l_{22} & l_{23} \\ l_{31} & l_{32} & l_{33} \end{bmatrix}, \tag{1.12}$$

and equations (1.6), (1.7) and (1.8) may, like (1.2), be regarded as matrix equations, but these are virtually the only points of resemblance. The existence of the transformation law (1.11) indicates that the matrix $[\varrho_{ij}]$ should properly be regarded as an entity of a different kind: just as the J_i are said to be the three components of a vector rather than the three components of a column matrix $[J_1 \ J_2 \ J_3]$, so the coefficients ϱ_{ij} are said to be the nine components of a *tensor*.

§ 4. POLAR AND AXIAL TENSORS

A scalar physical quantity, such as temperature, may be represented by a single number, whilst a vector quantity requires three numbers for its complete specification. These last three numbers are not, however, scalars; they are the three components of a vector, and the distinction becomes immediately apparent when a rotation of coordinate axes is considered. Such a rotation does not change the value of a scalar (such as temperature), but the components of a vector are altered because they are associated both with the axes, which have been rotated, and with the vector itself – a *physical entity* that retains its identity however the axes are changed. Since a vector has a meaning that is independent of the system of coordinates in which it is described, it is to be expected that a study of the relationship between its components in one system and those in another will provide an indication of the essential characteristics of a vector. It is, in fact, more satisfactory to *define* a vector, d, as a quantity with three components d_1, d_2, d_3 which transform according to

$$d_i' = l_{ip}d_p, \tag{1.13}$$

upon the transformation of coordinate axes discussed in § 3. Similarly a quantity such as ϱ_{ij} is said to be a tensor because it conforms to a transformation law of the form

$$d_{ij}' = l_{ip}l_{jq}d_{pq}. \tag{1.14}$$

The additional fact that a scalar is invariant upon a rotation of the coordinate axes reveals the existence of a sequence of transformation laws of the form

$$d' = d,$$
$$d_i' = l_{ip}d_p, \tag{1.15}$$
$$d_{ij}' = l_{ip}l_{jq}d_{pq},$$

and suggests that a tensor be defined, in general, as a quantity which transforms according to

$$d_{ijk...n}' = l_{ip}l_{jq}l_{kr} \cdots l_{nu}d_{pqr...u}. \tag{1.16}$$

The number of suffixes attached to $d_{ijk...n}$ determines the *rank* of the tensor: thus the resistivity tensor ϱ_{ij} is a second-rank tensor, whilst a vector such as E or J is a first-rank tensor and a scalar is a zero-rank tensor.

Since differentiation of equations (1.8) gives two identical values for l_{ip}, that is

$$\frac{\partial x_i'}{\partial x_p} = l_{ip} = \frac{\partial x_p}{\partial x_i'}, \tag{1.17}$$

equations (1.16) may be expressed in a number of alternative forms, two of which are

$$d_{ijk...n}' = \frac{\partial x_i'}{\partial x_p} \frac{\partial x_j'}{\partial x_q} \frac{\partial x_k'}{\partial x_r} \cdots \frac{\partial x_n'}{\partial x_u} d_{pqr...u}, \tag{1.18a}$$

$$d_{ijk...n}' = \frac{\partial x_p}{\partial x_i'} \frac{\partial x_q}{\partial x_j'} \frac{\partial x_r}{\partial x_k'} \cdots \frac{\partial x_u}{\partial x_n'} d_{pqr...u}. \tag{1.18b}$$

In tensor analysis both contravariant and covariant tensors are employed, the former transforming according to (1.18a) and the latter according to (1.18b). For example, an infinitesimal displacement, dx_i, is obviously a contravariant vector since

$$dx_i' = \frac{\partial x_i'}{\partial x_p}\, dx_p, \qquad (1.19)$$

whilst the gradient, $\partial\phi/\partial x_i$, of a scalar, ϕ, is a covariant vector since

$$\frac{\partial \phi}{\partial x_i'} = \frac{\partial \phi}{\partial x_p}\frac{\partial x_p}{\partial x_i'}. \qquad (1.20)$$

Although the distinction between contravariant and covariant tensors is important when curvilinear coordinates are employed, equation (1.17) shows that they transform in the same way upon a rotation of rectangular cartesian coordinate axes. If the coordinate axes are not orthogonal then (1.8) must be replaced by equations of the form

$$x_i' = m_{ip}x_p \qquad (m_{ip} \equiv \partial x_i'/\partial x_p), \qquad (1.21a)$$

$$x_i = n_{ip}x_p' \qquad (n_{ip} \equiv \partial x_i/\partial x_p'), \qquad (1.21b)$$

where the matrix m_{ip} is reciprocal to the matrix n_{ip} (i.e. $m_{ik}n_{kp} = \delta_{ip}$). For rectangular cartesian coordinate axes, however, $m_{ip} = l_{ip}$ and

$$l_{ik}n_{kp} = \delta_{ip}, \qquad (1.22a)$$

whilst, from (1.5a),

$$l_{ik}l_{pk} = \delta_{ip}, \qquad (1.22b)$$

so that l_{kp} is orthogonal (its reciprocal n_{kp} being equal to its transpose l_{pk}) and there is no distinction between contravariant and covariant tensors.

Although a true tensor transforms according to equation (1.16), there are numerous physical quantities which obey the transformation law

$$d_{ijk...n}' = \pm l_{ip}l_{jq}l_{kr} \cdots l_{nu}d_{pqr...u}, \qquad (1.23)$$

where the negative sign is taken for transformations which change right-handed coordinate axes into left-handed and vice versa, and the positive sign for transformations which do not change the hand of the axes. Quantities which transform according to (1.23) are called *axial* tensors whilst a true tensor, which transforms according to (1.16), is referred to as a *polar* tensor. A rotation of the coordinate axes does not, of course, change the hand of the axes: a transformation which does change the hand of the axes can always be considered to be a combination of a rotation of the axes and a reversal of their sense (i.e. the inversion $x_i' = -x_i$).

The most familiar examples of axial tensors are provided by axial vectors (tensors of the first rank). A true vector, for example a displacement, is a polar vector, that is it may be represented by a directed segment of length – an arrow. The direction in which the arrow points is unambiguous and a polar vector does not change sign upon a transformation which changes the hand of the coordinate axes. An axial vector, however, does change sign (the sign of the *coefficients* remaining the same). An example of an axial vector is the vector product of two polar vectors. This has the directional properties of an element of area rather than an arrow; the direction of the arrow may be defined as normal to the area but there is no unequivocal rule as to which side of the element of area is the positive direction of the vector. The area fixes the shank of the arrow but it does not determine which end should bear the point and this must be decided by some purely arbitrary (e.g. right-hand) rule. Axial vectors are sometimes called pseudo-vectors, and their three components are actually the three components of a true (i.e. polar) second-rank antisymmetrical tensor in three dimensions: indeed it is only in three dimensions that it is possible to represent an antisymmetrical tensor by an axial vector. Similarly the scalar product of a polar and an axial vector, which changes sign upon inversion, is called a pseudoscalar to distinguish it from a true scalar which does not. An example of a pseudoscalar is the rotary power of an optically active crystal, the rotary power being defined as positive when the sense of the rotation is the same as the hand of the axes. An example of a second-rank axial tensor is the optical gyration tensor (NYE [1960]).

A useful corollary of equation (1.22b) is that, since the determinants of a matrix and its transpose are equal, $|l_{ip}|^2 = 1$ and $|l_{ip}| = \pm 1$, the negative sign being appropriate for transformations which change the hand of the axes and the positive sign for those which do not. The $\pm$ sign may therefore be removed from equations (1.23) by writing

$$d'_{ijk...n} = |l| \, l_{ip}l_{jq}l_{kr} \, ... \, l_{nu}d_{pqr...u},$$ (1.24)

for the transformation law for axial tensors.

§ 5. PROPERTY TENSORS AND PHYSICAL TENSORS

A physical property of a crystal is defined by, and consists of, a relationship between two or more particular measurable quantities associated with the crystal. Because these measurable quantities are usually tensors (or the components of tensors) most physical properties of crystals will themselves be represented by tensors. For example, the resistivity tensor, ϱ_{ij}, of (1.2d) relates the electric field, E, in the crystal to the current density, J, in the crystal. Because E and J are vectors, ϱ_{ij} is a tensor of the second rank. Of course, not all physical properties of crystals are tensors, for not all the measurable quantities associated with a crystal are tensors. For example the dielectric breakdown strength is a measurable quantity of a crystal; it is also an anisotropic property since it depends upon the direction of measurement, but it does not appear to be possible to represent it by a tensor. Similarly, many surface properties of crystals may not be directly represented by tensors. Nevertheless, most physical properties of crystals are defined by the relationship between two or more tensors and may therefore themselves be represented by tensors.

If a crystal is subjected to an influence, represented by a tensor $i_{j_1 j_2 \ldots j_n}$, which gives rise to a resultant physical effect, represented by a tensor $e_{i_1 i_2 \ldots i_m}$, then a linear relationship between influence and effect defines a property tensor $d_{i_1 i_2 \ldots i_m j_1 j_2 \ldots j_n}$ according to the equation

$$e_{i_1 i_2 \ldots i_m} = d_{i_1 i_2 \ldots i_m j_1 j_2 \ldots j_n} i_{j_1 j_2 \ldots j_n}. \tag{1.25}$$

The tensors $i_{j_1 j_2 \ldots j_n}$ and $e_{i_1 i_2 \ldots i_m}$ may be called *physical* (or field) tensors in order to differentiate them from the property (or matter) tensor $d_{i_1 i_2 \ldots i_m j_1 j_2 \ldots j_n}$. The invariance of this equation under space-inversion (i.e. the transformation $x_i' = -x_i$) enables the property tensor to be immediately classified as polar or axial provided the physical tensors are already so classified. Thus, if $e_{i_1 i_2 \ldots i_m}$ and $i_{j_1 j_2 \ldots j_n}$ are both polar or both axial then $d_{i_1 i_2 \ldots i_m j_1 j_2 \ldots j_n}$ is polar, whilst if one of the physical tensors is polar and the other axial then the property tensor is axial. This rule – which is analogous to the rule $(-1) \times (-1) = (+1)$ – has obvious extensions to cases where two or more influences are acting on the crystal simultaneously, and it may be conveniently referred to as the 'product' rule.

Hence, for example, the dielectric permittivity tensor ε_{ij}, which inter-connects electric field strength E and dielectric displacement D and is defined by

$$D_i = \varepsilon_{ij} E_j, \tag{1.26}$$

relates two polar vectors and is therefore a polar tensor of second rank. The magnetic permeability tensor μ_{ij}, which inter-connects the magnetic field strength H and magnetic induction B and is defined by

$$B_i = \mu_{ij} H_j, \tag{1.27}$$

is also a polar tensor of second rank, since B and H are both axial vectors. The assumption that E and D are polar whilst H

and B are axial may be justified by considering the invariance of Maxwell's equations, viz.

$$\text{curl } H = \frac{1}{c}\left[\frac{\partial D}{\partial t} + 4\pi J\right], \qquad (1.28a)$$

$$\text{div } D = 4\pi\varrho, \qquad (1.28b)$$

$$\text{curl } E = -\frac{1}{c}\frac{\partial B}{\partial t}, \qquad (1.28c)$$

$$\text{div } B = 0, \qquad (1.28d)$$

under space-inversion. Thus, if E is a polar vector, it may be immediately deduced from (1.28c) that B is an axial vector. Similarly, the invariance of charge under space-inversion (or the fact that D and E are indistinguishable in vacuo) may be used in (1.28b) to predict that D is a polar vector, whence, from (1.28a) J must be a polar vector and H an axial vector. That E actually is a polar vector is deduced from the fact that crystals like tourmaline with polar shape (which is related to polar inner structure) possess an inner electric field, which is revealed by heating (pyroelectricity) or deforming the crystal (piezoelectricity). Similarly, the fact that H is an axial vector may be deduced from the existence of the Faraday effect, which represents a difference between the refractive indices for light rays the E vectors of which rotate clockwise and anticlockwise around a constant magnetic field (ZOCHER and TÖRÖK [1953]).

§6. CRYSTAL SYMMETRY

The transformation law (1.11) may now be used in reconsidering the hexagonal close-packed crystal lattice part of which is shown in Fig. 1.1b. Fig. 1.2a illustrates schematically the orientation of the lattice relative to the axes Ox_1, Ox_2, Ox_3 of Fig. 1.1b by indicating the position of the triangle formed by the three atoms denoted by p, q and r. Fig. 1.2b illustrates its orientation relative to axes Ox'_1, Ox'_2, Ox'_3 which are rotated by 120° about the Ox_3 axis with respect to the axes Ox_1, Ox_2, Ox_3. Since the angle between Ox'_i and Ox_p is $\cos^{-1}l_{ip}$, the coefficients l_{ip} of § 3 are given, for such a rotation of axes, by the matrix

$$[l_{ip}] = \begin{bmatrix} \cos 120° & \cos 30° & 0 \\ \cos 210° & \cos 120° & 0 \\ 0 & 0 & \cos 0 \end{bmatrix} = \begin{bmatrix} -\tfrac{1}{2} & \tfrac{1}{2}\sqrt{3} & 0 \\ -\tfrac{1}{2}\sqrt{3} & -\tfrac{1}{2} & 0 \\ 0 & 0 & 1 \end{bmatrix}. \quad (1.29)$$

Figs. 1.2c and 1.2d illustrate, relative to the two sets of axes, a situation in which the crystal has also been rotated through an angle of 120° in the same sense as the rotation from Ox_i to Ox'_i. However, it may be seen from a consideration of the crystal structure that these two positions are entirely equivalent and indistinguishable from one another, and this rotation is therefore said to

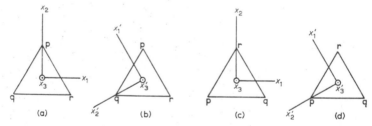

Fig. 1.2

be a symmetry transformation or symmetry operation. Consequently, the situations depicted in Figs. 1.2a and 1.2c are both described by the single resistivity tensor ϱ_{ij}, whilst those appropriate to Figs. 1.2b and 1.2d are described by the tensor

$$\varrho'_{ij} = l_{ip}l_{jq}\varrho_{pq}. \quad (1.30)$$

Further, since free space is isotropic, the resistivity tensor can depend only on the relative orientation of the crystal and the coordinate axes, and not on their absolute orientation in space. The situations depicted in Figs. 1.2a and 1.2d are therefore indistinguishable, so that

$$\varrho'_{ij} = \varrho_{ij}.$$ (1.31)

This equation permits the matrix $[l_{ij}]$ to be used to simplify the form of the resistivity tensor, for substitution of (1.31) into (1.30) yields

$$\varrho_{ij} = l_{ip}l_{jq}\varrho_{pq}.$$ (1.32)

The two results, $\varrho_{31} = 0$ and $\varrho_{32} = 0$, derived in § 2 may now be readily obtained by using equations (1.29) and (1.32), thus:

$$\varrho_{31} = l_{3p}l_{1q}\varrho_{pq}$$

$$= l_{33}l_{11}\varrho_{31} + l_{33}l_{12}\varrho_{32}$$

$$= -\tfrac{1}{2}\varrho_{31} + \tfrac{1}{2}\sqrt{3}\,\varrho_{32},$$ (1.33a)

$$\varrho_{32} = l_{3p}l_{2q}\varrho_{pq}$$

$$= l_{33}l_{21}\varrho_{31} + l_{33}l_{22}\varrho_{32}$$

$$= -\tfrac{1}{2}\sqrt{3}\,\varrho_{31} - \tfrac{1}{2}\varrho_{32},$$ (1.33b)

and these two equations can only be satisfied simultaneously if $\varrho_{31} = \varrho_{32} = 0$. One obvious advantage of employing equation (1.32) rather than proceeding as indicated in § 2 is that the form of the tensor ϱ_{ij} may be further simplified by repeating the process with different values of i and j. Thus it may be shown in a similar way that ϱ_{13} and ϱ_{23} must also be zero.

However, the rotation of 120° about the axis Ox_3 considered above is not the only transformation which produces entirely equivalent positions: so, for example, does a rotation of 180° about the axis Ox_2, and this is therefore another symmetry operation. To obtain the *maximum* simplification in the form of a particular property tensor it is necessary to consider other symmetry operations and to evolve a system for their classification.

CHAPTER 2

SPATIAL SYMMETRY

§ 1. SYMMETRY OPERATIONS

The description of the symmetry of a physical crystal in terms of symmetry operations is complicated by the fact that the inter-atomic spacing is usually small enough for the crystal to be considered, in many respects, as an array of atoms of infinite extent. However, a consideration of the symmetry of an object of finite extent brings out many useful points.

§ 1.1. *The Symmetry of a Two-dimensional Finite Object*

Consider the equilateral triangle lmn shown in Fig. 2.1a – a simple two-dimensional finite object the position of which is defined relative to the axes Ox_1, Ox_2, (or the axes Oa, Ob, Oc) which are fixed in space. A symmetry operation or transformation is one which moves the triangle into a position in which it is indistinguishable from the triangle in the original position, that is an operation which 'sends the triangle into itself'. There are obviously only six such equivalent positions and they are illustrated in Figs. 2.1. If an anticlockwise rotation through an angle of $2\pi/n$ is denoted by C_n and a reflection in a line by σ, then the six symmetry operations which transform the original triangle (Fig. 2.1a) into the triangles shown in Figs. 2.1a, b, c, d, e and f are, in that order,

$E(= C_1)$, the identity operation,
C_3,   anticlockwise rotation through 120° about the centre of the triangle,

C_3^2,   anticlockwise rotation through 240° about the centre of the triangle,

σ^a,   reflection through the line Oa, fixed in space,

σ^b,   reflection through the line Ob, fixed in space,

σ^c,   reflection through the line Oc, fixed in space.

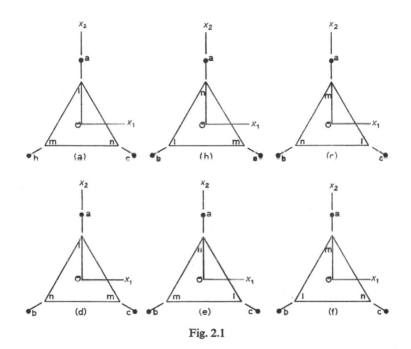

Fig. 2.1

A sequence of two symmetry operations obviously itself constitutes a symmetry operation. For example, consider the operation σ^a followed by the operation σ^b: this will be denoted by $\sigma^b\sigma^a$, the first operation appearing on the right in the product and the second on the left. The triangle shown in Fig. 2.1a is transformed to that shown in Fig. 2.1d by the operation σ^a, and this is then transformed to that shown in Fig. 2.1c by the operation σ^b. This is the same result as would have been obtained by using the operation C_3^2 directly. Thus, since a succession of operations is represented by multiplication, it is possible to write

$$C_3^2 = \sigma^b \sigma^a. \tag{2.1}$$

In a similar way, the products of all pairs of operations may be found and the results presented in the form of a 'multiplication table' thus:

TABLE 1

	E	C_3	C_3^2	σ^a	σ^b	σ^c
E	E	C_3	C_3^2	σ^a	σ^b	σ^c
C_3	C_3	C_3^2	E	σ^c	σ^a	σ^b
C_3^2	C_3^2	E	C_3	σ^b	σ^c	σ^a
σ^a	σ^a	σ^b	σ^c	E	C_3	C_3^2
σ^b	σ^b	σ^c	σ^a	C_3^2	E	C_3
σ^c	σ^c	σ^a	σ^b	C_3	C_3^2	E

The six symmetry operations considered above form the elements of a *group* in the mathematical sense. A group $\mathscr{G}$ is defined as a set of distinct elements A, B, C, ... for which an operation of combining (called multiplication) is specified, and for which the following conditions are satisfied.

(a) The product of two elements A and B of the set is itself a member of the set.

(b) Multiplication is associative: this means that for any three elements of the set, A, B, C,

$$(AB)C = A(BC).$$

(c) The set contains an element E called the identity such that $AE = EA = A$ for every element A of the set.

(d) For every element A of the set there must exist an element B such that $AB = BA = E$. The element B is called the inverse of A and denoted by $B = A^{-1}$.

If the number of elements in $\mathcal{G}$ is finite, the group is said to be a finite group. The number of elements in a finite group is called the *order* of the group. It should be noted that, although the law of combination is referred to as multiplication, this does not necessarily imply ordinary multiplication. The set of rational fractions (excluding zero) forms a group under ordinary multiplication, whilst the set of integers (positive, negative and zero) forms a group if the law of combination is ordinary addition.

It may now be seen that the set of six elements

$$E, \; C_3, \; C_3^2, \; \sigma^a, \; \sigma^b, \; \sigma^c$$

forms a finite group of order six. Inspection of Table 1 shows that the product of any pair of operations is once again an operation of the set. These operations are associative, and the operation which leaves the triangle unmoved is the identity operation for the group. The multiplication table also confirms that an inverse exists for every element of the group; thus,

$$E^{-1} = E, \qquad C_3^{-1} = C_3^2, \qquad (C_3^2)^{-1} = C_3,$$
$$(\sigma^a)^{-1} = \sigma^a, \quad (\sigma^b)^{-1} = \sigma^b, \qquad (\sigma^c)^{-1} = \sigma^c. \tag{2.2}$$

This group is often denoted, in a notation due to Schönflies, by the symbol C_{3v}. It may be noted that the postulates (a), (b), (c), (d) given above do not require multiplication to be commutative, and indeed, for this group, $\sigma^b\sigma^a = C_3^2$ whilst $\sigma^a\sigma^b = C_3$.

Although all six elements of the group C_{3v} are symmetry operations for the triangle lmn of Fig. 2.1a, the symmetry of the triangle may actually be fully specified by a smaller number of symmetry operations. It is evident that the identity operation, E, contributes nothing to the specification of the symmetry of the triangle. Moreover, it is unnecessary to retain both C_3 and C_3^2 in such a specification for if a rotation of 120° sends the triangle into itself, so will two successive rotations of 120°, that is a rotation of 240°. This last observation illustrates the general principle that the symmetry of an object can be completely specified by a set of elements from which all products of those elements remaining in the set have been eliminated. Any set of elements from which all the elements of a group may be obtained by multiplication is called a set of generating elements. In addition, the set of elements E, C_3, C_3^2 is itself a group, denoted in the Schönflies notation by the symbol C_3, and, since $C_3 C_3 = C_3^2$ and $C_3 C_3 C_3 = E$, the element C_3 generates the whole group. That the elements E, C_3, C_3^2 do form a group is evident from Table 1: the two broken lines divide the group multiplication table into four squares and all the inverses and products of pairs of the elements E, C_3, C_3^2 are contained in the upper left-hand square. Since the other requirements for a group are automatically satisfied, this square comprises the multiplication table of the group C_3, which is therefore a sub-group of the group C_{3v}. The *index* of the sub-group, that is the ratio of the order of the group to the order of the sub-group, is two, since there are twice as many elements in the group C_{3v} as in the sub-group C_3.

It may be observed that the lower right-hand square of Table 1 is occupied exclusively by the elements of the group C_3. Moreover, the symmetry operations σ^a, σ^b, σ^c, which are contained in the group C_{3v} but not in the group C_3, form a set, called a complex, the members of which are distributed only over the remaining two squares. Consequently, the complex σ^a, σ^b, σ^c is generated by multiplying the elements E, C_3, C_3^2 by any one member of the complex – for example, by σ^a. This result may be written symbolically in the form

$$C_{3v} = C_3 + \sigma^a C_3, \qquad (2.3)$$

which is familiar in group theory as a special case of Lagrange's theorem, the complex $\sigma^a C_3$ being a left-hand coset of C_{3v} relative to C_3. (Here the equality sign means that the two sets contain the same elements.) Thus the elements C_3 and σ^a are a set of generating elements of the group C_{3v}. The symmetry of the group C_{3v} and of the triangle lmn may therefore be fully characterized by the two elements C_3 and σ^a or, in general, by one element chosen from the set C_3, C_3^2 and one from the complex σ^a, σ^b, σ^c.

§ 1.2. The Symmetry of a Three-dimensional Finite Object

The three-dimensional analogue of the triangle lmn of § 1.1 is the equilateral triangular prism shown in Fig. 2.2. This prism possesses all the symmetry of the original triangle and the corresponding symmetry operations may be denoted by

$$E,\ C_3,\ C_3^2,\ \sigma_v^a,\ \sigma_v^b,\ \sigma_v^c.$$

E is again the identity operation, whilst C_3 and C_3^2 are right-handed rotations through 120° and 240° respectively about the axis Ox_3. Reflection in lines Oa, Ob, Oc is now replaced by reflection in planes each containing one of these lines and the axis Ox_3. The corresponding symmetry operations are denoted by σ_v^a, σ_v^b, σ_v^c, the suffix v being added because Ox_3 is conventionally assumed to be directed vertically. However, it is obvious from a consideration of Fig. 2.2, that the symmetry operations listed above are not the only ones. For example the plane defined by the triangle abc is a 'horizontal' reflection plane, the corresponding symmetry operation being denoted by σ_h.

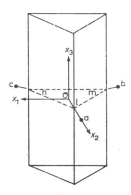

The complete symmetry of the triangular prism shown in Fig. 2.2 is, in fact, characterized by the twelve symmetry operations

$$E,\quad C_3,\quad C_3^2,\quad \sigma_v^a,\quad \sigma_v^b,\quad \sigma_v^c,$$

$$\sigma_h,\quad U_2^a,\quad U_2^b,\quad U_2^c,\quad S_3,\quad S_3',$$

Fig. 2.2

where U_2^a, U_2^b, U_2^c are rotations of 180° about 'horizontal' axes Oa, Ob, Oc respectively, and where S_3 and S_3' are composite operations representing rotation through 120° and 240° respectively about the 'vertical' axis Ox_3 followed in each case by reflection in the 'horizontal' plane abc. All twelve symmetry operations form a group for which the multiplication table is:

TABLE 2

	E	C_3	C_3^2	σ_v^a	σ_v^b	σ_v^c	σ_h	U_2^a	U_2^b	U_2^c	S_3	S_3'
E	E	C_3	C_3^2	σ_v^a	σ_v^b	σ_v^c	σ_h	U_2^a	U_2^b	U_2^c	S_3	S_3'
C_3	C_3	C_3^2	E	σ_v^c	σ_v^a	σ_v^b	S_3	U_2^c	U_2^a	U_2^b	S_3'	σ_h
C_3^2	C_3^2	E	C_3	σ_v^b	σ_v^c	σ_v^a	S_3'	U_2^b	U_2^c	U_2^a	σ_h	S_3
σ_v^a	σ_v^a	σ_v^b	σ_v^c	E	C_3	C_3^2	U_2^a	σ_h	S_3	S_3'	U_2^b	U_2^c
σ_v^b	σ_v^b	σ_v^c	σ_v^a	C_3^2	E	C_3	U_2^b	S_3'	σ_h	S_3	U_2^c	U_2^a
σ_v^c	σ_v^c	σ_v^a	σ_v^b	C_3	C_3^2	E	U_2^c	S_3	S_3'	σ_h	U_2^a	U_2^b
σ_h	σ_h	S_3	S_3'	U_2^a	U_2^b	U_2^c	E	σ_v^a	σ_v^b	σ_v^c	C_3	C_3^2
U_2^a	U_2^a	U_2^b	U_2^c	σ_h	S_3	S_3'	σ_v^a	E	C_3	C_3^2	σ_v^b	σ_v^c
U_2^b	U_2^b	U_2^c	U_2^a	S_3'	σ_h	S_3	σ_v^b	C_3^2	E	C_3	σ_v^c	σ_v^a
U_2^c	U_2^c	U_2^a	U_2^b	S_3	S_3'	σ_h	σ_v^c	C_3	C_3^2	E	σ_v^a	σ_v^b
S_3	S_3	S_3'	σ_h	U_2^c	U_2^a	U_2^b	C_3	σ_v^c	σ_v^a	σ_v^b	C_3^2	E
S_3'	S_3'	σ_h	S_3	U_2^b	U_2^c	U_2^a	C_3^2	σ_v^b	σ_v^c	σ_v^a	E	C_3

This group, denoted in the Schönflies notation by the symbol D_{3h}, has twice as many elements as the group C_{3v} of § 1.1.

Inspection of Table 2 reveals that the two broken lines divide the group multiplication table into four squares of which the upper left-hand square is the multiplication table of the group C_{3v}.

Hence C_{3v} is a sub-group of the group D_{3h} of index 2, just as C_3 is a sub-group of the group C_{3v} of index 2. As before, the complex σ_h, U_2^a, U_2^b, U_2^c, S_3, S_3' is generated by multiplying the elements of C_{3v} by any one member of the complex – for example, by σ_h, and this result may be written symbolically (Lagrange's theorem) in the form

$$D_{3h} = C_{3v} + \sigma_h C_{3v}. \qquad (2.4)$$

Thus the elements C_3, σ_v^a, σ_h are a set of generating elements of the group D_{3h}. The symmetry of the group D_{3h} and of the triangular prism may therefore be fully characterized by the three elements C_3, σ_v^a and σ_h or, in general, by one element chosen from the set C_3, C_3^2, one from the complex σ_v^a, σ_v^b, σ_v^c and one from the complex σ_h, U_2^a, U_2^b, U_2^c, S_3, S_3'.

It may be noted that, although the symmetry of a triangular lamina is characterized in three dimensions by the group D_{3h}, the symmetry of a triangle in *two dimensions* is characterized merely by the group C_{3v} since, for example, a rotation about an axis other than Ox_3 is conceptually impossible. Similarly, the extension to a crystalline lattice appropriate to an array of triangular prisms introduces further symmetry operations. However, before proceeding to a consideration of the symmetry of an extended crystalline lattice, it is desirable to introduce a more systematic notation for symmetry operations, and this may be done in two ways.

First, the symmetry operations may be classified in terms of n-fold rotation and rotation–reflection axes. For example, an allowable symmetry operation might be repetition of an object at successive angular intervals θ, provided that periodic repetition at this interval eventually superposes the repeated object on the original object. Thus θ must be of the form $2\pi/n$ where n is an integer and, if this rotation is a permissible symmetry operation, the object is said to possess an n-fold axis of rotation, denoted by the symbol n. Another possibility is the existence of an n-fold rotation–reflection axis, denoted by $\tilde{n}$, corresponding to a rotation of $2\pi/n$ followed by a reflection in a plane perpendicular to the axis of rotation. As an illustration of this method of classification, consider the symmetry operations of the group D_{3h}, which may be written in the compact form

$$E, \quad 3(U_2), \quad 3(\sigma_v), \quad \sigma_h, \quad C_3, \quad C_3^2, \quad S_3, \quad S_3'.$$

The identity operation, E, is equivalent to a one-fold rotation axis (rotation through 2π), U_2 to a two-fold rotation axis and σ to a one-fold rotation–reflection axis. Futhermore the two rotations C_3 and C_3^2 correspond to three-fold rotation axes of either sense (i.e. to ± 3) whilst S_3 and S_3' correspond to three-fold rotation–reflection axes of either sense (i.e. to $\pm \tilde{3}$). The symmetry operations of the group D_{3h} may therefore be enumerated in terms of rotation and rotation-reflection axes as follows:

$$1, \quad 3(2_\perp), \quad 3(\tilde{1}_\perp), \quad \tilde{1}_z, \quad \pm 3_z, \quad \pm \tilde{3}_z,$$

where, by convention, the suffixes z and $\perp$ refer to 'vertical' and 'horizontal' directions respectively.

The second method of classifying symmetry operations, which is generally to be preferred, again uses rotation axes but employs rotation–inversion axes rather than rotation–reflection axes. An n-fold rotation–inversion axis, denoted by $\bar{n}$, corresponds to the rotation of an object through an angle of $2\pi/n$ followed by inversion through a fixed point. This repetition operation is called an improper rotation – to distinguish it from the proper rotation associated with a true n-fold rotation axis – and it consists of a combination of a rotation and a reversal of sense. Thus, for example, an initial right-handed object would be repeated left-handed, and then right-handed again, and so on, so that an improper rotation generates neighbouring enantiomorphous objects and alternate congruent objects. Improper rotations are readily expressible in terms of either rotation–inversion or rotation–

reflection axes; thus, since $\bar{2} = \tilde{1}$ and $\pm\bar{6} = \mp\tilde{3}$, the symmetry operations of the group D_{3h} may also be enumerated as follows:

$$1, \quad 3(2_\perp), \quad 3(\bar{2}_\perp), \quad \bar{2}_z, \quad \pm 3_z, \quad \pm\bar{6}_z.$$

The group itself may also be denoted by several different symbols: in the international notation (based on one devised by Mauguin and Hermann) it is denoted by $\mathbf{\bar{6}m2}$†. The symbol m indicates the presence of a mirror reflection plane parallel to the a-axis, and the complete symbol indicates the existence of the three symmetry operations $\bar{6}_z$, $\bar{2}_\perp$ and $2_\perp$, that is of S_3, σ_v^a and U_2^a. Although it is not, perhaps, immediately obvious, S_3, σ_v^a and U_2^a are, in fact, a set of generating elements for the group, since it may readily be verified from Table 2 that

$$E = \sigma_v^a \sigma_v^a, \qquad \bar{C}_3 = \sigma_v^a U_2^a S_3, \qquad C_3^2 = \sigma_v^a S_3 U_2^a,$$

$$\sigma_v^b = U_2^a S_3, \qquad \sigma_v^c = S_3 U_2^a, \qquad \sigma_h = \sigma_v^a U_2^a, \qquad (2.5)$$

$$U_2^b = \sigma_v^a S_3, \qquad U_2^c = S_3 \sigma_v^a, \qquad S_3' = U_2^a S_3 U_2^a.$$

§ 1.3. *The Symmetry of an Extended Crystalline Lattice*

By stacking together the equilateral triangular prisms of § 1.2, an extended structure may be formed, part of which is shown in Fig. 2.3. The intersecting lines corresponding to the edges of the triangular prisms form a three-dimensional lattice which may be imagined to be of infinite extent. It is obvious that the symmetry of the *extended* lattice, considered to be unbounded by any surface, is at least as high as that of an individual triangular prism, although the symmetry of the irregular prism comprising that part

† To conform to a notation that is followed in later chapters, bold-face type is used for the international symbols (but not for the individual symmetry operations). This is necessitated by the need to distinguish, as explained in Ch. 3, § 1, between magnetic and non-magnetic groups.

of the lattice which is depicted in Fig. 2.3 is, of course, much lower. The symmetry operations for the extended lattice therefore include all those of the group $\overline{6}\mathrm{m}2$ ($= D_{3\mathrm{h}}$), that is

$$1, \quad 3(2_{\perp}), \quad 3(\overline{2}_{\perp}), \quad \overline{2}_z, \quad \pm3_z, \quad \pm\overline{6}_z.$$

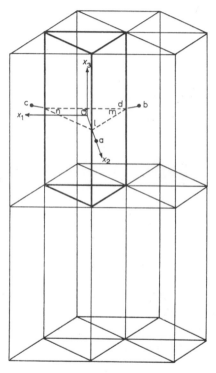

Fig. 2.3

Comparison of Fig. 2.3 with Fig. 2.2 confirms that any one of these operations sends the heavily outlined triangular prism of Fig. 2.3 into itself. For triangular prisms other than that in heavy outline, all these operations except the identity operation also replace one prism by another in the extended lattice. However,

this does not exhaust the list of symmetry operations which inter-
change pairs of triangular prisms: a consideration of Fig. 2.3
reveals that, for example, the 'vertical' line through d is actually a
six-fold rotation axis (denoted by 6_z), whilst the point d itself is a
centre of inversion (denoted by $\bar{1}$). The symmetry of the extended
lattice is thus higher than that of an individual triangular prism.

Because the operations which send a prism into itself may be
augmented by those which replace one prism by another, the symmetry of the extended lattice is, in fact, characterized not by the
group $\bar{6}m2$ but by the group $6/mmm$, obtained from $\bar{6}m2$ by
counting the symmetry operation $\bar{1}$ (for example) as an *additional*
generating element. The addition of the centre of inversion as a
generating element is indicated symbolically (Lagrange's theorem)
by the equation

$$(6/mmm) = (\bar{6}m2) + \bar{1}(\bar{6}m2), \qquad (2.6)$$

and the group $6/mmm$, so formed, contains the 24 elements

$$1, \quad \bar{1}, \quad 6(2_\perp), \quad 2_z, \quad 6(\bar{2}_\perp),$$

$$\bar{2}_z, \quad \pm 3_z, \quad \pm \bar{3}_z, \quad \pm 6_z, \quad \pm \bar{6}_z.$$

A set of generating elements of this group may, of course, be
formed by adding any one of the complex of elements contained in
the group $6/mmm$ but not in the sub-group $\bar{6}m2$ to any set of
generating elements of the group $\bar{6}m2$ (e.g. to 3_z, $\bar{2}_\perp$, $\bar{2}_z$). The symbol $6/mmm$ itself indicates that the symmetry of the lattice is
characterized by a six-fold rotation axis perpendicular to a 'horizontal' mirror reflection plane and by two 'vertical' mirror reflection planes.

To relate the geometrical lattice shown in Fig. 2.3 to an actual
crystalline lattice it is necessary to specify the positions of the
atoms, ions or molecules of which the physical crystal is composed.
For example, to identify this geometrical lattice with the hexagonal close-packed crystalline lattice of Fig. 1.1b, individual

atoms (indicated by open circles) must be situated at each lattice
point and also at intermediate points such as o, p, q and r as
shown in Fig. 2.4. Although the crystal structure is hexagonal it
can be adequately represented by the parallelepiped shown in
heavy outline in Fig. 2.4, since the extended crystal may be reproduced by stacking together similar parallelepipeds in similar
orientations. This parallelepiped is therefore referred to as a unit

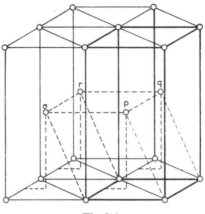

Fig. 2.4

cell of the crystal and, since it contains the atom p in addition to
exhibiting an atom at each corner, it is called a multiply primitive
unit cell. It may be noted that the parallelepiped indicated by broken lines in Fig. 2.4 is not a unit cell since an identical parallelepiped, when placed in the same orientation on the face opqr,
does not reproduce the positions of the atoms in the 'top layer'
correctly.

   The symmetry of a crystalline lattice, such as that shown in
Fig. 2.4, is conventionally described by considering it to be an
array formed by infinite regular repetition in space of identical
structural units: the crystal symmetry is then characterized by the
allowable symmetry operations, that is by the operations or trans-

formations which transform the array into itself. The existence of a spatial lattice restricts the number of possible rotation axes and, for example, rules out the occurrence of a five-fold axis: one-, two-, three-, four- and six-fold axes of rotation are permissible, the corresponding symmetry operations being denoted respectively by the symbols 1, 2, 3, 4 and 6. Similarly, an improper rotation may be represented either by one of five rotation–reflection operations or by one of five rotation–inversion operations, the relations between the two sets being $\bar{1} = \tilde{2}$, $\bar{2} = \tilde{1}$, $\pm\bar{3} = \mp\tilde{6}$, $\pm\bar{4} = \mp\tilde{4}$, $\pm\bar{6} = \mp\tilde{3}$. The symmetry operations discussed above are of the same type as those used (e.g. in §§ 1.1 and 1.2) to specify the symmetry of an object of finite dimensions. For such an object, the application of a symmetry operation must leave at least one point in its original position. It follows that all the axes and planes of symmetry of a finite object must have at least one common point of intersection, for successive rotation of the object about two non-intersecting axes or successive reflection in two non-intersecting planes results in a translation of the object, which obviously cannot then be left unaltered. The groups of symmetry operations used to describe the symmetry of finite objects are therefore called *point groups*.

Although the symmetry of an extended crystalline lattice may be described in terms of n-fold rotation and rotation–inversion axes, it is obvious that it cannot be completely specified in this way, because finite displacements of the lattice parallel to particular directions are also symmetry operations for the crystal, considered to be of infinite extent. Hence, to the symmetry operations discussed above must be added those provided by combinations of these operations with translations and by translations alone, the set of symmetry operations so formed characterizing the complete spatial symmetry of the crystal. Since a succession of two symmetry operations is also a symmetry operation, and every operation has an inverse which is also a symmetry operation, the symmetry operations form the elements of a group, called the *space group*. Classical crystallography is, however, concerned particularly with the point group, a special sub-group of the space group in which the translational components of symmetry operations are completely suppressed and only rotation and rotation–inversion symmetry operations are considered. This is because the translational symmetries of actual crystals have such a small period that they can only be detected by special (e.g. X-ray) techniques, and the immediately apparent elements of symmetry of a crystal are those of the point group. The macroscopic properties of crystals thus depend on the symmetry of their point groups and not on the (230) spatial symmetries obtained by combining a point group symmetry with the translational symmetry of the corresponding infinite lattice.

Although the translational components of symmetry operations are completely suppressed in forming the point group from the appropriate space group, it must not be assumed that the symmetry operations of the point group of a crystal are merely those appropriate to a unit cell of the lattice considered as a finite object. Thus, for example, the symmetry of the unit cell shown in heavy outline in Fig. 2.4 – including, of course, the atom situated at p – is characterized by only four symmetry operations, namely

$$1, \quad \bar{2}_z, \quad 2_\perp, \quad \bar{2}_\perp,$$

where the last two operations correspond to axes through the centre of the cell parallel to oq and pr respectively. Nor should it be imagined that this restriction can be removed by investigating the symmetry of a larger cell such as that shown in Fig. 1.1b. Thus, the complete symmetry of this cell, again considered as a finite object, is characterized by the group **6̄m2** whilst the extended crystalline lattice of which the cell is a part exhibits the higher symmetry characterized by the group **6/mmm**. This discrepancy arises because the presence of the three atoms at p, q and r is inconsistent with the existence of a 'vertical' six-fold rotation axis for the cell.

That such a six-fold rotation is a symmetry operation for the extended crystalline lattice can best be appreciated by considering Figs. 2.5, which represent projections of the positions of the atoms in a hexagonal close-packed structure on to a basal (i.e. 'horizontal') plane. Fig. 2.5a depicts the positions of the three 'layers' of atoms shown in Fig. 1.1b: the 'upper' and 'lower' layers of

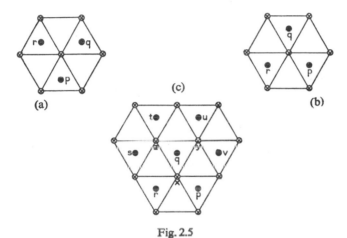

Fig. 2.5

atoms are denoted by crosses and open circles respectively, whilst the 'middle' layer (i.e. p, q and r) is denoted by closed circles. A similar projection of the same portion of the lattice after the crystal has been rotated anticlockwise through an angle of 60° is shown in Fig. 2.5b, whilst Fig. 2.5c is an extension of Fig. 2.5b to include a few neighbouring atoms. It may now be seen that the three atoms p, q and r are in exactly the same relationship to the seven atoms denoted by open circles in Fig. 2.5a as the three atoms denoted by crosses at x, y and z are to the seven atoms p, q, r, s, t, u and v in Fig. 2.5c. Since all the atoms are of the same type, this means that a symmetry operation for the extended crystalline lattice is a rotation of 60° about the centre of the triangle pqr followed by a displacement of the whole lattice so as to translate the atom at the position indicated by the cross at x to the position indicated by the closed circle at q. However, since the translational component of this symmetry operation is completely suppressed in forming the point group from the space group, the point group of the crystal contains as an element a 'vertical' six-fold rotation axis rather than merely a 'vertical' three-fold rotation axis. It should be noted, however, that if, in Fig. 1.1b, the atoms at p, q and r were of one type whilst the remainder were of another type (as in a compound), then the above considerations would not apply and the point group of the crystal would contain a three-fold rather than a six-fold 'vertical' rotation axis.

These considerations emphasize the important fact that, whilst the point group appropriate to a finite object may be obtained directly, the point group appropriate to an extended crystalline lattice may often only be obtained via the space group characterizing the complete spatial symmetry of the crystal. It should also be noted that, in forming the point group, the symmetry operations of the space group must not only be deprived of any translational components but they must also be imagined to be 'collapsed' so as to pass through a common point, although this point does not, of course, have any definite location in the lattice.

§ 1.4. The Thirty-two Crystal Classes

A monaxial crystal is one that exhibits a single n-fold axis of symmetry: this may be either a rotation axis, or a rotation–inversion axis, or both may be present simultaneously. Hence for each value of n there exist three possible symmetries which may be denoted by n, $\bar{n}$ and $n/\bar{n}$. Since n can only take on the values 1, 2, 3, 4 and 6, there are five possible symmetries of type n and five of type $\bar{n}$. The number of type $n/\bar{n}$ is, however, reduced since $1/\bar{1}$ is identical with $\bar{1}$, and $3/\bar{3}$ is identical with $\bar{3}$. The remaining three, $2/\bar{2}$, $4/\bar{4}$ and $6/\bar{6}$, may also be designated by 2/m, 4/m and 6/m respectively, where /m (:m in the Shubnikov notation) denotes a reflection (or mirror) plane perpendicular to the symmetry axis. There are therefore 13 possible symmetries for monaxial crystals and a simple extension to polyaxial crystals (BUERGER [1956]) augments this number by 19. The total possible number of classes of crystal symmetry is thus 32 and they are customarily divided amongst the seven crystal systems as shown in Table 3.

Several different sets of symbols are used to designate the 32 crystal classes but the international notation (based on one devised by Mauguin and Hermann) is to be preferred †. The crystal may possess more symmetry operations than those appearing in the Hermann–Mauguin symbol but the stated ones are always sufficient, and sometimes more than sufficient, to generate equivalent points from which the other, implied, operations may be inferred. For example, the identity operation, 1, is omitted from the designation of the classes 2 and $m(= \bar{2})$, whilst both 1 and $\bar{1}$ are omitted from $2/m$ (= $2/\bar{2}$), and so on. Futher simplification is afforded by omitting any reference to the sense of the axes for $n > 2$ although the operations 3, 4, 6, $\bar{3}$, $\bar{4}$ and $\bar{6}$ may be of either sign. The complete set of symmetry operations is listed for each crystal class in column 6 of Table 3, the maximum number being 18, for the class **m3m**. The subscripts x, y, z, xy, $-xy$ on the symbols n and $\bar{n}$ indicate the direction of the rotation or rotation–inversion axis; the subscript $\perp$ on 2 and $\bar{2}$ indicates that the two-fold axis is perpendicular to the main crystal axis of three-fold or higher symmetry. The z-axis is the axis of symmetry or normal to the reflection plane for monoclinic crystals: for tetragonal, trigonal and hexagonal crystals the z-axis is the main axis and the y-axis is a two-fold axis or a normal to a crystal surface. For orthorhombic crystals all three axes are symmetry axes or normals to reflection planes and for cubic crystals the four three-fold axes are the cube-body diagonals.

The symmetry operations listed in column 6 of Table 3 may also

† Again, with the modification that bold-face type is used to conform to a notation that is followed in later chapters.

36

TABLE 3

System	Symbol of symmetry class			Shubnikov	Symmetry operations	Number of symmetry operations	Generating matrices
	International		Schönflies				
	Abbreviated	Full					
Triclinic	1	1	C_1	1	1	1	$\sigma^{(0)}$
	$\bar{1}$	$\bar{1}$	$C_1(S_2)$	$\bar{2}$	$1, \bar{1}$	2	$\sigma^{(1)}$
Monoclinic	2	2	C_2	2	$1, 2_z$	2	$\sigma^{(3)}$
	m	m	$C_s(C_{1h})$	m	$1, \bar{2}_z$	2	$\sigma^{(5)}$
	2/m	$\dfrac{2}{m}$	C_{2h}	2:m	$1, \bar{1}, 2_z, \bar{2}_z$	4	$\sigma^{(1)}, \sigma^{(3)}$
Ortho-rhombic	222	222	$D_2(V)$	2:2	$1, 2_x, 2_y, 2_z$	4	$\sigma^{(2)}, \sigma^{(3)}$
	mm2	mm2	C_{2v}	2·m	$1, 2_z, \bar{2}_x, \bar{2}_y$	4	$\sigma^{(3)}, \sigma^{(4)}$
	mmm	$\dfrac{2\,2\,2}{mmm}$	$D_{2h}(V_h)$	m·2:m	$1, \bar{1}, 2_x, 2_y, 2_z, \bar{2}_x, \bar{2}_y, \bar{2}_z$	8	$\sigma^{(1)}, \sigma^{(2)}, \sigma^{(3)}$

System	International (full)	International (short)	Schoenflies	Symbol	Symmetry operations	Order	Mirror planes
Tetra-gonal	4	4	C_4	4	$1,\ 2_z,\ \pm 4_z$	4	$\sigma^{(7)}$
	$\bar{4}$	$\bar{4}$	S_4	$\bar{4}$	$1,\ 2_z,\ \pm \bar{4}_z$	4	$\sigma^{(8)}$
	4/m	$\dfrac{4}{m}$	C_{4h}	4:m	$1,\ \bar{1},\ 2_z,\ \bar{2}_z,\ \pm 4_z,\ \pm \bar{4}_z$	8	$\sigma^{(1)},\ \sigma^{(7)}$
	422	422	D_4	4:2	$1,\ 2_x,\ 2_y,\ 2_z,\ 2_{xy},\ 2_{-xy},\ \pm 4_z$	8	$\sigma^{(2)},\ \sigma^{(7)}$
	4mm	4mm	C_{4v}	4·m	$1,\ 2_z,\ \bar{2}_x,\ \bar{2}_y,\ \bar{2}_{xy},\ \bar{2}_{-xy},\ \pm 4_z$	8	$\sigma^{(4)},\ \sigma^{(7)}$
	$\bar{4}$2m	$\bar{4}$2m	$D_{2d}(V_d)$	$\bar{4}$·m	$1,\ 2_z,\ 2_y,\ 2_z,\ \bar{2}_{xy},\ \bar{2}_{-xy},\ \pm \bar{4}_z$	8	$\sigma^{(2)},\ \sigma^{(8)}$
	4/mmm	$\dfrac{4\,2\,2}{mmm}$	D_{4h}	m·4:m	$1,\ \bar{1},\ 2_x,\ 2_y,\ 2_z,\ 2_{xy},\ 2_{-xy},\ \bar{2}_x,\ \bar{2}_y,\ \bar{2}_z,$ $\bar{2}_{xy},\ \bar{2}_{-xy} \equiv 4_z,\ \pm \bar{4}_z$	16	$\sigma^{(1)},\ \sigma^{(2)},\ \sigma^{(7)}$
Trigonal	3	3	C_3	3	$1,\ \pm 3_z$	3	$\sigma^{(6)}$
	$\bar{3}$	$\bar{3}$	$C_{3i}(S_6)$	$\bar{6}$	$1,\ \bar{1},\ \pm 3_z,\ \equiv \bar{3}_z$	6	$\sigma^{(1)},\ \sigma^{(6)}$
	32	32	D_3	3:2	$1,\ 3(2_\perp),\ \pm 3_z$	6	$\sigma^{(2)},\ \sigma^{(6)}$
	3m	3m	C_{3v}	3·m	$1,\ 3(\bar{2}_\perp),\ \pm 3_z$	6	$\sigma^{(4)},\ \sigma^{(6)}$
	$\bar{3}$m	$\bar{3}\dfrac{2}{m}$	D_{3d}	$\bar{6}$·m	$1,\ \bar{1},\ 3(2_\perp),\ 3(\bar{2}_\perp),\ \pm 3_z,\ \pm \bar{3}_z$	12	$\sigma^{(1)},\ \sigma^{(2)},\ \sigma^{(6)}$

TABLE 3 (continued)

Hexagonal	6	6	C_6	6	$1, 2_z, \pm 3_z, \pm 6_z$	6	$\sigma^{(3)}, \sigma^{(6)}$
	$\bar{6}$	$\bar{6}$	C_{3h}	$3{:}m$	$1, \bar{2}_z, \pm 3_z, \pm \bar{6}_z$	6	$\sigma^{(5)}, \sigma^{(6)}$
	$6/m$	$\dfrac{6}{m}$	C_{6h}	$6{:}m$	$1, \bar{1}, 2_z, \bar{2}_z, \pm 3_z, \pm \bar{3}_z, \pm 6_z, \pm \bar{6}_z$	12	$\sigma^{(1)}, \sigma^{(3)}, \sigma^{(6)}$
	622	622	D_6	$6{:}2$	$1, 6(2_\perp), 2_z, \pm 3_z, \pm 6_z$	12	$\sigma^{(2)}, \sigma^{(3)}, \sigma^{(6)}$
	6mm	6mm	C_{6v}	$6 \cdot m$	$1, 2_z, 6(\bar{2}_\perp), \pm 3_z, \pm 6_z$	12	$\sigma^{(4)}, \sigma^{(4)}, \sigma^{(6)}$
	$\bar{6}m2$	$\bar{6}m2$	D_{3h}	$m \cdot 3{:}m$	$1, 3(2_\perp), 3(\bar{2}_\perp), \bar{2}_z, \pm 3_z, \pm \bar{6}_z$	12	$\sigma^{(2)}, \sigma^{(5)}, \sigma^{(6)}$
	$6/mmm$	$\dfrac{6\,2\,2}{m\,m\,m}$	D_{6h}	$m \cdot 6{:}m$	$1, \bar{1}, 6(2_\perp), 2_z, 6(\bar{2}_\perp), \bar{2}_z, \pm 3_z, \pm \bar{3}_z, \pm 6_z, \pm \bar{6}_z$	24	$\sigma^{(1)}, \sigma^{(2)}, \sigma^{(3)}, \sigma^{(6)}$
Cubic	23	23	T	$3/2$	$1, 3(2), 4(\pm 3)$	12	$\sigma^{(3)}, \sigma^{(9)}$
	m3	$\dfrac{2}{m}\bar{3}$	T_h	$\bar{6}/2$	$1, \bar{1}, 3(2), 3(\bar{2}), 4(\pm 3), 4(\pm \bar{3})$	24	$\sigma^{(1)}, \sigma^{(3)}, \sigma^{(9)}$
	432	432	O	$3/4$	$1, 9(2), 4(\pm 3), 3(\pm 4)$	24	$\sigma^{(7)}, \sigma^{(9)}$
	$\bar{4}3m$	$\bar{4}3m$	T_d	$3/\bar{4}$	$1, 3(2), 6(\bar{2}), 4(\pm 3), 3(\pm \bar{4})$	24	$\sigma^{(8)}, \sigma^{(9)}$
	m3m	$\dfrac{4}{m}\bar{3}\dfrac{2}{m}$	O_h	$\bar{6}/4$	$1, \bar{1}, 9(2), 9(\bar{2}), 4(\pm 3), 4(\pm \bar{3}), 3(\pm 4), 3(\pm \bar{4})$	48	$\sigma^{(1)}, \sigma^{(7)}, \sigma^{(9)}$

be exhibited diagrammatically by means of the stereograms presented in Fig. 2.6. In constructing the right-hand diagram of any pair illustrated in Fig. 2.6, the crystallographic axes of symmetry are drawn in such a way that they intersect at the centre of a sphere: the stereogram then shows the projection on to an equatorial plane of the points of intersection of the symmetry axes and the surface of the sphere. If the z-axis is assumed to be directed out of the plane of the paper, then the setting of the crystal relative to the stereogram corresponds to the symmetry operations listed in Table 3, except that for monoclinic crystals a second setting has been used, for clarity, in which the two-fold rotation and rotation–inversion axes are assumed to lie in the plane of the paper. For all the other crystal classes, the principal n-fold axis is represented by the n-sided figure in the centre of the (right-hand) diagram. Three-, four- and six-fold rotation inversion axes are represented by the symbols △, ◇ and ⬢ respectively, and reflection planes are indicated by heavy lines (an outer circle in heavy outline corresponding to a reflection plane normal to the principal axis). Symmetry axes perpendicular to the main axis are denoted by the appropriate symbol placed at the ends of the line through the centre of the diagram, the y- and x-axes being parallel to rows and columns of diagrams respectively. (For the trigonal and hexagonal classes the orientations of the two-fold axes are not completely specified in column 6 of Table 3 but the generating matrices may be used to remove the ambiguity in the absolute directions of these axes.)

The left-hand set of diagrams indicates the positions of equivalent points, that is the positions of all the points which can be obtained from any one of them by successive application of all the symmetry operations of the appropriate point group. The symbols • and o represent points above and below the plane of the paper respectively. Although a crystal and its stereogram are in a definite mutual orientation, the stereogram cannot be thought of as having a particular location relative to the crystalline lattice.

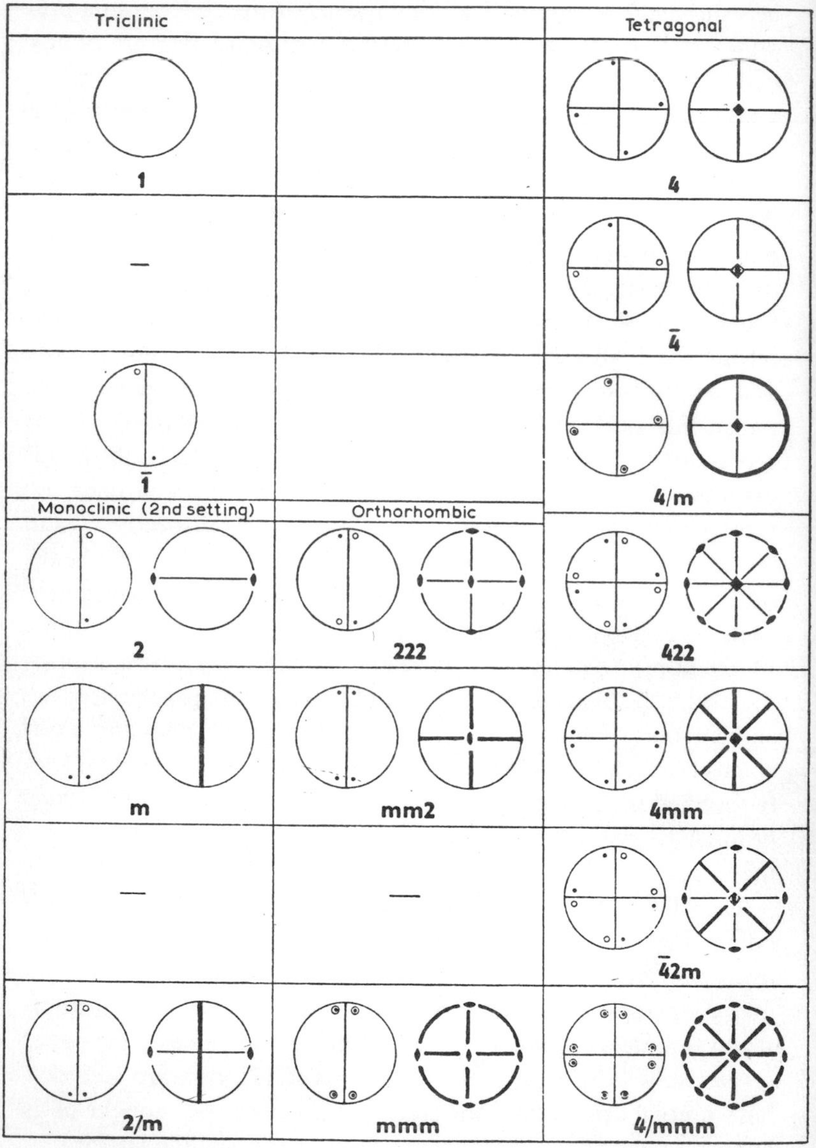

Fig. 2.6

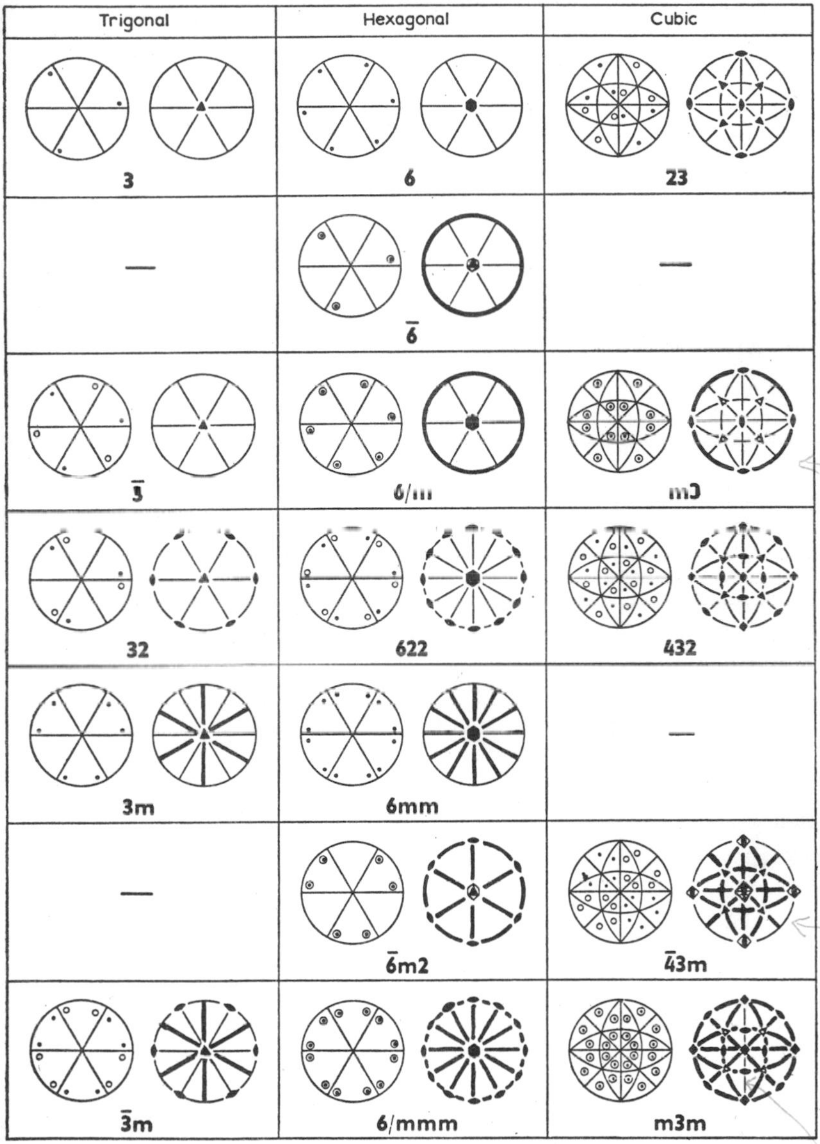

Trigonal	Hexagonal	Cubic
3	6	23
—	$\bar{6}$	—
$\bar{3}$	6/m	m3
32	622	432
3m	6mm	—
—	$\bar{6}$m2	$\bar{4}$3m
$\bar{3}$m	6/mmm	m3m

Fig. 2.6

The {100} planes are reflection planes.

There are no {100} reflection planes.

This should be a reflection plane.

§ 1.5. *Symmetry Operators and Matrices:*
the Time-inversion Operator

If a crystal exhibits an *n*-fold rotation axis then the simple example discussed in Ch. 1, § 6 indicates that the quantity to be used [e.g. in equation (1.32)] to simplify the form of a property tensor is the matrix $[l_{ip}]$ of Ch. 1, § 3 which corresponds to a rotation of the axes Ox_i' through an angle of $2\pi/n$ relative to the axes Ox_i. Such a rotation can be thought of as a linear *operator*, *n*, that transforms the vector *r* (with components x_p) into the vector $r' = nr$ (with components x_i') according to equation (1.8a) viz.

$$x_i' = l_{ip}x_p. \tag{2.7a}$$

Thus, for example, the *symmetry operator* $n = 3$ of Ch. 1, § 6, corresponding to a right-handed rotation of $\theta = 120°$ about the Ox_3 axis, is represented by the *symmetry matrix*

$$[l_{ip}] = \begin{bmatrix} \cos 120° & \cos 30° & 0 \\ \cos 210° & \cos 120° & 0 \\ 0 & 0 & \cos 0 \end{bmatrix} = \begin{bmatrix} \cos\theta & \sin\theta & 0 \\ -\sin\theta & \cos\theta & 0 \\ 0 & 0 & 1 \end{bmatrix}. \tag{2.8}$$

More generally, the matrix representing a right-handed rotation through an angle θ about an axis with direction cosines m_i (relative to Ox_p) is given by (JEFFREYS and JEFFREYS [1950])

$$[l_{ip}] = \begin{bmatrix} \cos\theta + m_1^2(1-\cos\theta) & m_1 m_2(1-\cos\theta) + m_3\sin\theta & m_1 m_3(1-\cos\theta) - m_2\sin\theta \\ m_2 m_1(1-\cos\theta) - m_3\sin\theta & \cos\theta + m_2^2(1-\cos\theta) & m_2 m_3(1-\cos\theta) + m_1\sin\theta \\ m_3 m_1(1-\cos\theta) + m_2\sin\theta & m_3 m_2(1-\cos\theta) - m_1\sin\theta & \cos\theta + m_3^2(1-\cos\theta) \end{bmatrix}$$

$$\tag{2.9}$$

For various values of m_i and θ this matrix represents *any* rotation about the point O and it may readily be verified that it is ortho-

gonal, that is its transpose and reciprocal are equal, in agreement
with (1.8b) viz.

$$x_i = l_{pi} x_p'. \tag{2.7b}$$

Equations (2.7a) and (2.7b) also hold simultaneously when the
operation under consideration is a combination of a rotation and
an inversion rather than a pure rotation, but then each component
of the matrix in (2.9) must be multiplied by -1. (This is equivalent to the multiplication of the matrix $[l_{ip}]$ of (2.9) by the matrix, $[-\delta_{pq}]$, corresponding to the operator $\bar{I}$, inversion through a
centre of symmetry.)

Another important symmetry operator which has not so far
been discussed and which cannot, in three dimensions, be directly
represented by a matrix is the time-inversion operator. It will be
shown in Ch. 3, § 1 that this operator reverses the direction of the
(spin) magnetic moment of an electron, and its significance in a
consideration of crystal symmetry is as follows. The component
parts of an actual crystal are continually in motion, and it is the
time-average of the positions of these component parts that is
represented by the geometrical description of the crystal lattice. It
is obvious that the structure of the crystal depends on the average
positions of its component parts, but, if there is, on a microscopic
scale, relative motion of various parts of the crystal which possesses a non-zero time-average, then this information is not contained in any specification of average positions. Further, if the
motion which possesses a non-zero time-average recurs in an identical manner in each unit cell of the crystal, this constitutes an
additional repetitive feature of the crystal structure that is not
included in the geometrical description of the crystal lattice. For
example, a ferromagnetic, ferrimagnetic or antiferromagnetic crystal is characterized by an orderly distribution of spin magnetic
moments which constitutes just such a repetitive feature, so that,
for these materials, the geometrical description of the crystal lattice
is not necessarily a faithful representation of the physical crystal.

Diamagnetic and paramagnetic crystals do not exhibit such ordered arrays of spin magnetic moments and they are time-symmetric, that is they are invariant under time-inversion, which is equivalent to reversing the direction of spin. For these non-magnetic crystals, the geometrical description of classical symmetry is a faithful representation of the physical crystal and the concepts of classical crystallography discussed in the present chapter may be applied without modification. The fact that the time-inversion operator, denoted by R, is an additional symmetry operator for non-magnetic crystals has, however, important consequences which are examined in § 7. Ferromagnetic, ferrimagnetic and certain antiferromagnetic crystals, on the other hand, exhibit a spontaneous magnetization, in other words the resultant spin magnetic moment does not vanish when averaged over many unit cells. Such crystals cannot be time-symmetric, since time-inversion reverses the spontaneous magnetization. However, the fact that R is not a symmetry operator does not preclude the combination of R and a spatial operator being a symmetry operator for these crystals, and for this reason classical crystallography cannot be applied without modification. The physical properties of such magnetic crystals may only be adequately described when the concepts of classical crystallography are extended to include the possibility of time-inversion. The way in which this is done is discussed in detail in Chapter 3.

§ 2. NEUMANN'S PRINCIPLE

In the simple example discussed in Ch. 1, § 6, it was shown that the form of the resistivity tensor, ϱ_{ij}, could be simplified by substituting the coefficients of a *symmetry matrix* $[l_{ip}]$ into equation (1.31) to give

$$\varrho_{ij} = l_{ip}l_{jq}\varrho_{pq}. \qquad (2.10)$$

The generalization of this particular relation between the symmetry of a crystal and the symmetry of its macroscopic physical

properties is furnished by Neumann's principle which states that
any type of symmetry which is exhibited by the point group of the
crystal is possessed by every physical property of the crystal. To
investigate the effect of crystal symmetry on the components of a
property (or matter) tensor – representing a macroscopic physical
property of the crystal – it is therefore necessary to formulate
mathematically the requirement that the tensor be invariant under
all the permissible symmetry operations appropriate to the particular crystal class. For a rotation of the coordinate axes the components $d_{ijk...n}$ of a polar tensor transform according to the
relations

$$d'_{ijk...n} = l_{ip}l_{jq}l_{kr} \cdots l_{nu}d_{pqr...u}. \tag{2.11}$$

Hence, if $d_{ijk...n}$ is a polar property tensor, the requirement that it
is invariant under all permissible symmetry operations appropriate to the particular crystal class is equivalent to the requirement that the components $d_{ijk...n}$ satisfy the set of equations

$$d_{ijk...n} = \sigma_{ip}\sigma_{jq}\sigma_{kr} \cdots \sigma_{nu}d_{pqr...u}, \tag{2.12}$$

where σ is the matrix corresponding to a particular permissible
symmetry operation for the crystal class. Since any symmetry
matrix may be used, there are as many equations as there are
symmetry operators. An axial tensor, however, transforms according to

$$d'_{ijk...n} = |l|l_{ip}l_{jq}l_{kr} \cdots l_{nu}d_{pqr...u}, \tag{2.13}$$

so that, for an axial property tensor, equation (2.12) must be
replaced by

$$d_{ijk...n} = |\sigma|\sigma_{ip}\sigma_{jq}\sigma_{kr} \cdots \sigma_{nu}d_{pqr...u}. \tag{2.14}$$

Thus, (2.14) must be employed for axial tensors and (2.12) for
polar tensors, there being, in both cases, as many equations as
there are symmetry operators. An immediate consequence of this
is that axial tensors of even rank and polar tensors of odd rank

must vanish identically for centrosymmetrical classes (i.e. those classes for which the inversion, $\bar{1}$, is a permissible symmetry operator), since these equations reduce, with

$$\sigma = \begin{bmatrix} -1 & 0 & 0 \\ 0 & -1 & 0 \\ 0 & 0 & -1 \end{bmatrix}, \qquad (2.15)$$

to the equation $d_{ijk...n} = -d_{ijk...n}$.

A particularly illuminating formulation of Neumann's principle is in terms of asymmetry rather than symmetry for, as remarked by CURIE [1908], "C'est la dissymétrie, qui crée le phénomène". Expressed in terms of asymmetry, Neumann's principle states that no asymmetry can appear in an effect which does not already exist in the crystal, in the influence which is exerted upon it, or in the combination of both. Thus no asymmetry can manifest itself in the form of a property tensor which does not already exist in the crystal which exhibits the property. When applied to (three-dimensional) spatial symmetry, Neumann's principle is therefore essentially a statement that free space is intrinsically isotropic – that there is no preferred direction in space. When the physical situation is described in terms of three spatial coordinates and a time coordinate, Neumann's principle is essentially an affirmation of the isotropy of space-time. As will be seen in Ch.3, § 3, this affirmation is correct for static properties but not for dynamic properties, such as transport phenomena, where a system has reached a steady state but is permanently in non-equilibrium.

§3. GENERATING MATRICES

It may be seen from Table 3 that the symmetry class of a crystal can be specified by a symbol (columns 2, 3, 4 or 5) which in many cases contains far fewer elements than the total number (column 7) of symmetry operators (column 6) appropriate to that class. It would be surprising therefore if it were necessary to employ *all* the symmetry operators (e.g. 48 for class **m3m**) in equations (2.12) or (2.14) in order to secure the maximum simplification in the form of the tensor $d_{ijk...n}$. In fact, it is only rarely that all the symmetry operators need be invoked, for the symmetry class is completely specified by any set of generating elements of the corresponding point group. Just as all the elements of a group may be obtained by 'multiplication' (in the sense of group theory) of generating elements, so all the symmetry matrices corresponding to a particular crystal class may be obtained from a smaller number of matrices by matrix multiplication.

For example, consider the crystal class **6/m**, which possesses the twelve symmetry operators $1, \bar{1}, 2_z, \bar{2}_z, \pm 3_z, \pm \bar{3}_z, \pm 6_z, \pm \bar{6}_z$. If the corresponding symmetry matrices are denoted by $[1], [\bar{1}], [2_z]$, and so on, it may readily be verified (using equation (2.9) and the ordinary rules of matrix multiplication) that

$$[\bar{1}] = \begin{bmatrix} -1 & 0 & 0 \\ 0 & -1 & 0 \\ 0 & 0 & -1 \end{bmatrix}, \quad [2_z] = \begin{bmatrix} -1 & 0 & 0 \\ 0 & -1 & 0 \\ 0 & 0 & 1 \end{bmatrix},$$

$$[+3_z] = \begin{bmatrix} -\tfrac{1}{2} & \tfrac{1}{2}\sqrt{3} & 0 \\ -\tfrac{1}{2}\sqrt{3} & -\tfrac{1}{2} & 0 \\ 0 & 0 & 1 \end{bmatrix}, \quad [1] = [\bar{1}][\bar{1}],$$

$$\quad (2.16)$$

$$[\bar{2}_z] = [\bar{1}][2_z], \qquad\qquad [+\bar{3}_z] = [\bar{1}][+3_z],$$

$$[-3_z] = [+3_z][+3_z], \qquad [-\bar{3}_z] = [\bar{1}][+3_z][+3_z],$$

$$[+6_z] = [2_z][+3_z][+3_z], \qquad [+\bar{6}_z] = [\bar{1}][2_z][+3_z][+3_z],$$

$$[-6_z] = [2_z][+3_z], \qquad\qquad [-\bar{6}_z] = [\bar{1}][2_z][+3_z].$$

Thus all twelve symmetry matrices may be obtained from suitable combinations of three basic matrices $[\bar{1}]$, $[2_z]$ and $[+3_z]$. Any set of symmetry matrices from which all the symmetry matrices of a particular crystal class may be obtained by multiplication is known as a set of generating matrices: similarly the corresponding symmetry operators are known as the generators of the particular point group. If all the members of a particular set of *generating* matrices have been used to simplify the form of a tensor $d_{ijk...n}$, no further simplification is secured by employing products of two or more of these matrices, so that the application of (2.12) or (2.14) with each of the generating matrices in turn is sufficient to exploit the maximum simplification imposed on a tensor by the symmetry of any particular crystal class. The members of a set of generating matrices are not determined uniquely by the crystal class but may be chosen with a certain degree of freedom. A convenient assemblage from which to choose the various sets of generating matrices is the following:

$$\sigma^{(0)} = [1] = \begin{bmatrix} 1 & 0 & 0 \\ 0 & 1 & 0 \\ 0 & 0 & 1 \end{bmatrix}, \quad \sigma^{(1)} = [\bar{1}] = \begin{bmatrix} -1 & 0 & 0 \\ 0 & -1 & 0 \\ 0 & 0 & -1 \end{bmatrix},$$

$$\sigma^{(2)} = [2_y] = \begin{bmatrix} -1 & 0 & 0 \\ 0 & 1 & 0 \\ 0 & 0 & -1 \end{bmatrix}, \quad \sigma^{(3)} = [2_z] = \begin{bmatrix} -1 & 0 & 0 \\ 0 & -1 & 0 \\ 0 & 0 & 1 \end{bmatrix},$$

$$\sigma^{(4)} = [\bar{2}_y] = \begin{bmatrix} 1 & 0 & 0 \\ 0 & -1 & 0 \\ 0 & 0 & 1 \end{bmatrix}, \quad \sigma^{(5)} = [\bar{2}_z] = \begin{bmatrix} 1 & 0 & 0 \\ 0 & 1 & 0 \\ 0 & 0 & -1 \end{bmatrix},$$

$$(2.17)$$

$$\sigma^{(6)} = [3_z] = \begin{bmatrix} -\frac{1}{2} & \frac{1}{2}\sqrt{3} & 0 \\ -\frac{1}{2}\sqrt{3} & -\frac{1}{2} & 0 \\ 0 & 0 & 1 \end{bmatrix}, \quad \sigma^{(7)} = [4_z] = \begin{bmatrix} 0 & 1 & 0 \\ -1 & 0 & 0 \\ 0 & 0 & 1 \end{bmatrix},$$

$$\tag{2.17}$$

$$\sigma^{(8)} = [\bar{4}_z] = \begin{bmatrix} 0 & -1 & 0 \\ 1 & 0 & 0 \\ 0 & 0 & -1 \end{bmatrix}, \quad \sigma^{(9)} = \begin{bmatrix} 0 & 1 & 0 \\ 0 & 0 & 1 \\ 1 & 0 & 0 \end{bmatrix}.$$

This assemblage is so chosen that the number of generating matrices in any set is small and the relations satisfied by the tensor components are simple. Substitution into equations (2.12) or (2.14) of the matrices $\sigma^{(1)}$, ... $\sigma^{(5)}$ leads to a number of tensor components being equated to zero, whilst substitution of the matrices $\sigma^{(6)}$, ... $\sigma^{(9)}$ ($\sigma^{(9)}$ represents a three-fold rotation axis parallel to a cube-body diagonal) yields linear relationships between the non-vanishing components. Sets of generating matrices (chosen from this assemblage) for the 32 crystal classes are listed in column 8 of Table 3.

To summarize, it may be said that the limitations of crystal symmetry are imposed on the tensor $d_{ijk...n}$ by means of equations of the form

$$d_{ijk...n} = \sigma_{ip}\sigma_{jq}\sigma_{kr} \cdots \sigma_{nu}d_{pqr...u}, \tag{2.18a}$$

for polar tensors, and

$$d_{ijk...n} = |\sigma|\,\sigma_{ip}\sigma_{jq}\sigma_{kr} \cdots \sigma_{nu}d_{pqr...u}, \tag{2.18b}$$

for axial tensors, where the σ's are generating matrices embodying the symmetry characteristics of the particular crystal class under consideration. For any particular rank of the tensor $d_{ijk...n}$, the appropriate set of equations from (2.18) successively employs the coefficients $\sigma_{ip}, \sigma_{jq}, \sigma_{kr}, \ldots, \sigma_{nu}$ corresponding to *any one* generating matrix in turn. These sets of generating matrices never possess more than four members and they are listed for the 32 crystal classes in column 8 of Table 3. As an example of their use it is instructive to consider a particular crystal class.

§4. THE FORM OF A FOURTH-RANK TENSOR
IN THE CRYSTAL CLASS 6/mmm

Consider the hexagonal close-packed structure discussed in Ch. 1 and in § 1.3 and illustrated in Fig. 1.1b. The appropriate crystal class is **6/mmm** and Table 3 indicates that a set of generating matrices is

$$\sigma^{(1)} = \begin{bmatrix} -1 & 0 & 0 \\ 0 & -1 & 0 \\ 0 & 0 & -1 \end{bmatrix}, \quad \sigma^{(2)} = \begin{bmatrix} -1 & 0 & 0 \\ 0 & 1 & 0 \\ 0 & 0 & -1 \end{bmatrix},$$

$$\sigma^{(3)} = \begin{bmatrix} -1 & 0 & 0 \\ 0 & -1 & 0 \\ 0 & 0 & 1 \end{bmatrix}, \quad \sigma^{(6)} = \begin{bmatrix} -\tfrac{1}{2} & \tfrac{1}{2}\sqrt{3} & 0 \\ -\tfrac{1}{2}\sqrt{3} & -\tfrac{1}{2} & 0 \\ 0 & 0 & 1 \end{bmatrix}. \tag{2.19}$$

Since $\sigma^{(1)}$ is a generating matrix, the crystal class is centrosymmetrical and all axial fourth-rank tensors vanish identically. For polar tensors, the coefficients d_{ijkl} must all satisfy the relations

$$d_{ijkl} = \sigma_{ip}\sigma_{jq}\sigma_{kr}\sigma_{ls}d_{pqrs}, \tag{2.20}$$

where the σ's are, in turn, any one of the symmetry operators in (2.19). Thus, if $\sigma^{(2)}$ is used in equations (2.20), it may be observed that the σ's are separately non-zero only if $i = p$ or $j = q$ or $k = r$ or $l = s$. Further the product $\sigma_{ip}\sigma_{jq}\sigma_{kr}\sigma_{ls}$ is -1 when the subscript 2 appears (as p, q, r or s) an odd number of times. Since this implies that $d_{ijkl} = -d_{ijkl}$, all the coefficients d_{ijkl} in which the subscript 2 appears an odd number of times must be identically zero. Similarly, if $\sigma^{(3)}$ is used, it may be shown that all the coefficients d_{ijkl} in which the subscript 3 appears an odd number of times must be zero. These two restrictions taken together ensure that the coefficients in which *any* subscript appears an odd number of times must be zero. The remaining coefficients are therefore

$$
\begin{array}{ccc}
d_{1111} & d_{1122} & d_{1133} \\[4pt]
d_{2211} & d_{2222} & d_{2233} \\[4pt]
d_{3311} & d_{3322} & d_{3333}
\end{array}
$$

$$
\begin{array}{cccc}
d_{2323} & d_{2332} & d_{3223} & d_{3232} \\[4pt]
d_{3131} & d_{3113} & d_{1331} & d_{1313} \\[4pt]
d_{1212} & d_{1221} & d_{2112} & d_{2121}.
\end{array}
$$

(2.21)

If, finally, $\sigma^{(6)}$ is used in equations (2.20), the following relations are obtained

$$
\begin{aligned}
d_{1111} = {} & \tfrac{1}{16}d_{1111} \\
& + \tfrac{3}{16}(d_{1122} + d_{2211} + d_{1212} + d_{2121} + d_{1221} + d_{2112}) \\
& + \tfrac{9}{16}d_{2222}, \\[6pt]
d_{1122} = {} & \tfrac{3}{16}d_{1111} + \tfrac{1}{16}d_{1122} + \tfrac{9}{16}d_{2211} + \tfrac{3}{16}d_{2222} \\
& - \tfrac{3}{16}(d_{1212} + d_{1221} + d_{2121} + d_{2112}), \\[6pt]
d_{1133} = {} & \tfrac{1}{4}d_{1133} + \tfrac{3}{4}d_{2233}, \\[6pt]
d_{2211} = {} & \tfrac{3}{16}d_{1111} + \tfrac{9}{16}d_{1122} + \tfrac{1}{16}d_{2211} + \tfrac{3}{16}d_{2222} \\
& - \tfrac{3}{16}(d_{1212} + d_{1221} + d_{2121} + d_{2112}),
\end{aligned}
$$

(2.22)

$$d_{2222} = \tfrac{9}{16}d_{1111}$$
$$+ \tfrac{3}{16}(d_{1122} + d_{2211} + d_{1212} + d_{2121} + d_{1221} + d_{2112})$$
$$+ \tfrac{1}{16}d_{2222},$$

$$d_{2233} = \tfrac{1}{4}d_{2233} + \tfrac{3}{4}d_{1133},$$

$$d_{3311} = \tfrac{1}{4}d_{3311} + \tfrac{3}{4}d_{3322},$$

$$d_{3322} = \tfrac{1}{4}d_{3322} + \tfrac{3}{4}d_{3311},$$

$$d_{3333} = d_{3333},$$

$$d_{2323} = \tfrac{1}{4}d_{2323} + \tfrac{3}{4}d_{1313},$$

$$d_{2332} = \tfrac{1}{4}d_{2332} + \tfrac{3}{4}d_{1331},$$

$$d_{3223} = \tfrac{1}{4}d_{3223} + \tfrac{3}{4}d_{3113}, \qquad\qquad (2.22)$$

$$d_{3232} = \tfrac{1}{4}d_{3232} + \tfrac{3}{4}d_{3131},$$

$$d_{3131} = \tfrac{1}{4}d_{3131} + \tfrac{3}{4}d_{3232},$$

$$d_{3113} = \tfrac{1}{4}d_{3113} + \tfrac{3}{4}d_{3223},$$

$$d_{1331} = \tfrac{1}{4}d_{1331} + \tfrac{3}{4}d_{2332},$$

$$d_{1313} = \tfrac{1}{4}d_{1313} + \tfrac{3}{4}d_{2323},$$

$$d_{1212} = \tfrac{1}{16}d_{1212} + \tfrac{9}{16}d_{2121}$$
$$+ \tfrac{3}{16}(d_{1111} + d_{2222} - d_{1122} - d_{2211} - d_{1221} - d_{2112}),$$

$$d_{1221} = \tfrac{1}{16}d_{1221} + \tfrac{9}{16}d_{2112}$$
$$+ \tfrac{3}{16}(d_{1111} + d_{2222} - d_{1122} - d_{2211} - d_{1212} - d_{2121}),$$

$$d_{2112} = \tfrac{1}{16}d_{2112} + \tfrac{9}{16}d_{1221}$$
$$+ \tfrac{3}{16}(d_{1111} + d_{2222} - d_{1122} - d_{2211} - d_{2121} - d_{1212}),$$
$$\text{(2.22)}$$
$$d_{2121} = \tfrac{1}{16}d_{2121} + \tfrac{9}{16}d_{1212}$$
$$+ \tfrac{3}{16}(d_{1111} + d_{2222} - d_{1122} - d_{2211} - d_{2112} - d_{1221}).$$

These equations reduce the number of independent components of d_{ijkl} and many of the coefficients are equal in pairs. It is possible to write the complete scheme of coefficients in an extremely compact form as may be seen by reference to the following sets of equations.

$$
\begin{array}{lll}
d_{1111} = d_{1122} & xxxx = xxyy & xxxx = xxyy \\
\quad |\ d_{1212} & +\ xyxy & +\ xyxy \\
\quad +\ d_{1221} & +\ yxxy & +\ yxxy \\
\quad = d_{2222} & =\ yyyy & =\ yyyy \\
\end{array}
$$

$$
\begin{array}{lll}
d_{1122} = d_{2211} & xxyy = yyxx & \\
d_{1212} = d_{2121} & xyxy = yxyx & \left.\begin{array}{}\\\\\\\end{array}\right\} \quad xxyy(x{:}3) = yyxx(y{:}3) \\
d_{1221} = d_{2112} & xyyx = yxxy & \\
\end{array}
$$

$$
\begin{array}{lll}
d_{3333} = d_{3333} & zzzz = zzzz & zzzz = zzzz \\
\end{array}
$$

$$\text{(2.23)}$$

$$
\begin{array}{lll}
d_{2323} = d_{1313} & yzyz = xzxz & \\
d_{2332} = d_{1331} & yzzy = xzzx & \\
d_{3223} = d_{3113} & zyyz = zxxz & \left.\begin{array}{}\\\\\\\\\\\\\end{array}\right\} \quad xxzz(6) = yyzz(6) \\
d_{3232} = d_{3131} & zyzy = zxzx & \\
d_{1133} = d_{2233} & xxzz = yyzz & \\
d_{3311} = d_{3322} & zzxx = zzyy & \\
\end{array}
$$

The equations in the first column display the non-zero components of the general polar tensor d_{ijkl} and exhibit the equalities between them: ten of these components are independent. The same information is given in a slightly condensed form in the second column where only the corresponding suffixes have been written down and where, for clarity, 1, 2 and 3 have been replaced by x, y and z respectively. The equations in the third column represent a compact way of writing those in the second: notations of the type $xxyy(x\!:\!3)$ denote the three distinct components which may be obtained from the component $xxyy$ by keeping its first index fixed and permutating all the others, whilst notations of the type $xxzz(6)$ denote the six components which may be obtained from the component $xxzz$ by unrestricted permutations of its indices.

§ 5. EXTENSION TO GENERAL TENSORS IN ANY CRYSTAL CLASS

The form of a property tensor of any rank in any particular crystal class may be found by the procedure employed in § 4, that is by systematic substitution of the appropriate generating matrices into equations (2.18). However, a certain simplification is afforded by the existence of equalities between tensors of the same rank in different crystal classes. For example, consider the crystal classes **2**, **m** and **2/m**.

The generating matrix for class **2** is $\sigma^{(3)}$ and for class **m** is $\sigma^{(5)}$, whilst it may be observed that $|\sigma^{(3)}| = 1$, $|\sigma^{(5)}| = -1$ and $\sigma^{(3)} = -\sigma^{(5)}$. Thus, for a tensor of *even* rank,

$$\sigma_{ip}^{(3)}\sigma_{jq}^{(3)}\sigma_{kr}^{(3)} \cdots \sigma_{nu}^{(3)}d_{pqr\ldots u} = \sigma_{ip}^{(5)}\sigma_{jq}^{(5)}\sigma_{kr}^{(5)} \cdots \sigma_{nu}^{(5)}d_{pqr\ldots u}, \quad (2.24\text{a})$$

and, for a tensor of *odd* rank,

$$|\sigma^{(3)}|\sigma_{ip}^{(3)}\sigma_{jq}^{(3)}\sigma_{kr}^{(3)} \cdots \sigma_{nu}^{(3)}d_{pqr\ldots u} = |\sigma^{(5)}|\sigma_{ip}^{(5)}\sigma_{jq}^{(5)}\sigma_{kr}^{(5)} \cdots \sigma_{nu}^{(5)}d_{pqr\ldots u}.$$

$$(2.24\text{b})$$

From a comparison with equations (2.18) it follows that, in the classes **2** and **m**, polar tensors of even rank are equal, and axial tensors of odd rank are equal. Further, since $|\sigma^{(3)}| = 1$, polar and axial tensors of the same rank are equal in class **2**. These equalities are displayed in Table 4a, where an axial tensor of odd rank in class **m** and polar and axial tensors of odd rank in class **2** are denoted by B_n, and where a polar tensor of even rank in class **m** and polar and axial tensors of even rank in class **2** are denoted by B_m.

For the centrosymmetrical class **2/m**, the generating matrices are $\sigma^{(1)}$ and $\sigma^{(3)}$. Thus polar tensors of odd rank and axial tensors of even rank vanish identically, whilst polar tensors of even rank and axial tensors of odd rank have, respectively, the same form as the corresponding tensors in class **2**. This is indicated in Table 4a by the presence of the symbols B_n and B_m in the row appropriate to class **2/m**. Similar considerations hold in the other crystal classes: classes which do not admit improper rotations as symmetry operators are equivalent for polar and axial tensors; classes which differ by the centre of symmetry are equivalent for polar tensors of even rank and for axial tensors of odd rank; polar tensors of odd rank and axial tensors of even rank vanish identically in the centrosymmetrical classes.

The equalities between property tensors in the various crystal classes are displayed in Table 4a. The occurrence of the same symbol in various rows and columns of the table indicates equality of the various property tensors. The actual form of the tensor which is represented by a given symbol may be obtained from Tables 4c, d, e and f for tensors of rank 1, 2, 3 and 4 respectively. These tables have been constructed (FIESCHI [1957]; FUMI [1952]) by systematic substitution into equations (2.18) of the generating matrices given in column 8 of Table 3. For completeness, the form of tensors of rank 0, i.e. scalars, is indicated in Table 4b. Each column displays, in the notation of equations (2.23), the tensor components to which the component at the top of the column reduces in the various crystal classes: each row is therefore a list

TABLE 4a

System	International symbol of symmetry class	Orientation of reference axes	Polar tensor of even rank m	Axial tensor of even rank m	Polar tensor of odd rank n	Axial tensor of odd rank n
Triclinic	1	any	A_m	A_m	A_n	A_n
	$\bar{1}$	any	A_m	–	–	A_n
Mono-clinic	2	$2//z$	B_m	B_m	B_n	B_n
	m	$\bar{2}//z$	B_m	C_m	C_n	B_n
	2/m	$2//z$	B_m	–	–	B_n
Ortho-rhombic	222	$2//x, 2//y$	D_m	D_m	D_n	D_n
	mm2	$\bar{2}//x, \bar{2}//y$	D_m	E_m	E_n	D_n
	mmm	$2//x, 2//y$	D_m	–	–	D_n
Tetra-gonal	4	$4//z$	F_m	F_m	F_n	F_n
	$\bar{4}$	$\bar{4}//z$	F_m	G_m	G_n	F_n
	4/m	$4//z$	F_m	–	–	F_n
	422	$4//z, 2//y$	H_m	H_m	H_n	H_n
	4mm	$4//z, \bar{2}//y$	H_m	I_m	I_n	H_n
	$\bar{4}2m$	$\bar{4}//z, 2//y$	H_m	J_m	J_n	H_n
	4/mmm	$4//z, 2//y$	H_m	–	–	H_n

of equalities between pairs of components, and of identities of components to zero. Notations of the type $xz(2)$, $xxy(3)$, $yxxx(x \cdot 3)$, $xxxz(4)$, $xxyy(x:3)$, $xxyz(c4)$ and $zzxy(xy:6)$ indicate certain permutations which must be applied to every component in the column. Thus, in considering a permutation of a component at the top of a column, the same permutation must be applied to all the components listed in that column for the various crystal classes. Notations of the type $xz(2)$ denote the two components which may be obtained from the component xz by unrestricted permutations

TABLE 4a (continued)

System	International symbol of symmetry class	Orientation of reference axes	Polar tensor of even rank m	Axial tensor of even rank m	Polar tensor of odd rank n	Axial tensor of odd rank n
Trigonal	3	$3//z$	K_m	K_m	K_n	K_n
	$\bar{3}$	$\bar{3}//z$	K_m	–	–	K_n
	32	$3//z, 2//y$	L_m	L_m	L_n	L_n
	3m	$3//z, \bar{2}//y$	L_m	M_m	M_n	L_n
	$\bar{3}$m	$3//z, 2//y$	L_m	–	–	L_n
Hexa-gonal	6	$6//z$	N_m	N_m	N_n	N_n
	$\bar{6}$	$3//z$	N_m	O_m	O_n	N_n
	6/m	$6//z$	N_m	–	–	N_n
	622	$6//z, 2//y$	P_m	P_m	P_n	P_n
	6mm	$6//z, \bar{2}//y$	P_m	Q_m	Q_n	P_n
	$\bar{6}$m2	$3//z, \bar{2}//y$	P_m	R_m	R_n	P_n
	6/mmm	$6//z, 2//y$	P_m	–	–	P_n
Cubic	23	$2//x, 2//y$	S_m	S_m	S_n	S_n
	m3	$2//x, 2//y$	S_m	–	–	S_n
	432	$4//x, 4//y$	T_m	T_m	T_n	T_n
	$\bar{4}$3m	$\bar{4}//x, \bar{4}//y$	T_m	U_m	U_n	T_n
	m3m	$4//x, 4//y$	T_m	–	–	T_n

of its indices; similarly $xxy(3)$ and $xxxz(4)$ denote the distinct unrestricted permutations of xxy and $xxxz$. Notations of the type $yxxx(x \cdot 3)$ denote the three distinct components which may be obtained from the component $yxxx$ by keeping its *last* index fixed and permutating all the others, whilst notations of the type $xxyy(x:3)$ denote the three distinct components which may be obtained from the component $xxyy$ by keeping its *first* index fixed and permutating all the others. Notations of the type $xxyz(c4)$

TABLE 4b

$m = 0$	x
A_0	x
B_0	x
C_0	0
D_0	x
E_0	0
F_0	x
G_0	0
H_0	x
I_0	0
J_0	0
K_0	x
L_0	x
M_0	0
N_0	x
O_0	0
P_0	x
Q_0	0
R_0	0
S_0	x
T_0	x
U_0	0

TABLE 4c

$n = 1$	x	y	z
A_1	x	y	z
B_1	0	0	z
C_1	x	y	0
D_1	0	0	0
E_1	0	0	z
F_1	0	0	z
G_1	0	0	0
H_1	0	0	0
I_1	0	0	z
J_1	0	0	0
K_1	0	0	z
L_1	0	0	0
M_1	0	0	z
N_1	0	0	z
O_1	0	0	0
P_1	0	0	0
Q_1	0	0	z
R_1	0	0	0
S_1	0	0	0
T_1	0	0	0
U_1	0	0	0

TABLE 4d

$m = 2$	xx	yy	zz	xy	yx	$xz(2)$	$yz(2)$
A_2	xx	yy	zz	xy	yx	xz	yz
B_2	xx	yy	zz	xy	yx	0	0
C_2	0	0	0	0	0	xz	yz
D_2	xx	yy	zz	0	0	0	0
E_2	0	0	0	xy	yx	0	0
F_2	xx	xx	zz	xy	$-xy$	0	0
G_2	xx	$-xx$	0	xy	xy	0	0
H_2	xx	xx	zz	0	0	0	0
I_2	0	0	0	xy	$-xy$	0	0
J_2	xx	$-xx$	0	0	0	0	0
K_2	xx	xx	zz	xy	$-xy$	0	0
L_2	xx	xx	zz	0	0	0	0
M_2	0	0	0	xy	$-xy$	0	0
N_2	xx	xx	zz	xy	$-xy$	0	0
O_2	0	0	0	0	0	0	0
P_2	xx	xx	zz	0	0	0	0
Q_2	0	0	0	xy	$-xy$	0	0
R_2	0	0	0	0	0	0	0
S_2	xx	xx	xx	0	0	0	0
T_2	xx	xx	xx	0	0	0	0
U_2	0	0	0	0	0	0	0

TABLE 4e

$n = 3$	xxx	yyy	zzz	$xxy(3)$	$yyx(3)$	$xxz(3)$	$yyz(3)$
A_3	xxx	yyy	zzz	xxy	yyx	xxz	yyz
B_3	0	0	zzz	0	0	xxz	yyz
C_3	xxx	yyy	0	xxy	yyx	0	0
D_3	0	0	0	0	0	0	0
E_3	0	0	zzz	0	0	xxz	yyz
F_3	0	0	zzz	0	0	xxz	xxz
G_3	0	0	0	0	0	xxz	$-xxz$
H_3	0	0	0	0	0	0	0
I_3	0	0	zzz	0	0	xxz	xxz
J_3	0	0	0	0	0	0	0
K_3	xxx	yyy	zzz	$-yyy$	$-xxx$	xxz	xxz
L_3	0	yyy	0	$-yyy$	0	0	0
M_3	xxx	0	zzz	0	$-xxx$	xxz	xxz
N_3	0	0	zzz	0	0	xxz	xxz
O_3	xxx	yyy	0	$-yyy$	$-xxx$	0	0
P_3	0	0	0	0	0	0	0
Q_3	0	0	zzz	0	0	xxz	xxz
R_3	xxx	0	0	0	$-xxx$	0	0
S_3	0	0	0	0	0	0	0
T_3	0	0	0	0	0	0	0
U_3	0	0	0	0	0	0	0

TABLE 4e (continued)

$n = 3$	$zzx(3)$	$zzy(3)$	xyz	xzy	zxy	yxz	yzx	zyx
A_3	zzx	zzy	xyz	xzy	zxy	yxz	yzx	zyx
B_3	0	0	xyz	xzy	zxy	yxz	yzx	zyx
C_3	zzx	zzy	0	0	0	0	0	0
D_3	0	0	xyz	xzy	zxy	yxz	yzx	zyx
E_3	0	0	0	0	0	0	0	0
F_3	0	0	xyz	xzy	zxy	$-xyz$	$-xzy$	$-zxy$
G_3	0	0	xyz	xzy	zxy	xyz	xzy	zxy
H_0	0	0	xyz	xzy	zxy	$-xyz$	$-xzy$	$-zxy$
I_3	0	0	0	0	0	0	0	0
J_3	0	0	xyz	xzy	zxy	xyz	xzy	zxy
K_3	0	0	xyz	xzy	zxy	$-xyz$	$-xzy$	$-zxy$
L_3	0	0	xyz	xzy	zxy	$-xyz$	$-xzy$	$-zxy$
M_3	0	0	0	0	0	0	0	0
N_3	0	0	xyz	xzy	zxy	$-xyz$	$-xzy$	$-zxy$
O_3	0	0	0	0	0	0	0	0
P_3	0	0	xyz	xzy	zxy	$-xyz$	$-xzy$	$-zxy$
Q_3	0	0	0	0	0	0	0	0
R_3	0	0	0	0	0	0	0	0
S_3	0	0	xyz	xzy	xyz	xzy	xyz	xzy
T_3	0	0	xyz	$-xyz$	xyz	$-xyz$	xyz	$-xyz$
U_3	0	0	xyz	xyz	xyz	xyz	xyz	xyz

TABLE 4f (pp. 62–66)

$m = 4$	$xxxx$	$yyyy$	$zzzz$	$xxxy$
A_4	$xxxx$	$yyyy$	$zzzz$	$xxxy$
B_4	$xxxx$	$yyyy$	$zzzz$	$xxxy$
C_4	0	0	0	0
D_4	$xxxx$	$yyyy$	$zzzz$	0
E_4	0	0	0	$xxxy$
F_4	$xxxx$	$xxxx$	$zzzz$	$xxxy$
G_4	$xxxx$	$-xxxx$	0	$xxxy$
H_4	$xxxx$	$xxxx$	$zzzz$	0
I_4	0	0	0	$xxxy$
J_4	$xxxx$	$-xxxx$	0	0
K_4	$yyxx + xyyx + yxyx$	$xxxx$	$zzzz$	$yyxy + xyyy + yxyy$
L_4	$yyxx + xyyx + yxyx$	$xxxx$	$zzzz$	0
M_4	0	0	0	$yyxy + xyyy + yxyy$
N_4	$yyxx + xyyx + yxyx$	$xxxx$	$zzzz$	$yyxy + xyyy + yxyy$
O_4	0	0	0	0
P_4	$yyxx + xyyx + yxyx$	$xxxx$	$zzzz$	0
Q_4	0	0	0	$yyxy + xyyy + yxyy$
R_4	0	0	0	0
S_4	$xxxx$	$xxxx$	$xxxx$	0
T_4	$xxxx$	$xxxx$	$xxxx$	0
U_4	0	0	0	0

TABLE 4f (continued)

$m = 4$	$yxxx(x\cdot3)$	$yyyx$	$xyyy(y\cdot3)$	$xxxz(4)$	$yyyz(4)$	$zzzx(4)$
A_4	$yxxx$	$yyyx$	$xyyy$	$xxxz$	$yyyz$	$zzzx$
B_4	$yxxx$	$yyyx$	$xyyy$	0	0	0
C_4	0	0	0	$xxxz$	$yyyz$	$zzzx$
D_4	0	0	0	0	0	0
E_4	$yxxx$	$yyyx$	$xyyy$	0	0	0
F_4	$yxxx$	$-xxxy$	$-yxxx$	0	0	0
G_4	$yxxx$	$xxxy$	$yxxx$	0	0	0
H_4	0	0	0	0	0	0
I_4	$yxxx$	$-xxxy$	$-yxxx$	0	0	0
J_4	0	0	0	0	0	0
K_4	$yxxx$	$-xxxy$	$-yxxx$	$xxxz$	$yyyz$	0
L_4	0	0	0	$xxxz$	0	0
M_4	$yxxx$	$-xxxy$	$-yxxx$	0	$yyyz$	0
N_4	$yxxx$	$-xxxy$	$-yxxx$	0	0	0
O_4	0	0	0	$xxxz$	$yyyz$	0
P_4	0	0	0	0	0	0
Q_4	$yxxx$	$-xxxy$	$-yxxx$	0	0	0
R_4	0	0	0	0	$yyyz$	0
S_4	0	0	0	0	0	0
T_4	0	0	0	0	0	0
U_4	0	0	0	0	0	0

TABLE 4f (continued)

$m = 4$	$zzzy(4)$	$xxyy(x:3)$	$yyxx(y:3)$	$xxzz(x:3)$	$zzxx(z:3)$
A_4	$zzzy$	$xxyy$	$yyxx$	$xxzz$	$zzxx$
B_4	0	$xxyy$	$yyxx$	$xxzz$	$zzxx$
C_4	$zzzy$	0	0	0	0
D_4	0	$xxyy$	$yyxx$	$xxzz$	$zzxx$
E_4	0	0	0	0	0
F_4	0	$xxyy$	$xxyy$	$xxzz$	$zzxx$
G_4	0	$xxyy$	$-xxyy$	$xxzz$	$zzxx$
H_4	0	$xxyy$	$xxyy$	$xxzz$	$zzxx$
I_4	0	0	0	0	0
J_4	0	$xxyy$	$-xxyy$	$xxzz$	$zzxx$
K_4	0	$xxyy$	$xxyy$	$xxzz$	$zzxx$
L_4	0	$xxyy$	$xxyy$	$xxzz$	$zzxx$
M_4	0	0	0	0	0
N_4	0	$xxyy$	$xxyy$	$xxzz$	$zzxx$
O_4	0	0	0	0	0
P_4	0	$xxyy$	$xxyy$	$xxzz$	$zzxx$
Q_4	0	0	0	0	0
R_4	0	0	0	0	0
S_4	0	$xxyy$	$yyxx$	$yyxx$	$xxyy$
T_4	0	$xxyy$	$xxyy$	$xxyy$	$xxyy$
U_4	0	$xxyy$	$-xxyy$	$-xxyy$	$xxyy$

TABLE 4f (continued)

$m = 4$	$yyzz(y:3)$	$zzyy(z:3)$	$xxyz(c4)$	$xyxz(c4)$	$yxxz(c4)$
A_4	$yyzz$	$zzyy$	$xxyz$	$xyxz$	$yxxz$
B_4	$yyzz$	$zzyy$	0	0	0
C_4	0	0	$xxyz$	$xyxz$	$yxxz$
D_4	$yyzz$	$zzyy$	0	0	0
E_4	0	0	0	0	0
F_4	$xxzz$	$zzxx$	0	0	0
G_4	$-xxzz$	$-zzxx$	0	0	0
H_4	$xxzz$	$zzxx$	0	0	0
I_4	0	0	0	0	0
J_4	$-xxzz$	$-zzxx$	0	0	0
K_4	$xxzz$	$zzxx$	$-yyyz$	$-yyyz$	$-yyyz$
L_4	$xxzz$	$zzxx$	0	0	0
M_4	0	0	$-yyyz$	$-yyyz$	$-yyyz$
N_4	$xxzz$	$zzxx$	0	0	0
O_4	0	0	$-yyyz$	$-yyyz$	$-yyyz$
P_4	$xxzz$	$zzxx$	0	0	0
Q_4	0	0	0	0	0
R_4	0	0	$-yyyz$	$-yyyz$	$-yyyz$
S_4	$xxyy$	$yyxx$	0	0	0
T_4	$xxyy$	$xxyy$	0	0	0
U_4	$xxyy$	$-xxyy$	0	0	0

TABLE 4f (continued)

$m = 4$	$yyxz$(c4)	$yxyz$(c4)	$xyyz$(c4)	$zzxy$(xy:6)	$zzyx$(yx:6)
A_4	$yyxz$	$yxyz$	$xyyz$	$zzxy$	$zzyx$
B_4	0	0	0	$zzxy$	$zzyx$
C_4	$yyxz$	$yxyz$	$xyyz$	0	0
D_4	0	0	0	0	0
E_4	0	0	0	$zzxy$	$zzyx$
F_4	0	0	0	$zzxy$	$-zzxy$
G_4	0	0	0	$zzxy$	$zzxy$
H_4	0	0	0	0	0
I_4	0	0	0	$zzxy$	$-zzxy$
J_4	0	0	0	0	0
K_4	$-xxxz$	$-xxxz$	$-xxxz$	$zzxy$	$-zzxy$
L_4	$-xxxz$	$-xxxz$	$-xxxz$	0	0
M_4	0	0	0	$zzxy$	$-zzxy$
N_4	0	0	0	$zzxy$	$-zzxy$
O_4	$-xxxz$	$-xxxz$	$-xxxz$	0	0
P_4	0	0	0	0	0
Q_4	0	0	0	$zzxy$	$-zzxy$
R_4	0	0	0	0	0
S_4	0	0	0	0	0
T_4	0	0	0	0	0
U_4	0	0	0	0	0

denote the four distinct *cyclic* permutations of *xxyz*. Notations of
the type $zzxy(xy:6)$ denote the six components which can be obtained from the component $zzxy$ by permutating its indices subject to the restriction that the *order* of the indices x and y remains
unchanged (although x and y need not remain adjacent).

As an example of the use of Table 4, it may be noted that the
(polar) tensor d_{ijkl} in the class **6/mmm** discussed in § 4 is given as
P_4 from Table 4a. The form of the tensor may be ascertained from
the row appropriate to P_4 in Table 4f, the resulting equalities
corresponding to those given in the last column of (2.23).

§ 6. INTRINSIC SYMMETRY

In addition to the symmetry imposed by the crystal structure, a
property tensor may exhibit intrinsic symmetry, that is the physical
nature of the property it describes may cause some of its components to be equal or linearly related. In general, the schemes of
coefficients given in Table 4 may then be simplified still further,
and this further simplification is known as particularization. An
excellent example of particularization is provided by the equations for the energy relations governing magnetoelastic effects in
ferromagnetic crystals. This example is discussed below, with
special reference to fourth-rank tensors in the crystal class **6/mmm**,
i.e. to the tensors considered in § 4.

The magnetoelastic properties of a saturated ferromagnetic
crystal are formally expressed in terms of an energy density $U+V'$,
where U is the elastic energy density and V' is the magnetic energy
density. U is a quadratic function of the components, E_{ij}, of the
symmetrical strain tensor†, that is

$$U = a_{ijkl}E_{ij}E_{kl}. \qquad (2.25)$$

V' is a function of the E_{ij} and also of the α_i, the direction cosines,

† The propriety of assuming that the *symmetrical* strain tensor is the relevant
tensor is examined in Ch. 5, § 3.

relative to the crystallographic axes, of the saturation magnetization vector. For small strains, $V' = V^0 + V_{ij}^0 E_{ij}$, where V^0 and
the V_{ij}^0 are functions of the α_i only which may be written in the
form

$$V^0 = b_i\alpha_i + b_{ij}\alpha_i\alpha_j + b_{ijk}\alpha_i\alpha_j\alpha_k + b_{ijkl}\alpha_i\alpha_j\alpha_k\alpha_l$$

$$+ b_{ijklm}\alpha_i\alpha_j\alpha_k\alpha_l\alpha_m + \cdots, \tag{2.26}$$

$$V_{ij}^0 = c_{ij} + c_{kij}\alpha_k + c_{klij}\alpha_k\alpha_l + c_{klmij}\alpha_k\alpha_l\alpha_m + \cdots. \tag{2.27}$$

There are, therefore, three terms involving fourth-rank tensors in
the expression for the energy density $U + V'$, namely $a_{ijkl}E_{ij}E_{kl}$,
$b_{ijkl}\alpha_i\alpha_j\alpha_k\alpha_l$ and $c_{klij}\alpha_k\alpha_l E_{ij}$. The α_i are the components of an axial
vector and the E_{ij} are the components of a polar tensor, so that
a_{ijkl}, b_{ijkl} and c_{klij} are all polar tensors.

For the crystal class **6/mmm**, the complete scheme of coefficients
of a general fourth-rank polar tensor, d_{ijkl}, is given by (2.23). There
are ten independent components. If the d_{ijkl} are particularized to
the a_{ijkl} of (2.25), then $a_{ijkl} = a_{klij}$, since the two strain components are interchangeable in $a_{ijkl}E_{ij}E_{kl}$. The number of independent coefficients is thereby reduced from ten to eight. In addition,
since the E_{ij} are symmetrical, $E_{ij} = E_{ji}$, so that the first pair of
indices of any coefficient can be interchanged and the last pair can
be interchanged. The number of independent coefficients is thereby
further reduced from eight to five, namely a_{1122}, a_{1133}, a_{3333},
a_{2323} and a_{1212}. If the d_{ijkl} are identified with the c_{klij} then the
first pair of indices is interchangeable because α_k and α_l are interchangeable, whilst the last pair is interchangeable since $E_{ij} = E_{ji}$.
However, $c_{ijkl} \neq c_{klij}$ in this case, and the number of independent
coefficients is reduced from ten to six, namely c_{1122}, c_{1133}, c_{3311},
c_{3333}, c_{2323} and c_{1212}. Finally, if the d_{ijkl} are particularized to the
b_{ijkl}, the order of the subscripts is immaterial and the number of
independent coefficients is reduced from ten to three, namely
b_{1122}, b_{1133} and b_{3333}.

It may be noted that, for the crystal class **6/mmm**, polar tensors of lower rank than the fourth cannot be further simplified by particularization. Since this class is centrosymmetrical, polar tensors of first and third ranks vanish identically. The complete scheme of coefficients for a general second-rank polar tensor d_{ij} in the class $6/mmm$ is given by $d_{11} = d_{22}, d_{33} = d_{33}$, and this may not be further simplified by considerations of intrinsic symmetry. However, even for classes of the lowest symmetry, many property tensors of the second rank are observed to by symmetrical (i.e. $d_{ij} = d_{ji}$). For example, the second-rank property tensors characterizing magnetic permeabilities and susceptibilities, dielectric permittivities and susceptibilities and electrical and thermal conductivities and resistivities are all symmetrical. This is a consequence of intrinsic symmetry arising from thermodynamic (or thermostatic) considerations.

The permeability and permittivity tensors are examples of property tensors characterizing static properties, the symmetry of which follows from the second law of thermodynamics (or, more correctly, thermostatics). Because these properties are static, they may be described in terms of a succession of equilibrium states; changes between these states are reversible and changes in the free energy may be expressed as perfect differentials. Under these conditions, the symmetry of the permeability (or permittivity) tensor follows directly (NYE [1960]) from the reversibility of the order in which the free energy may be successively differentiated with respect to two components of the magnetic (or electric) field strength.

Thermal and electrical conduction are examples of transport processes, in which the property is characterized by dynamic – rather than static – equilibrium, and for which the laws for reversible processes do not apply. In a transport process, a 'force', such as a potential difference – i.e. a potential gradient – or a gradient of temperature or concentration, gives rise to a 'flux', such as an electric current, or a heat flow, or a flow of matter of a component in a mixture. In an isotropic medium the components of the vector representing the force, X_i, and those representing the corresponding flux, J_i, are usually proportional. Familiar examples of such proportionality for irreversible processes are provided by Ohm's law relating electrical current to potential gradient, Fourier's law relating heat flow to temperature gradient and Fick's law relating flow of matter of a component in a mixture to its concentration gradient. In anisotropic media, or where two or more irreversible processes occur simultaneously, the proportionality between X_i and J_i must be generalized to

$$J_i = L_{ij}X_j, \qquad (2.28)$$

indicating that any force (component) may give rise to any flux (component).

For irreversible processes, the concept of macroscopic reversibility implicit in the second law of thermostatics must be replaced by the concept of microscopic reversibility, leading to Onsager's theorem of irreversible thermodynamics. Onsager's theorem (ONSAGER [1931a, b]) states that the coefficients L_{ij} occurring in equation (2.28) form a symmetrical matrix (i.e. $L_{ij} = L_{ji}$), provided the forces and fluxes are correctly chosen. It is obviously important, for example, to choose the forces and fluxes in such a way that every flux is related to the correct force, otherwise the distinction between diagonal and off-diagonal terms in L_{ij} would be lost. The rules which permit the correct forces and fluxes to be chosen have been discussed by DE GROOT [1951]: in general, the X_i and J_i must be defined in such a way that the sum X_iJ_i is the rate at which entropy is produced in the system. (For example, consider an electric current of density J flowing in a crystal under the action of an electric field E: at (absolute) temperature T the rate of production of entropy is $(E \cdot J)/T$ per unit volume, so that, if J is chosen as the flux, the correct force is not E but E/T.) Onsager's theorem will not be considered further at this stage, but it may be noted that, in the presence of an externally applied magnetic field H, the relations $L_{ij} = L_{ji}$ must be replaced by $L_{ij}(H) = L_{ji}(-H)$.

Intrinsic symmetry has been discussed in greater detail and in a systematic manner by NIGGLI [1955], who has considered the simplifications imposed on tensors of ranks 0 to 4 by many different types of particularization. He has listed the number of independent components of such tensors for the various types of intrinsic symmetry, not only in three dimensions but also in one, two, four, five and six dimensions.

§ 7. NULL PROPERTY TENSORS: 'FORBIDDEN' EFFECTS

For tensors of high rank, the only crystal classes in which the requirements of spatial symmetry impose nullity on all the components of a property tensor are the centrosymmetrical classes, in which polar tensors of odd rank and axial tensors of even rank vanish identically. This is true for tensors of any rank greater than the third – and also for general third-rank tensors, although it should be noted that particularization can lead to a null tensor, (e.g. to $H_3 = 0$ for the class **422**). For general tensors of the first or second rank the situation is as indicated below.

In the centrosymmetrical classes general second-rank axial tensors vanish identically. However, in addition, O_2, R_2 and U_2 are all zero, so that such tensors also vanish in the classes $\bar{6}$, $\bar{6}$m2 and $\bar{4}$3m. Crystals of these or of the centrosymmetrical classes cannot therefore exhibit properties described by general second-rank axial tensors (e.g. the optical gyration tensor). Symmetry does not impose nullity on general second-rank polar tensors (e.g. permittivity) in any crystal class.

Similarly, properties characterized by polar vectors (e.g. pyroelectricity) cannot be exhibited by centrosymmetrical crystals nor (since D_1, G_1, H_1, J_1, L_1, O_1, P_1, R_1, S_1, T_1 and U_1 all vanish) by crystals belonging to the classes **222, $\bar{4}$, 422, $\bar{4}$2m, 32, $\bar{6}$, 622, $\bar{6}$m2, 23, 432** or **$\bar{4}$3m**. Properties characterized by axial vectors (e.g. pyromagnetism) may be exhibited only by crystals belonging to the classes **1, $\bar{1}$, 2, m, 2/m, 4, $\bar{4}$, 4/m, 3, $\bar{3}$, 6, $\bar{6}$** and **6/m**. Thus, although some tensors must vanish in certain crystal classes, crystal symmetry does not impose nullity on any tensor in *all* crystal classes. There are, therefore, no effects which are completely 'forbidden' from symmetry considerations. However, the restrictions imposed by symmetry are, in fact, more prohibitive than is indicated above and, to discuss this point in more detail, it is convenient to consider as examples pyroelectricity and pyromagnetism, properties characterized respectively by polar and axial vectors.

Although pyroelectricity is a well-known effect, pyromagnetic crystals are singularly elusive. Both CURIE [1908] and VOIGT [1928] tried to demonstrate the existence of pyromagnetism, but without success. It was commonly supposed (until recently) that no crystals were pyromagnetic, and eventually (ZOCHER and TÖRÖK [1953]) it was concluded that pyromagnetism is a 'forbidden' effect.

Zocher and Török pointed out that, for an equilibrium or a stationary state, it is possible to consider transformations both of the space coordinates and of the time coordinate as symmetry transformations. In particular, they considered the operation representing a reversal or inversion of time, the spatial coordinates being unaltered. Quantities like linear or rotational velocities are time-antisymmetric, that is time-inversion causes the sign of the quantity to be reversed. Other quantities related to movement may be time-symmetric, for instance those containing velocity to an even power (e.g. energy), or those containing acceleration (the second derivative). The laws of classical mechanics are invariant with respect to a reversal of time but magnetic moment – like angular momentum – is time-antisymmetric.

It is therefore possible, by considering the effect of time-inversion, to divide all property tensors into two types: tensors whose components are invariant under time-inversion – these may be called i-tensors, and tensors whose components all change sign under time-inversion – these may be called c-tensors. Since magnetic moment is time-antisymmetric, pyromagnetism (and also piezomagnetism) is characterized by a c-tensor. Zocher and

Török assumed that the structure of a crystal is time-symmetric and therefore concluded, from Neumann's principle, that all c-tensors must be null. The conclusion that static† properties characterized by c-tensors are forbidden for time-symmetric crystals is correct. However, the assumption that *all* crystals are time-symmetric is not.

As indicated in § 1.5, diamagnetic and paramagnetic crystals do not exhibit ordered arrays of (spin) magnetic moments and they are time-symmetric, that is they are invariant under time-inversion, which is equivalent to reversing the direction of spin. For these non-magnetic crystals, the geometrical description of classical symmetry is a faithful representation of the physical crystal; all static properties characterized by c-tensors are forbidden and pyromagnetism is impossible. Ferromagnetic, ferri-magnetic and certain antiferromagnetic crystals, on the other hand, exhibit a spontaneous magnetization, in other words the resultant spin magnetic moment does not vanish when averaged over many unit cells. Such crystals cannot be time-symmetric, since time-inversion reverses the spontaneous magnetization. Thus pyromagnetism may be a possible effect for some magnetic crystals. To investigate the actual restrictions imposed by symmetry on c-tensors for magnetic crystals, it is necessary to extend the concepts of crystal symmetry to include the possibility of time-inversion. This is discussed in detail in Chapter 3.

---

† The limitation to *static* properties is discussed in Ch. 3, § 3.

CHAPTER 3

SYMMETRY IN SPACE-TIME

§1. TIME-INVERSION

If the effect of time-inversion on property tensors is to be investigated, then it is necessary that the description of the symmetry of crystal structures be modified to accommodate the possibility of time-inversion. Since electron spin is associated with angular momentum it was assumed in Ch. 2, § 7 that time-inversion reverses the direction of spin. However, it must be remembered that, although electron spin is a vector quantity with the dimensions of angular momentum, and although the nearest classical analogue to electron spin is the angular momentum of a rotating body, nevertheless spin is essentially distinct from angular momentum: it is a quantum-mechanical quantity which does not exist in classical mechanics. The characteristic values of the component of the spin in any prescribed direction (measured in units of $\frac{1}{2}\hbar$) are $+1$ and -1, and the existence of only these two characteristic values means that a measurement of the component of the spin in any direction will always give one of the two results $+1$ or -1. It is in this fact that the distinction between spin and ordinary angular momentum becomes apparent (since the latter would not have only two eigenstates). It is therefore not immediately obvious that electron spin is reversed by time-inversion. Further, it is essential to clarify this point because it is the symmetry of the distribution of spin magnetic moments that is observed experimentally (e.g. by neutron diffraction) rather than the symmetry of the crystal under the operation of time-inversion.

74

The most complete theory of spin yet devised is provided by Dirac's relativistic treatment of the electron. However, when the velocities of electrons are small compared with the velocity of light, spin may be handled by the scheme outlined below, which was developed by Pauli. Since the three space coordinates, x_1, x_2, x_3, and the time coordinate, t, are insufficient to specify the complete state of an electron, a further 'spin coordinate' is introduced denoted by s_3. The hypothetical spin coordinates s_1 and s_2 are, in fact, never needed, so that the subscript 3 on s may be deleted and the wave function, or state function, of an electron written in the form $\psi(x_1, x_2, x_3, s, t)$. The success of Pauli's theory hinges on the postulate that the range of the variable s consists of only two points: $s = \pm 1$. If s has only these two values, then the state function may be treated as the pair of functions:

$$\psi_1 = f_1(x_1, x_2, x_3, 1, t),$$
$$\psi_2 = f_2(x_1, x_2, x_3, -1, t). \tag{3.1}$$

The quantity $|\psi_1|^2 = |f_1(x_1, x_2, x_3, 1, t)|^2$ is the probability that the electron has the coordinates x_1, x_2, x_3 with the spin $+1$ in the x_3 direction at time t, whilst $|\psi_2|^2 = |f_2(x_1, x_2, x_3, -1, t)|^2$ is the probability that the electron has the same value of the coordinates but with the other possible value of the 'spin in the x_3 direction'. In general, these two functions are different functions of (x_1, x_2, x_3).

It will be recalled that a scalar or a pseudoscalar, i.e. a tensor of rank 0, is invariant under all rotations of the coordinate axes (a pseudoscalar changes sign, however, upon space-inversion). Although the two quantities ψ_1 and ψ_2 are numbers (in general, complex) they are not scalar functions in the sense of being independent of the choice of the coordinate system. Under a transformation of coordinate axes, ψ_1 and ψ_2 transform between one another in a complicated way which may be most readily understood by introducing a two-dimensional spin-space in which ψ_1

and ψ_2 are the orthogonal components of a first-rank spinor†
represented by the column matrix

$$\psi = \begin{bmatrix} \psi_1 \\ \psi_2 \end{bmatrix}. \tag{3.2}$$

By a two-dimensional spin-space is meant an x, y coordinate system in which both x and y are complex numbers, so that the complex numbers ψ_1 and ψ_2 are 'components' (along the complex x
and y coordinate axes) of the spinor representing the complete
state function. This two-dimensional spin-space is not the same as
the Argand diagram, on which ψ_1 and ψ_2 would be represented by
two 'vectors'. The significance of saying that the state function is a
spinor is that it obeys the transformation laws of spinor analysis
(CORSON [1953]), just as a tensor obeys the transformation laws of
tensor analysis. However, the transformation laws for a first-rank
spinor are considerably different from those for a first-rank tensor,
i.e. a vector. For example, a right-handed rotation of the spatial
coordinate axes through an angle θ about an axis with direction
cosines m_1, m_2, m_3 transforms the state function according to the
relation

$$\psi'_\alpha = \lambda_{\alpha\beta}\psi_\beta \qquad (\alpha, \beta = 1, 2), \tag{3.3}$$

where

$$[\lambda_{\alpha\beta}] = \begin{bmatrix} \cos\tfrac{1}{2}\theta - im_3\sin\tfrac{1}{2}\theta & (m_2 - im_1)\sin\tfrac{1}{2}\theta \\ (-m_2 - im_1)\sin\tfrac{1}{2}\theta & \cos\tfrac{1}{2}\theta + im_3\sin\tfrac{1}{2}\theta \end{bmatrix}. \tag{3.4}$$

The right-hand side of (3.4) may be contrasted with the corresponding transformation matrix for a two-dimensional *vector*,
which may be obtained directly from (2.9).

If an electron is located at the point (x_1, x_2, x_3) at time t and
it is known with *certainty* that the spin in the x_3 direction is $+1$,

---

† When a system contains n electrons instead of 1, the state function may be
represented as a first-rank spinor in a spin-space of 2^n dimensions.

then $|\psi_2|^2 = 0$. By putting $\psi_1 = a + ib$, it may readily be verified, using equations (3.3) and (3.4), that a rotation through 180° about a line perpendicular to the z-axis ($m_3 = 0$) transforms ψ to ψ' where

$$|\psi_1'|^2 = 0 \tag{3.5}$$

and

$$|\psi_2'|^2 = (a^2 + b^2)(m_1^2 + m_2^2) = a^2 + b^2 = |\psi_1|^2. \tag{3.6}$$

This rotation of the spatial coordinate axes has therefore reversed the direction of spin.

In a similar way, the time-inversion operator R may be represented by a 2×2 matrix, thus

$$R \equiv [R_{\alpha\beta}] = \begin{bmatrix} R_{11} & R_{12} \\ R_{21} & R_{22} \end{bmatrix}. \tag{3.7}$$

However, since time-inversion (and, of course, space-inversion) is a discrete transformation rather than a continuous transformation like a (proper) rotation of the spatial coordinate axes, the $R_{\alpha\beta}$ will be numbers rather than variables as in (3.4). It might appear that an obvious choice of the $R_{\alpha\beta}$ is provided by

$$R\psi = \begin{bmatrix} 0 & 1 \\ 1 & 0 \end{bmatrix} \begin{bmatrix} \psi_1 \\ \psi_2 \end{bmatrix}, \tag{3.8}$$

since this interchanges ψ_1 and ψ_2 and therefore interchanges $|\psi_1|^2$ and $|\psi_2|^2$. However, this operator does not commute with the operator $\lambda \equiv \lambda_{\alpha\beta}$ of (3.4), and to ensure that $R\lambda\psi = \lambda R\psi$ it is necessary to operate on the complex conjugate ψ^* of ψ thus

$$R\psi = \begin{bmatrix} 0 & 1 \\ -1 & 0 \end{bmatrix} \psi^* = \begin{bmatrix} 0 & 1 \\ -1 & 0 \end{bmatrix} \begin{bmatrix} \psi_1^* \\ \psi_2^* \end{bmatrix}. \tag{3.9}$$

Consequently, if $\psi' = R\psi$, then

$$\psi' = \begin{bmatrix} \psi_2^* \\ -\psi_1^* \end{bmatrix}, \tag{3.10}$$

so that this operator also interchanges $|\psi_1|^2$ and $|\psi_2|^2$. This operator may be correctly identified with the time-inversion operator because the transformation (3.9) applied to first-rank spinors in two-dimensional spin-space corresponds directly to the transformation representing inversion of time, t, ($Rt = -t$ or $t \rightarrow -t$) applied to first-rank tensors in four-dimensional space-time. In the same way that the transformation (2.7a) using the l_{ij} of (2.9) applied to first-rank tensors corresponds directly to the transformation (3.3) using the $\lambda_{\alpha\beta}$ of (3.4) applied to first-rank spinors because first-rank tensors and spinors transform respectively according to irreducible representations of weight 1 and $\frac{1}{2}$ of the same group (the group of three-dimensional rotations of the co-ordinate axes), so the transformations (3.9) and $t \rightarrow -t$ correspond directly because they are both associated with representations of the four-dimensional rotation group. The fact that time-inversion is represented both by (3.9) and by the transformation $t \rightarrow -t$ may also be deduced from the invariance of the time-dependent Schrödinger equation under time-inversion†.

Although the operator R reverses ψ when applied twice ($RR\psi = -\psi$), this is of no direct physical significance because the physical meaning of a wave function or wave operator, ψ, is such that this transformation – and indeed quite general changes of phase (described by Pauli as gauge transformations of the first kind) – do not affect physically observable quantities. It may be

---

† The transformation (3.9) changes ψ_1 to ψ_2^*, ψ_2 to $-\psi_1^*$, and the time-dependent Schrödinger equation $H\psi = -i\hbar \, \partial\psi/\partial t$ to $H\psi^* = -i\hbar\partial\psi^*/\partial t$. However, since H is Hermitian, the additional transformation $t \rightarrow -t$ must be applied to this latter equation if it is to agree with the result obtained directly by the conjugation of both sides of the original Schrödinger equation, viz. $H\psi^* = i\hbar\partial\psi^*/\partial t$.

noted that charge is a time-symmetric quantity because R leaves $|\psi|^2 = |\psi_1|^2 + |\psi_2|^2$ invariant. Since current is proportional to the rate of decrease of $|\psi|^2$, it is to be expected that current will be reversed by time-inversion and this may be verified by applying the operator R of (3.9) to the quantum-mechanical current operator †.

The symmetry of property (and other) tensors with respect to the time-inversion operator, R, is discussed in detail in § 3 and § 4. To determine the (space-time) symmetry of the crystal, however, it is merely necessary to know that – as indicated in Ch. 2, § 7 – time-inversion reverses the direction of spin and of current whilst leaving charge invariant. Non-magnetic crystals are time-symmetric and the time-inversion operator, R, is a symmetry operator. R is therefore merely an additional symmetry operator which may, of course, be employed in conjunction with any of the permissible spatial symmetry operators. For magnetic crystals, R is not a symmetry operator, but this does not preclude the combination of R and a spatial operator being a symmetry operator. For example, X-ray or electron diffraction may reveal that a certain rotation of the crystal will bring similar atoms into coincidence, but, when the distribution of spins has been established (e.g. by neutron diffraction), it may transpire that the spins may only be brought into coincidence by a reversal of their sense. Thus it is not sufficient to enquire what spatial rotations and rotation–inversions are symmetry operators: what is also of interest is which combinations of such operators and the time-inversion operator, R, transform the crystal and its associated array of spin magnetic moments into itself.

The problem of finding the permissible symmetry operators is thus a four-dimensional one, since they represent generalized

---

† The operator R transforms ψ_1, ψ_1^*, ψ_2 and ψ_2^* to $\psi_2^*, \psi_2, -\psi_1^*$ and $-\psi_1$ respectively, and therefore transforms

$$J = \frac{ie\hbar}{2m} [(\psi_1^* \operatorname{grad} \psi_1 - \psi_1 \operatorname{grad} \psi_1^*) + (\psi_2^* \operatorname{grad} \psi_2 - \psi_2 \operatorname{grad} \psi_2^*)] \text{ to } -J.$$

transformations in space-time. However, from physical considerations, the only transformations of interest are those which can be represented by time-inversion, by a spatial transformation, or by the successive application of both – for example, no physical significance can be attached to a rotation in a generalized plane

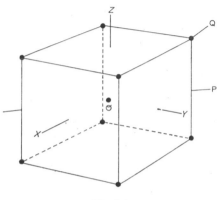

Fig. 3.1

defined by one spatial axis and the axis of time. Thus, although the problem is essentially four-dimensional, the space-time symmetry operators may be represented by the symbols which correspond to three-dimensional symmetry operators or products of these with R. Further, these symbols may be readily manipulated in these forms and, since the corresponding four-dimensional operators form a group, elementary group theory may be used to derive the space-time symmetry operators, a four-dimensional formulation being unnecessary.

As an example of the way in which combinations of spatial transformations with R can constitute symmetry operations, it is instructive to consider a metal which exhibits a body-centred cubic crystal structure as shown in Fig. 3.1, the metallic atoms being denoted by closed circles. For a diamagnetic metal such as cesium,

R is a symmetry operator and so are all the elements of the classical point group **m3m**, viz.

$$1, \quad 9(2), \quad 4(\pm 3), \quad 3(\pm 4),$$

$$\bar{1}, \quad 9(\bar{2}), \quad 4(\pm \bar{3}), \quad 3(\pm \bar{4}).$$

The three four-fold axes, which may, of course, be of either sign, are parallel to $\langle 100 \rangle$ directions such as OX, OY and OZ. These are also two-fold axes, and the other six two-fold axes are parallel to $\langle 110 \rangle$ directions, such as OP. The four three-fold axes are parallel to $\langle 111 \rangle$ directions, such as OQ.

Because the crystal has a centre of symmetry (such as O), denoted by $\bar{1}$, each rotation axis recurs as a rotation–inversion axis. However, R is also a symmetry operator, so that if n is a symmetry operator so is $\underline{n} \equiv Rn$, and if $\bar{n}$ is a symmetry operator so is $\underline{\bar{n}} \equiv R\bar{n}$. The operators $\underline{n}$ and $\underline{\bar{n}}$ represent spatial transformations followed by time-inversion. It may therefore be said that cesium belongs to the *non-magnetic* crystal class m3m for which the permissible symmetry operators, namely

$$1, \quad 9(2), \quad 4(\pm 3), \quad 3(\pm 4),$$

$$\bar{1}, \quad 9(\bar{2}), \quad 4(\pm \bar{3}), \quad 3(\pm \bar{4}),$$

$$\underline{1}, \quad 9(\underline{2}), \quad 4(\pm \underline{3}), \quad 3(\pm \underline{4}),$$

$$\underline{\bar{1}}, \quad 9(\underline{\bar{2}}), \quad 4(\pm \underline{\bar{3}}), \quad 3(\pm \underline{\bar{4}}),$$

are derived by augmenting the elements of the classical point group **m3m** with the time-inversion operator, R.

For a ferromagnetic metal such as iron, the crystal structure is again body-centred cubic but R is not a symmetry operator. If the spins of each metallic atom are parallel to the z-axis, OZ, of Fig. 3.1, then OZ is still a four-fold and also a two-fold axis, but axes such as OX and OP are two-fold axes only when the rotation is combined with time-inversion. The permissible symmetry operators are

$$1, \quad 2_z, \quad \pm 4_z,$$

$$\bar{1}, \quad \bar{2}_z, \quad \pm \bar{4}_z,$$

$$\underline{2}_x, \quad \underline{2}_y, \quad \underline{2}_{xy}, \quad \underline{2}_{-xy},$$

$$\underline{\bar{2}}_x, \quad \underline{\bar{2}}_y, \quad \underline{\bar{2}}_{xy}, \quad \underline{\bar{2}}_{-xy},$$

where the underlining of an operator indicates multiplication by R. These operators form the elements of a *magnetic* point group which is denoted by the symbol **4/mmm**. It will be shown in § 2 that there are 90 magnetic point groups: 32 have exactly the same elements as the 32 classical point groups (i.e. they do not contain R at all), whilst the remaining 58 contain R only in combination with symmetry operators other than the identity operator. The number of non-magnetic point groups is, of course, also 32, and, to distinguish these from the corresponding magnetic point groups, bold-face type is used for the Hermann–Mauguin symbols appropriate to the 90 magnetic groups but not for those appropriate to the 32 non-magnetic groups.

The allocation of cesium and iron to the non-magnetic class m3m and the magnetic class **4/mmm** respectively illustrates the general principle that diamagnetics and paramagnetics (for which R is a symmetry operator) must belong to non-magnetic crystal classes, whilst ferromagnetics and ferrimagnetics (for which R is not a symmetry operator) must belong to magnetic crystal classes. Antiferromagnetics may, however, belong to either. For example, consider an antiferromagnetic metal such as chromium, the crystal structure of which is, again, body-centred cubic. Chromium displays a simple antiferromagnetic structure in which, for example, the spins of all the chromium atoms shown in Fig. 3.1, except that at O, are parallel to OZ, whilst the spin at O is anti-parallel to OZ†. It might at first sight appear that R is not a symmetry operator, but it must be remembered that in the extended crystal lattice (of which the unit cell shown in Fig. 3.1 is a part) there is no way of distinguishing the chromium atoms at the cube-corners from those in the body-centred positions. In fact, the time-inverted lattice is identical with the original lattice if it is translated along a $\langle 111 \rangle$ direction, such as OQ, by half the length of the cube-body diagonal. Moreover, the macroscopic properties of the crystal depend on the symmetry of the point group, in which the translational component of the symmetry operators is completely suppressed, and for which, therefore, R must be admitted as a symmetry operator. The space-time symmetry of chromium is, in fact, tetragonal and it belongs to the non-magnetic crystal class 4/mmm. Nevertheless, it should be noted that antiferro-magnetics do not always belong to non-magnetic classes. For example, it may readily be seen that, for a crystalline compound with the same antiferromagnetic arrangement of spins as chromium, additional atoms may be present which are not brought into coincidence by the translation parallel to OQ.

§ 2. SPACE-TIME SYMMETRY OPERATORS

As stated in § 1, the space-time symmetry operators correspond to proper and improper spatial rotations and to combinations of such spatial transformations with time-inversion. They may be represented by symbols which correspond to three-dimensional symmetry operators or products of these with the time-inversion operator, R. If R is replaced by the identity operator, 1, the space-

† For the sake of clarity, chromium has been assumed to possess this simple antiferromagnetic structure. It seems likely, however, (LOMER [1963]) that, at room temperature, the antiferromagnetic array of spins in chromium is sinusoidally modulated in amplitude along a line of atoms with a period equal to about 28 times the interatomic spacing.

time symmetry operators must revert to the classical spatial symmetry operators appropriate to the point group of the crystal, that is to the *permissible* classical symmetry operators, $S_0 \equiv 1$, $S_1, S_2, ..., S_n$. The space-time symmetry operators can therefore be chosen *only* from the set $S_0 \equiv 1$, $S_1, S_2, ..., S_n$, from the set $RS_0 \equiv R$, $RS_1, RS_2, ..., RS_n$, or from both. It is immediately obvious (since the symmetry operators form a group) that the groups of space-time symmetry operators fall into two categories. If $R = RS_0$ is a symmetry operator, then the space-time symmetry group comprises all the $2(n + 1)$ elements $S_0, ... S_n$ and $RS_0, ... RS_n$. If $R = RS_0$ is not a symmetry operator then the group must include the identity operator, $S_0 = 1$, and at least n other elements drawn from the sets $S_1, ... S_n$ and $RS_1, ... RS_n$ so as to include each suffix $1, ... n$ at least once. Those groups falling into the former category differ from the classical point groups only by the presence of the additional element R: since these groups are those appropriate to non-magnetic crystals, they are called non-magnetic groups. (The non-magnetic groups, $\mathscr{G}'$, are denoted by the same Hermann–Mauguin symbols as the corresponding classical groups, $\mathscr{G}$, except that bold-face type is used for the latter but not for the former.) Those groups falling into the second category are the magnetic groups appropriate to magnetic crystals, and to identify the symmetry operators in any particular magnetic group it is necessary to know which of the classical symmetry operators $S_1, S_2, ..., S_n$ occur alone and which in combination with R (the two possibilities are, as shown below, mutually exclusive since R does not occur alone). In the limiting cases in which R does not occur *at all* the magnetic groups reduce to the 32 classical point groups. The problem is therefore to devise a scheme which will generate the remaining (58) magnetic groups from these 32 classical point groups. To avoid confusion, these (58) magnetic groups will be referred to as additional magnetic groups.

Let the classical symmetry operators of a particular crystal class be denoted by S_g, where the suffix g takes on all the *permissible* values appropriate to the point group, $\mathscr{G}$, of the crystal, and let the (magnetic) symmetry operators of a corresponding additional magnetic group, $\mathscr{M}$, be denoted by S_h and $\underline{S}_i = RS_i$, where all the S_h are of type S_g and all the $\underline{S}_i$ are of type RS_g. Thus,

$$S_g, S_h, S_i \in \mathscr{G}, \tag{3.11}$$

and

$$S_h, \underline{S}_i \in \mathscr{M}, \tag{3.12}$$

where the symbol $\in$ denotes that the element or elements on the left-hand side of the symbol are contained in the set on the right-hand side (in both the above cases the set is also a group). In fact, the two sets of indices h and i are mutually exclusive as may be seen from the following argument.

If h and i were *not* mutually exclusive, then for at least one value of i,

$$\underline{S}_i = RS_h, \tag{3.13}$$

and, if ν is the order of S_h,†

$$\underline{S}_i S_h^{\nu-1} = RS_h S_h^{\nu-1} = R. \tag{3.14}$$

But, since $\underline{S}_i$ and $S_h^{\nu-1}$ are members of a group ($\mathscr{M}$) of permissible symmetry operators, $\underline{S}_i S_h^{\nu-1} = R$ must also be a symmetry operator, which is impossible since $\mathscr{M}$ is a magnetic group. Thus the two sets of indices h and i are mutually exclusive and the additional magnetic group $\mathscr{M}$ may be obtained from the classical group $\mathscr{G}$ by multiplying some of the elements S_g by R and the remainder by 1, the identity operator. Further, any product of two symmetry operators of type S_h is itself of type S_g and hence cannot be of type RS_g. Since the S_h and the $\underline{S}_i$ form a group ($\mathscr{M}$), the product of any two elements of type S_h must itself be a member

† The order of a symmetry operator S is the smallest positive exponent ν for which S^ν is equal to the identity operator, 1.

of the set of elements S_h so that this set must form a sub-group of the group $\mathscr{G}$. Those elements S_h of $\mathscr{G}$ which must be multiplied by 1 (rather than by R) therefore form a sub-group, $\mathscr{H}$, of the classical point group $\mathscr{G}$, and the identification of such groups is greatly facilitated by the fact that they are all sub-groups of index 2. In fact, this is both a necessary and sufficient condition for $\mathscr{M}$ to be a group, and this is proved rigorously in the Appendix. However, it is felt that the proof given below is more readily understandable, although slightly less formal.

Tables 5a and b are schematic representations of the multiplication tables of the groups $\mathscr{M}$ and $\mathscr{G}$ respectively. Since the indices h and i are mutually exclusive, it is possible to separate the elements S_h from the elements S_i (or $\underline{S}_i$) as shown. The products formed by multiplying a particular member $\underline{S}_i^0$ of the set $R(\mathscr{G} - \mathscr{H})$ with each element of the group $\mathscr{M}$ in turn are all to be found within the shaded rectangle P + Q of Table 5a. Now, if $\mathscr{M}$ is a group these products may be placed in a one-to-one correspondence (denoted symbolically by =) with the group $\mathscr{M}$. Thus, if the set of elements within the rectangle P is *denoted* by P, and that within Q by Q,

$$P + Q = \mathscr{M}, \tag{3.15a}$$

or

$$P + Q = \mathscr{H} + R(\mathscr{G} - \mathscr{H}). \tag{3.15b}$$

But, the members of P cannot be elements of $\mathscr{H}$ (i.e. $\underline{S}_i^0 S_h \notin \mathscr{H}$) since they are all of the form RS_g. Further, R commutes with all the S_g and $R^2 = 1$ (as applied to the crystal), so that $\underline{S}_i^0 \underline{S}_i = S_i^0 S_i$, whence $\underline{S}_i^0 \underline{S}_i \notin R(\mathscr{G} - \mathscr{H})$ and the members of Q cannot be members of $R(\mathscr{G} - \mathscr{H})$. Thus

$$P = R(\mathscr{G} - \mathscr{H}) \tag{3.16a}$$

and

$$Q = \mathscr{H}, \tag{3.16b}$$

TABLE 5a

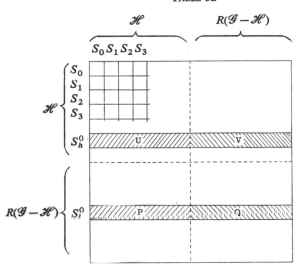

TABLE 5b

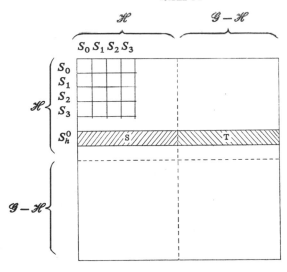

so that the number of elements in the sub-group $\mathscr{H}$ must be the same as the number of members in the set $R(\mathscr{G} - \mathscr{H})$. Hence, the ratio of the order of the group $\mathscr{G}$ to the order of the sub-group $\mathscr{H}$ is 2, i.e. the index of the sub-group is 2. Hence, a *necessary* condition for $M = \mathscr{H} + R(\mathscr{G} - \mathscr{H})$ to be a group is that $\mathscr{H}$ be a sub-group of $\mathscr{G}$ of index 2, and consequently only such sub-groups need be considered.

The requirement that $\mathscr{H}$ be a sub-group of $\mathscr{G}$ of index 2 is also a *sufficient* condition for $\mathscr{M}$ to be a group. This follows directly if the set $M = \mathscr{H} + R(\mathscr{G} - \mathscr{H})$ can be shown to be a closed set, for the associative property is obvious, and it is not necessary to prove the existence of a unit element or an inverse when the number of elements is finite. Consider the rectangle S + T in the multiplication table of $\mathscr{G}$, that is in Table 5b. Since $\mathscr{H}$ is a sub-group of $\mathscr{G}$

$$S = \mathscr{H}, \tag{3.17a}$$

whence

$$T = \mathscr{G} - \mathscr{H}. \tag{3.17b}$$

But R commutes with all the S_g and $R^2 = 1$, so that in the corresponding row of the multiplication table of the *set M*, that is in Table 5a,

$$U = \mathscr{H} \tag{3.18a}$$

and

$$V = R(\mathscr{G} - \mathscr{H}). \tag{3.18b}$$

Thus,

$$U + V = \mathscr{H} + R(\mathscr{G} - \mathscr{H}), \tag{3.19a}$$

or

$$U + V = M. \tag{3.19b}$$

It has thus been shown that any product of an S_h and a member of the set M is itself a member of the set. By considering both rows and columns in Table 5b, a similar result may be established for any $\underline{S}_t$, so that the set M must constitute a group. Hence, not only is it necessary for $\mathscr{H}$ to be a sub-group of $\mathscr{G}$ of index 2, but *all* sub-groups of index 2 satisfy the requirement that $M = \mathcal{H} + R(\mathcal{G} - \mathcal{H})$ be a group. However, in a few cases, a group, $\mathcal{M}$, so formed is inadmissible as a group of magnetic symmetry operators because an operator of odd order is a member of the set $\mathcal{G} - \mathcal{H}$. This is precluded since, if S_i is a classical symmetry operator of odd order ν, and if the corresponding $\underline{S}_i$ were a magnetic symmetry operator, then $\underline{S}_i^{\nu} = R^{\nu}S_i^{\nu} = RS_i^{\nu} = R$ would also be a magnetic symmetry operator, which is impossible. Only three classical symmetry operators are of odd order, namely 1, $+3$ and -3: thus, only those groups containing either $R(+3)$ or $R(-3)$ need be rejected (1 must be in the sub-group $\mathcal{H}$ and cannot therefore be in the set $\mathcal{G} - \mathcal{H}$).

To summarize, it may be said that the magnetic symmetry operators may be derived from the classical symmetry operators in the following way. For any particular crystal class, one group of magnetic symmetry operators is identical with the classical point group $\mathcal{G}$ and is denoted by $\mathcal{G}$. The remainder are found, first by selecting, from $\mathcal{G}$, all the possible sub-groups $\mathcal{H}$ of index 2, secondly by replacing all the elements S_i of $\mathcal{G}$ which do not belong to $\mathcal{H}$ by $\underline{S}_i = RS_i$, and finally by rejecting all the groups $\mathcal{M} - \mathcal{H} + R(\mathcal{G} - \mathcal{H})$ for which any S_i may be identified with either $+3$ or -3. The problem of ascertaining which elements of $\mathcal{G}$ form a sub-group $\mathcal{H}$ of index 2 – having, of course, half as many elements as $\mathcal{G}$ – is greatly facilitated by the fact that the only possible forms of these sub-groups are those of the 32 classical point groups.

The groups of magnetic symmetry operators, derived in this fashion are exhibited, for the various crystal classes, in Table 6. The 90 magnetic groups, denoted by $\mathcal{M}'$, comprise the 32 classical (magnetic) groups, $\mathcal{G}$, and the 58 additional magnetic groups, $\mathcal{M}$, and they are listed in columns 2 and 3 in the abbreviated international and Shubnikov notations. Columns 4 and 5 identify the (classical) sub-group $\mathcal{H}$ of the classical point group $\mathcal{G}$ corresponding to each of the 58 additional magnetic groups $\mathcal{M}$ listed in columns 2 and 3. The elements of each magnetic group $\mathcal{M}'$ listed in columns 2 and 3 are given in column 6, it being understood that the underlining of a symmetry operator indicates multiplication by the time-inversion operator R (i.e. $\underline{S_i} \equiv RS_i$). Corresponding generating matrices are listed in columns 7 and 8, the underlining of those in column 8 again indicating multiplication by R (i.e. $\underline{\sigma}^{(n)} \equiv R\sigma^{(n)}$). The procedure adopted in deriving these generating matrices for the additional magnetic groups, $\mathscr{M}$, is discussed below.

It follows from equations (3.15a) and (3.16b) that $\mathscr{M} = \mathscr{H} + P$, P being the set of products formed by multiplying a particular member $\underline{S_i^0}$ of the set $R(\mathscr{G} - \mathscr{H})$ with each element of the subgroup $\mathscr{H}$. Thus the group $\mathscr{M}$ may be built up by taking first all the elements of $\mathscr{H}$, and secondly all the products of the elements of $\mathscr{H}$ with *any one* element of the set $R(\mathscr{G} - \mathscr{H})$. Hence,

$$\mathscr{M} = \mathscr{H} + \underline{S_i^0}\mathscr{H}, \qquad (3.20)$$

which is a special case of Lagrange's theorem, $\underline{S_i^0}\mathscr{H} = R(\mathscr{G} - \mathscr{H})$ being a left-hand coset of $\mathscr{M}$ relative to $\mathscr{H}$. Similarly,

$$\mathscr{G} = \mathscr{H} + S_i^0\mathscr{H}. \qquad (3.21)$$

The group $\mathscr{M}$ can therefore be generated from the sub-group $\mathscr{H}$ provided only one element $\underline{S_i^0}$ of the set $\mathscr{M} - \mathscr{H}$ is known. Generators of the additional magnetic point group $\mathscr{M}$ are therefore the generators of the sub-group $\mathscr{H}$ plus any one element of $\mathscr{M}$ which is not contained in $\mathscr{H}$. For example, for the magnetic point group $\mathscr{M} = 4/\underline{mmm}$ considered in § 1, $\mathscr{G} = 4/mmm$ with generating matrices $\sigma^{(1)}$, $\sigma^{(2)}$, $\sigma^{(7)}$, whilst $\mathscr{H} = 4/m$ with generating matrices $\sigma^{(1)}$, $\sigma^{(7)}$, so that generating matrices of $\mathscr{M}$ are $\sigma^{(1)}$, $\sigma^{(7)}$, $\underline{\sigma}^{(2)}$. When one or more of the generating matrices of $\mathscr{H}$, obtained from Table 3, is not a generating matrix of $\mathscr{G}$, an arbitrary choice may be made from $\mathscr{G} - \mathscr{H}$ for the additional generating matrix.

TABLE 5

1	2	3	4	5	6	7	8
System	Symbol of symmetry class and magnetic point group $\mathscr{M}''$		Symbol of classical sub-group $\mathscr{H}$		Symmetry operators of group $\mathscr{M}''$	Generating matrices of group $\mathscr{M}'$	
	International	Shubnikov	International	Shubnikov		Generating matrices of sub-group $\mathscr{H}$	Additional generating matrix
Triclinic	1	1	—	—	1	$\sigma^{(0)}$	—
	$\bar{1}$	$\bar{2}$	—	—	$1, \bar{1}$	$\sigma^{(1)}$	—
	$\underline{\bar{1}}$	$\underline{\bar{2}}$	1	1	$1, \underline{\bar{1}}$	$\sigma^{(0)}$	$\underline{\sigma}^{(1)}$
Monoclinic	2	2	—	—	$1, 2_z$	$\sigma^{(3)}$	—
	$\underline{2}$	$\underline{2}$	1	1	$1, \underline{2}_z$	$\sigma^{(0)}$	$\underline{\sigma}^{(3)}$
	m	m	—	—	$1, \bar{2}_z$	$\sigma^{(5)}$	—
	$\underline{m}$	$\underline{m}$	1	1	$1, \underline{\bar{2}}_z$	$\sigma^{(0)}$	$\underline{\sigma}^{(5)}$
	$2/m$	$2{:}m$	—	—	$1, \bar{1}, 2_z, \bar{2}_z$	$\sigma^{(1)}, \sigma^{(3)}$	—
	$\underline{2/m}$	$\underline{2{:}m}$	$\bar{1}$	$\bar{2}$	$1, \bar{1}, \underline{2}_z, \underline{\bar{2}}_z$	$\sigma^{(1)}$	$\underline{\sigma}^{(3)}$
	$\underline{2}/m$	$\underline{2}{:}m$	2	2	$1, 2_z, \underline{\bar{1}}, \underline{\bar{2}}_z$	$\sigma^{(3)}$	$\underline{\sigma}^{(1)}$
	$2/\underline{m}$	$2{:}\underline{m}$	m	m	$1, \bar{2}_z, \underline{\bar{1}}, \underline{2}_z$	$\sigma^{(5)}$	$\underline{\sigma}^{(1)}$

TABLE 6 (continued)

					Generators	σ	σ_1
Ortho-rhombic							
222	2:2	—	—	$1, 2_x, 2_y, 2_z$	$\sigma^{(2)}, \sigma^{(3)}$	—
$\underline{\textbf{222}}$	$\underline{2:2}$	2	2	$1, 2_z, \underline{2}_x, \underline{2}_y$	$\sigma^{(3)}$	$\sigma_1^{(2)}$
mm2	$2\cdot m$	—	—	$1, 2_z, \bar{2}_x, \bar{2}_y$	$\sigma^{(3)}, \sigma^{(4)}$	—
$\underline{\textbf{mm2}}$	$2\cdot\underline{m}$	2	2	$1, 2_z, \underline{\bar{2}}_x, \underline{\bar{2}}_y$	$\sigma^{(3)}$	$\sigma_1^{(4)}$
$\underline{\textbf{2mm}}$	$\underline{2}\cdot m$	m	m	$1, \bar{2}_z, \underline{2}_x, \underline{\bar{2}}_y$	$\sigma^{(5)}$	$\sigma_1^{(4)}$
mmm	$m\cdot 2{:}m$	—	—	$1, 2_x, 2_y, 2_z, \bar{2}_x, \bar{2}_y, \bar{2}_z$	$\sigma^{(1)}, \sigma^{(2)}, \sigma^{(3)}$	—
$\underline{\textbf{mmm}}$	$\underline{m}\cdot 2{:}m$	2/m	2:m	$1, \bar{1}, 2_z, \bar{2}_z, \underline{2}_x, \underline{2}_y, \underline{\bar{2}}_x, \underline{\bar{2}}_y$	$\sigma^{(1)}, \sigma^{(3)}$	$\sigma_1^{(2)}$
$\underline{\textbf{mmm}}$	$m\cdot 2{:}\underline{m}$	222	2:2	$1, 2_x, 2_y, 2_z, \bar{1}, \underline{\bar{2}}_x, \underline{\bar{2}}_y, \underline{\bar{2}}_z$	$\sigma^{(2)}, \sigma^{(3)}$	$\sigma_1^{(1)}$
$\underline{\textbf{mmm}}$	$m\cdot 2{:}\underline{m}$	mm2	$2\cdot m$	$1, 2_z, \bar{2}_x, \bar{2}_y, \bar{1}, \underline{2}_x, \underline{2}_y, \underline{\bar{2}}_z$	$\sigma^{(3)}, \sigma^{(4)}$	$\sigma_1^{(1)}$
Tetra-gonal							
4	4	—	—	$1, 2_z, \pm 4_z$	$\sigma^{(7)}$	—
$\underline{\textbf{4}}$	$\underline{4}$	2	2	$1, 2_z, \pm \underline{4}_z$	$\sigma^{(3)}$	$\sigma_1^{(7)}$
$\bar{\textbf{4}}$	$\bar{4}$	—	—	$1, 2_z, \pm \bar{4}_z$	$\sigma^{(8)}$	—
$\underline{\bar{\textbf{4}}}$	$\bar{4}$	2	2	$1, 2_z, \pm \underline{\bar{4}}_z$	$\sigma^{(3)}$	$\sigma_1^{(8)}$
4/m	4:m	—	—	$1, \bar{1}, 2_z, \bar{2}_z, \pm 4_z, \pm \bar{4}_z$	$\sigma^{(1)}, \sigma^{(7)}$	—
$\underline{\textbf{4/m}}$	$\underline{4}{:}m$	2/m	2:m	$1, \bar{1}, 2_z, \bar{2}_z, \pm \underline{4}_z, \pm \underline{\bar{4}}_z$	$\sigma^{(1)}, \sigma^{(3)}$	$\sigma_1^{(7)}$

					Operations	σ	σ₁
Tetra-gonal	4/m	4:m	4	4	$1, 2_z, \pm 4_z, \bar{1}, \bar{2}_z, \pm\bar{4}_z$	$\sigma^{(7)}$	$\sigma_1^{(1)}$
	4/m	4:m	4̄	4̄	$1, 2_z, \pm\bar{4}_z, \bar{1}, \bar{2}_z, \pm 4_z$	$\sigma^{(8)}$	$\sigma_1^{(1)}$
	422	4:2	—	—	$1, 2_x; 2_y, 2_z, 2_{xy}, 2_{-xy}, \pm 4_z$	$\sigma^{(2)}, \sigma^{(7)}$	—
	422	4:2	222	2:2	$1, 2_x; 2_y, 2_z, \underline{2}_{xy}, \underline{2}_{-xy}, \pm\underline{4}_z$	$\sigma^{(2)}, \sigma^{(3)}$	$\sigma_1^{(7)}$
	422	4:2	4	4	$1, 2_z, \pm 4_z, \underline{2}_x, \underline{2}_y, \underline{2}_{xy}, \underline{2}_{-xy}$	$\sigma^{(7)}$	$\sigma_1^{(2)}$
	4mm	4·m	—	—	$1, 2_z, \bar{2}_x, \bar{2}_y, \bar{2}_{xy}, \bar{2}_{-xy}, \pm 4_z$	$\sigma^{(4)}, \sigma^{(7)}$	—
	4mm	4·m	mm2	2·m	$1, 2_z, \bar{2}_x, \bar{2}_y, \underline{2}_{xy}, \underline{2}_{-xy}, \pm\underline{4}_z$	$\sigma^{(3)}, \sigma^{(4)}$	$\sigma_1^{(7)}$
	4mm	4·m	4	4	$1, 2_z, \pm 4_z, \bar{2}_x, \bar{2}_y, \bar{2}_{xy}, \bar{2}_{-xy}$	$\sigma^{(7)}$	$\sigma_1^{(4)}$
	4̄2m	4̄·m	—	—	$1, 2_x, 2_y, 2_z, \bar{2}_{xy}, \bar{2}_{-xy}, \pm\bar{4}_z$	$\sigma^{(2)}, \sigma^{(8)}$	—
	4̄2m	4̄·m	222	2:2	$1, 2_x, \bar{2}_x, \bar{2}_y, \underline{2}_{xy}, \underline{2}_{-xy}, \pm\bar{4}_z$	$\sigma^{(2)}, \sigma^{(3)}$	$\sigma_1^{(8)}$
	4̄m2	4̄·m	mm2	2·m	$1, 2_x, \bar{2}_x, \bar{2}_y, \bar{2}_{xy}, \bar{2}_{-xy}, \pm\bar{4}_z$	$\sigma^{(3)}, \sigma^{(4)}$	$\sigma_1^{(8)}$
	4̄2m	4̄·m	4̄	4̄	$1, 2_z, \pm\bar{4}_z, \bar{2}_x, \bar{2}_y, \bar{2}_{xy}, \bar{2}_{-xy}$	$\sigma^{(8)}$	$\sigma_1^{(2)}$
	4/mmm	m·4:m	—	—	$1, \bar{1}, 2_x, 2_y, 2_z, 2_{xy}, 2_{-xy}, \pm 4_z, \pm\bar{4}_z,$ $\bar{2}_{xy}, \bar{2}_z, \bar{2}_z, \bar{2}_{xy=}, \bar{2}_{-xy}$	$\sigma^{(1)}, \sigma^{(2)}, \sigma^{(7)}$	—
	4/mmm	m·4:m	mmmm	m·2:m	$1, \bar{1}, 2_x, 2_y, 2_z, 2_z, \bar{2}_x, \bar{2}_y, \bar{2}_z,$ $\underline{2}_{xy}, \underline{2}_{-xy}, \underline{2}_{xy}, \underline{2}_{-xy}, \pm 4_z, \pm\bar{4}_z$	$\sigma^{(1)}, \sigma^{(2)}, \sigma^{(3)}$	$\sigma_1^{(7)}$

TABLE 6 (continued)

					Elements		
Tetra-gonal	$4/\underline{mmmm}$	$m\cdot4{:}\underline{m}$	$4/m$	$4{:}m$	$1, \bar{1}, 2_z\,\bar{2}_z, \pm4_z, \pm\bar{4}_z\,2_x, 2_y,$ $\underline{2}_{xy}, \underline{2}_{-xy}, \bar{2}_x, \bar{2}_y, \underline{\bar{2}}_{xy}, \underline{\bar{2}}_{-xy}$	$\sigma^{(1)}, \sigma^{(7)}$	$\underline{\sigma}^{(2)}$
	$4/\underline{mmmm}$	$\underline{m}\cdot4{:}\underline{m}$	422	$4{:}2$	$1, 2_x, 2_y, 2_z, 2_{xy}, 2_{-xy}, \pm4_z,$ $\bar{1}, \underline{\bar{2}}_x, \underline{\bar{2}}_y, \underline{\bar{2}}_z, \underline{\bar{2}}_{xy}, \underline{\bar{2}}_{-xy}, \pm\underline{\bar{4}}_z$	$\sigma^{(2)}, \sigma^{(7)}$	$\underline{\sigma}^{(1)}$
	$4/\underline{\underline{m}}mmm$	$m\cdot4{:}\underline{\underline{m}}$	$4mm$	$4\cdot m$	$1, 2_z, \bar{2}_x, \bar{2}_y, \bar{2}_{xy}, \bar{2}_{-xy}, \pm4_z,$ $\bar{1}, \underline{2}_x, \underline{2}_y, \underline{2}_{xy}, \underline{2}_{-xy}, \underline{\bar{2}}_z, \pm\underline{\bar{4}}_z$	$\sigma^{(4)}, \sigma^{(7)}$	$\underline{\sigma}^{(1)}$
	$4/\underline{\underline{mmmm}}$	$m\cdot4{:}\underline{m}$	$\bar{4}2m$	$\bar{4}\cdot m$	$1, 2_x, 2_y, 2_z, \bar{2}_{xy}, \bar{2}_{-xy}, \pm\bar{4}_z,$ $\bar{1}, \underline{2}_{xy}, \underline{2}_{-xy}, \underline{2}_x, \underline{2}_y, \underline{\bar{2}}_z, \pm\underline{4}_z$	$\sigma^{(2)}, \sigma^{(8)}$	$\underline{\sigma}^{(1)}$
Tri-gonal	3	3	—	—	$1, \pm3_z$	$\sigma^{(6)}$	—
	$\bar{3}$	$\bar{6}$	—	—	$1, \bar{1}, \pm3_z, \pm\bar{3}_z$	$\sigma^{(1)}, \sigma^{(6)}$	—
	$\underline{\bar{3}}$	$\underline{\bar{6}}$	3	3	$1, \pm3_z, \underline{\bar{1}}, \pm\underline{\bar{3}}_z$	$\sigma^{(6)}$	$\underline{\sigma}^{(1)}$
	32	$3{:}2$	—	—	$1, 3(2_{\perp}), \pm3_z$	$\sigma^{(2)}, \sigma^{(6)}$	—
	$3\underline{2}$	$3{:}\underline{2}$	3	3	$1, \pm3_z, 3(\underline{2}_{\perp})$	$\sigma^{(6)}$	$\underline{\sigma}^{(2)}$
	$3m$	$3\cdot m$	—	—	$1, 3(\bar{2}_{\perp}), \pm3_z$	$\sigma^{(4)}, \sigma^{(6)}$	—
	$3\underline{m}$	$3\cdot\underline{m}$	3	3	$1, \pm3_z, 3(\underline{\bar{2}}_{\perp})$	$\sigma^{(6)}$	$\underline{\sigma}^{(4)}$

System					Operators	σ set	σ
Tri‑gonal	$\bar{3}m$	$\bar{6}\!\cdot\! m$	—	—	$1,\ \bar{1},\ 3(2_\perp),\ \bar{3}(\bar{2}_\perp),\ \pm 3_z,\ \pm\bar{3}_z$	$\sigma^{(1)},\sigma^{(2)},\sigma^{(6)}$	—
	$\bar{3}\underline{m}$	$\bar{6}\!\cdot\!\underline{m}$	3	$\underline{2}$	$1,\ \bar{1},\ \pm 3_z,\ \equiv\bar{3}_z,\ 3(\underline{2}_\perp),\ 3(\bar{\underline{2}}_\perp)$	$\sigma^{(1)},\sigma^{(6)}$	$\underline{\sigma}^{(2)}$
	$\underline{\bar{3}m}$	$\underline{\bar{6}}\!\cdot\!\underline{m}$	32	$3{:}2$	$1,\ 3(2_\perp),\ \pm\hat{3}_z,\ \bar{1},\ 3(\bar{2}_\perp),\ \pm\bar{3}_z$	$\sigma^{(2)},\sigma^{(6)}$	$\underline{\sigma}^{(1)}$
	$\bar{3}\underline{m}$	$\underline{\bar{6}}\!\cdot\! m$	$3m$	$3\!\cdot\! m$	$1,\ 3(\underline{2}_\perp),\ \pm\hat{3}_z,\ \bar{1},\ 3(\bar{\underline{2}}_\perp),\ \pm\bar{3}_z$	$\sigma^{(4)},\sigma^{(6)}$	$\underline{\sigma}^{(1)}$
Hexa‑gonal	6	6	—	—	$1,\ 2_z,\ \pm 3_z,\ \pm 6_z$	$\sigma^{(3)},\sigma^{(6)}$	—
	$\underline{6}$	$\underline{6}$	3	3	$1,\ \pm 3_z,\ \underline{2}_z,\ \pm\underline{6}_z$	$\sigma^{(6)}$	$\underline{\sigma}^{(3)}$
	$\bar{6}$	$3{:}m$	—	—	$1,\ \bar{2}_z,\ \pm 3_z,\ \pm\bar{6}_z$	$\sigma^{(5)},\sigma^{(6)}$	—
	$\underline{\bar{6}}$	$3{:}\underline{m}$	3	3	$1,\ \pm 3_z,\ \bar{\underline{2}}_z,\ \pm\bar{\underline{6}}_z$	$\sigma^{(6)}$	$\underline{\sigma}^{(5)}$
	$6/m$	$6{:}m$	—	—	$1,\ \bar{1},\ 2_z,\ \bar{2}_z,\ \equiv 3_z,\ \pm\bar{3}_z,\ \pm 6_z,\ \pm\bar{6}_z$	$\sigma^{(1)},\sigma^{(3)},\sigma^{(6)}$	—
	$\underline{6}/\underline{m}$	$\underline{6}{:}\underline{m}$	$\underline{3}$	$\underline{6}$	$1,\ \bar{1},\ \pm 3_z,\ \pm\bar{3}_z,\ \underline{2}_z,\ \bar{\underline{2}}_z,\ \pm\bar{\underline{6}}_z,\ \pm\underline{6}_z$	$\sigma^{(1)},\sigma^{(6)}$	$\underline{\sigma}^{(3)}$
	$\underline{6}/\underline{m}$	$\underline{6}{:}\underline{m}$	6	6	$1,\ 2_z,\ \pm 3_z,\ \pm 6_z,\ \bar{\underline{1}},\ \bar{\underline{3}}_z,\ \pm\bar{\underline{6}}_z$	$\sigma^{(3)},\sigma^{(6)}$	$\underline{\sigma}^{(1)}$
	$6/\underline{m}$	$\underline{6}{:}m$	$\underline{6}$	$3{:}m$	$1,\ \bar{\underline{2}}_z,\ \pm 3_z,\ \equiv\bar{\underline{6}}_z,\ \underline{1},\ \underline{2}_z,\ \pm\bar{3}_z,\ \pm 6_z$	$\sigma^{(5)},\sigma^{(6)}$	$\underline{\sigma}^{(1)}$

TABLE 6 (continued)

					Elements	σ	
Hexa-gonal	622	6:2	—	—	$1, 6(2_\perp), 2_z, \pm 3_z, \pm 6_z$	$\sigma^{(2)}, \sigma^{(3)}, \sigma^{(6)}$	—
	$\underline{6}\,\underline{2}2$	$\underline{6}{:}2$	32	3:2	$3(2_\perp), \pm 3_z, 3(\underline{2_\perp}), 2_z, \pm 6_z$	$\sigma^{(2)}, \sigma^{(6)}$	$\sigma_1^{(3)}$
	$62\underline{2}$	$6{:}\underline{2}$	6	6	$1, 2_z, \pm 3_z, \pm 6_z, 6(\underline{2_\perp})$	$\sigma^{(3)}, \sigma^{(6)}$	$\sigma_1^{(2)}$
	6mm	$6{\cdot}m$	—	—	$1, 2_z, 6(\overline{2_\perp}), \pm 3_z, \pm 6_z$	$\sigma^{(3)}, \sigma^{(4)}, \sigma^{(6)}$	—
	$\underline{6}mm$	$\underline{6}{\cdot}m$	3m	3·m	$1, 3(\overline{2_\perp}), \pm 3_z, 2_z, 3(\overline{2_\perp}), \pm 6_z$	$\sigma^{(4)}, \sigma^{(6)}$	$\sigma_1^{(3)}$
	$6mm$	$6{\cdot}\underline{m}$	6	6	$1, 2_z, \pm 3_z, \pm 6_z, 6(\overline{2_\perp})$	$\sigma^{(3)}, \sigma^{(6)}$	$\sigma_1^{(4)}$
	$\bar{6}m2$	$m{\cdot}3{:}m$	—	—	$1, 3(2_\perp), 3(\overline{2_\perp}), \bar{2}_z, \pm 3_z, \pm \bar{6}_z$	$\sigma^{(4)}, \sigma^{(5)}, \sigma^{(6)}$	—
	$\bar{6}\underline{2}m$	$\underline{m}{\cdot}3{:}m$	32	3:2	$1, 3(2_\perp), \pm 3_z, 3(\overline{2_\perp}), \bar{2}_z, \pm \bar{6}_z$	$\sigma^{(2)}, \sigma^{(6)}$	$\sigma_1^{(5)}$
	$\bar{6}m\underline{2}$	$m{\cdot}3{:}\underline{m}$	3m	3·m	$1, 3(\overline{2_\perp}), \pm 3_z, 3(2_\perp), \bar{2}_z, \pm \bar{6}_z$	$\sigma^{(4)}, \sigma^{(6)}$	$\sigma_1^{(5)}$
	$\bar{6}m\underline{2}$	$\underline{m}{\cdot}3{:}m$	$\bar{6}$	3:m	$1, \bar{2}_z, \pm 3_z, \pm \bar{6}_z, 3(2_\perp), 3(\overline{2_\perp})$	$\sigma^{(5)}, \sigma^{(6)}$	$\sigma_1^{(4)}$
	6/mmm	$m{\cdot}6{:}m$	—	—	$1, \bar{1}, 6(2_\perp), 2_z, 6(\overline{2_\perp}), \bar{2}_z, \pm 3_z, \pm \bar{3}_z, \pm 6_z, \pm \bar{6}_z$	$\sigma^{(1)}, \sigma^{(2)}, \sigma^{(3)}, \sigma^{(6)}$	—
	$6/\underline{mmm}$	$m{\cdot}\underline{6}{:}\underline{m}$	$\bar{3}m$	$\bar{6}{\cdot}m$	$1, \bar{1}, 3(2_\perp), 3(\overline{2_\perp}), \pm 3_z, \pm \bar{3}_z, 3(2_\perp), 2_z, 3(\overline{2_\perp}), \bar{2}_z, \pm 6_z, \pm \bar{6}_z$	$\sigma^{(1)}, \sigma^{(2)}, \sigma^{(6)}$	$\sigma_1^{(2)}$
	$6/\underline{mmm}$	$\underline{m}{\cdot}6{:}m$	6/m	6:m	$1, \bar{1}, 2_z, \bar{2}_z, \pm 3_z, \pm \bar{3}_z, \pm 6_z, \pm \bar{6}_z, 6(2_\perp), 6(\overline{2_\perp})$	$\sigma^{(1)}, \sigma^{(2)}, \sigma^{(3)}, \sigma^{(6)}$	$\underline{\sigma}_1^{(2)}$

					Operators	σ (group)	σ_1
Hexagonal	$6/\underline{mmm}m$	$m\cdot6\!:\!\underline{m}$	622	6:2	$1, 6(2_\perp), 2_z, \pm3_{zz}, \pm6_z, \bar{1}, 6(\bar{2}_\perp), \bar{2}_z, \pm\bar{3}_{zz}, \pm\bar{6}_z$	$\sigma^{(2)}, \sigma^{(3)}, \sigma^{(6)}$	$\sigma_1^{(1)}$
	$6/\underline{mmm}m$	$m\cdot6\!:\!\underline{m}$	6mm	6·m	$1, 2_z, 6(\bar{2}_\perp), \pm3_{zz}, \pm6_z, \bar{1}, \bar{2}_z, \pm\bar{3}_{zz}, \pm\bar{6}_z$	$\sigma^{(3)}, \sigma^{(4)}, \sigma^{(6)}$	$\sigma_1^{(1)}$
	$6/\underline{mmm}m$	$m\cdot6\!:\!m$	$\bar{6}m2$	m·3:m	$1, 3(2_\perp), 3(\bar{2}_{\_}), \bar{6}_z, \pm3_{zz}, \pm\bar{6}_z, \bar{1}, 3(2_\perp), 2_z, 3(\bar{2}_\perp), \pm\bar{3}_{zz}, \pm6_z$	$\sigma^{(2)}, \sigma^{(5)}, \sigma^{(6)}$	$\sigma_1^{(1)}$
Cubic	23	3/2	—	—	$1, 3(2), 4(\pm3)$	$\sigma^{(3)}, \sigma^{(9)}$	—
	m3	$\bar{6}/2$	—	—	$1, \bar{1}, 3(2), 3(\bar{2}), 4(\pm3), 4(\pm\bar{3})$	$\sigma^{(11)}, \sigma^{(13)}, \sigma^{(9)}$	—
	$\underline{m}3$	$\underline{6}/2$	23	3/2	$1, 3(2), 4(\pm3), \bar{1}, 3(\bar{2}), 4(\pm\bar{3})$	$\sigma^{(3)}, \sigma^{(9)}$	$\sigma_1^{(1)}$
	432	3/4	—	—	$1, 9(2), 4(\pm3), 3(\pm4)$	$\sigma^{(7)}, \sigma^{(9)}$	—
	$43\underline{2}$	$3/\underline{4}$	23	3/2	$1, 3(2), 4(\pm3), 6(2), 3(\pm4)$	$\sigma^{(3)}, \sigma^{(9)}$	$\sigma_1^{(7)}$
	$\bar{4}3m$	$3/\bar{4}$	—	—	$1, 3(2), 6(\bar{2}), 4(\pm3), 3(\pm\bar{4})$	$\sigma^{(8)}, \sigma^{(9)}$	—
	$\bar{4}3\underline{m}$	$3/\underline{4}$	23	3/2	$1, 3(2), 4(\pm3), 6(\bar{2}), 3(\pm\bar{4})$	$\sigma^{(3)}, \sigma^{(9)}$	$\sigma_1^{(8)}$
	m3m	$\bar{6}/4$	—	—	$1, \bar{1}, 9(2), 9(\bar{2}), 4(\pm\bar{3}), 3(\pm4), 3(\pm\bar{4})$	$\sigma^{(11)}, \sigma^{(7)}, \sigma^{(9)}$	—

TABLE 6 (continued)

Cubic							
	m3m	$\overline{6}/4$	m3	$\overline{6}/2$	$1,\ \overline{1},\ 3(2),\ 3(\overline{2}),\ 4(\pm 3),\ 4(\pm \overline{3}),$ $6(\underline{2}),\ 6(\overline{\underline{2}}),\ 3(\pm \underline{4}),\ 3(\pm \overline{4})$	$\sigma^{(1)},\ \sigma^{(3)},\ \sigma^{(9)}$	$\sigma_1^{(7)}$
	$\underline{\text{m3m}}$	$\underline{\overline{6}/4}$	432	3/4	$1,\ 9(2),\ 4(\pm 3),\ 3(\pm 4),\ \overline{1},\ 9(\overline{\underline{2}}),$ $4(\pm \overline{3}),\ 3(\pm \overline{4})$	$\sigma^{(7)},\ \sigma^{(9)}$	$\sigma_1^{(1)}$
	$\underline{\text{m3m}}$	$\underline{\overline{6}/4}$	$\overline{4}3\text{m}$	$3/\overline{4}$	$1,\ 3(2),\ 6(\overline{2}),\ 4(\pm 3),\ 3(\pm 4),$ $\overline{\underline{1}},\ 6(\underline{2}),\ 3(\overline{\underline{2}}),\ 4(\pm \overline{3}),\ 3(\pm 4)$	$\sigma^{(8)},\ \sigma^{(9)}$	$\sigma_1^{(1)}$

§ 3. NEUMANN'S PRINCIPLE IN SPACE-TIME:

TRANSPORT PROPERTIES

As indicated in Ch. 2, § 2, Neumann's principle remains valid in
four-dimensional space-time for static properties but not for dynamic properties, such as transport phenomena, where a system
is permanently in non-equilibrium but has reached a steady state.
When the physical situation is described in terms of three spatial
coordinates and a time coordinate, t, Neumann's principle is essentially an affirmation of the isotropy of space-time. In other
words, it is a statement that there are no preferred directions in
space-time except those introduced, solely or jointly, by the crystal
and by the influence which is exerted upon it. However, it has
already been seen that the coordinate t differs from the spatial
coordinates in that it is subject only to the transformation
$t \rightarrow -t$: rotations in a generalised plane defined by one spatial
axis and the axis of time, for example, are impossible from physical
considerations. Further, the time coordinate is different from the
three spatial coordinates in another respect, namely that it may
sometimes be deduced that one direction of time (the real direction of time) must be regarded as infinitely more probable from
thermodynamic considerations. This is because it is a consequence of the second law of thermodynamics that the entropy of
a system never decreases. If the entropy does not remain constant,
then there is an intrinsically preferred direction of time – the direction for which the entropy of the system increases. It must not
be concluded, however, that the operation of time-inversion is in
any way inadmissible: as applied to a property tensor, the act of
inversion is not a physical act but merely a change from the
description of events in terms of the coordinate t to one in terms
of the coordinate $-t$. It represents the study of the opposite
chronological order of the same events, and can best be envisaged
as the act of running a cine-film backwards. When a film is run in
the reverse direction, events are seen proceeding backwards into

the past, and this is a perfectly valid description, provided it is recognised that some processes appear to be occurring in definite contradiction to the laws of nature: the corpse is resurrected and the river draws its water from the sea. Similarly, positively charged particles are observed to be moving from regions of lower potential to regions of higher potential.

This last observation is particularly relevant to a consideration of transport properties. If the particles are moving freely, their motion is governed by Newton's second law, that force is equal to rate of increase of momentum. The fact that positively charged particles move towards regions of higher potential is not in contradiction with this law, since *accelerations* are not reversed by time-inversion. That the *velocities* are reversed can be explained by assuming that the particles possessed reversed initial velocities at $t = 0$, and this contravenes no natural physical law. Unnatural behaviour immediately manifests itself, however, when the particles are imagined to be moving steadily in some sort of resistive medium which opposes their motion. In this case Newton's second law is still obeyed (the accelerations being zero), but upon time-inversion the resistive medium is observed to be exerting forces on the particles which *assist* their motion.

As an example of a transport property, consider an electric current of density J flowing in a crystal under the action of an electric field E, the resistivity tensor ϱ_{ij} being defined by equation (1.2d). The rate of production of entropy is proportional to $(E \cdot J)/T$, at absolute temperature T. Under time-inversion (as will be shown in § 4) J is reversed whilst E remains unchanged, so that the rate of production of entropy is now negative instead of positive, corresponding to a physically impossible situation. Thus the two directions of time are not equivalent and Neumann's principle cannot be applied in space-time because there is an intrinsically preferred direction of time. Indeed, if Neumann's principle were to apply in space-time, non-magnetic (i.e. diamagnetic and paramagnetic) crystals could not exhibit properties which were time-antisymmetric, and the property of electrical conduction would be prohibited for all non-magnetic crystals. It may therefore be concluded that, for a dynamic process, that is one in which the entropy of a system is changing, Neumann's principle cannot be applied in space-time because there is an intrinsically preferred direction of time to be taken into consideration as well as any asymmetry which might be expected to arise from the crystal or from the influence which is exerted upon it. For static phenomena, however, the rate of production of entropy is zero and the two directions of time are equivalent whilst, in both real time and inverse time, the entropy of the system conforms to the thermodynamical requirement that it shall never decrease.

§ 3.1. *The Symmetry of Property Tensors representing Static Phenomena*

For static phenomena the two directions of time are equivalent and Neumann's principle remains valid in four-dimensional space-time. Consequently any type of space-time symmetry which is exhibited by the point group of the crystal is possessed by every physical property of the crystal. The requirement that a static property tensor is invariant under all the permissible space-time symmetry operations appropriate to a particular crystal class is formulated mathematically as indicated below.

For a non-magnetic point group, $\mathscr{G}'$, that is for a diamagnetic or paramagnetic crystal, the matrix of every symmetry element S_g of the corresponding classical point group, $\mathscr{G}$, may be substituted for S into the equations

$$d_{ijk...n} = S_{ip}S_{jq}S_{kr} \cdots S_{nu}d_{pqr...u}, \qquad (3.22a)$$

for polar tensors, and

$$d_{ijk...n} = |S|S_{ip}S_{jq}S_{kr} \cdots S_{nu}d_{pqr...u}, \qquad (3.22b)$$

for axial tensors. In addition, R is a symmetry operator as the crystal is time-symmetrical. Thus, for non-magnetic crystals, all time-antisymmetric tensors vanish identically, whilst the forms of time-symmetric tensors may be obtained directly from Table 4 without any further simplification except that imposed by particularization.

For the 32 classical magnetic point groups, $\mathscr{G}$, every element S_g of $\mathscr{G}$ may again be used in (3.22a) and (3.22b): since R is not a symmetry operator, the forms of both time-symmetric and time-antisymmetric tensors may be obtained directly from Table 4. For the 58 additional magnetic point groups, $\mathscr{M}$, it is necessary to distinguish not only between polar and axial tensors but also between time-symmetric and time-antisymmetric tensors, that is between tensors which are invariant (i-tensors) under time-inversion and those whose components all change sign (c-tensors) under time-inversion.

Remembering that the symmetry operator $\underline{S}_i$ is equivalent to the consecutive application of the two operators R and S_i, it may be seen that, for i-tensors, the matrices of all the symmetry elements S_h and S_i (of § 2) may be substituted directly into equations (3.22). This is, of course, the same as using all the S_g of $\mathscr{G}$ in (3.22), so that the form of i-tensors for an additional magnetic group $\mathscr{M}$ is the same as that of tensors for the corresponding classical group $\mathscr{G}$. For c-tensors, however, equations (3.22) may only be used for the symmetry operators S_h. The symmetry operators $\underline{S}_i$ must be employed by substituting the matrices of the S_i into the equations

$$d_{ijk...n} = (-1)\, S_{ip}S_{jq}S_{kr} \cdots S_{nu}d_{pqr...u}, \qquad (3.23a)$$

for polar tensors, and

$$d_{ijk...n} = (-1)\, |S|S_{ip}S_{jq}S_{kr} \cdots S_{nu}d_{pqr...u}, \qquad (3.23b)$$

for axial tensors, the additional (-1) arising from the reversal of c-tensors under time-inversion. The forms of property tensors in

1	2	3	4	5	6	7	8	9	10	11	12
System	Magnetic point group $\mathcal{M}'$	Associated classical groups $\mathcal{A}$	Associated classical groups $\mathcal{B}$	i-tensors: Polar tensor of even rank m	i-tensors: Axial tensor of even rank m	i-tensors: Polar tensor of odd rank n	i-tensors: Axial tensor of odd rank n	c-tensors: Polar tensor of even rank m	c-tensors: Axial tensor of even rank m	c-tensors: Polar tensor of odd rank n	c-tensors: Axial tensor of odd rank n
Tri-clinic	1	—	—	A_m	A_m	A_n	A_n	A_m	A_m	A_n	A_n
	$\bar{1}$	—	—	A_m	—	—	A_n	A_m	—	—	A_n
	$\underline{\bar{1}}$	1	$\bar{1}$	A_m	—	—	A_n	—	A_m	A_n	—
Mono-clinic	2	—	—	B_m	B_m	B_n	B_n	B_m	B_m	B_n	B_n
	$\underline{2}$	m	m	B_m	B_m	B_n	B_n	C_m	C_m	C_n	C_n
	m	—	—	B_m	C_m	C_n	B_n	B_m	C_m	C_n	B_n
	$\underline{m}$	2	m	B_m	C_m	C_n	B_n	C_m	B_m	B_n	C_n
	2/m	—	—	B_m	—	—	B_n	B_m	—	—	B_n
	$\underline{2}$/m	2/m	m	B_m	—	—	B_n	C_m	—	—	C_n
	2/$\underline{m}$	2	2/m	B_m	—	—	B_n	—	B_m	B_n	—
	$\underline{2}$/$\underline{m}$	m	2/m	B_m	—	—	B_n	—	C_m	C_n	—

TABLE 7 (continued)

System											
Ortho-rhombic	222	—	—	D_m	D_m	D_n	D_n	D_m	D_m	D_n	D_n
	222	mm2	mm2	D_m	D_m	D_n	D_n	E_m	E_m	E_n	E_n
	mm2	—	—	D_m	E_m	E_n	D_n	D_m	E_m	E_n	D_n
	mm2	222	mm2	D_m	E_m	E_n	D_n	E_m	D_m	D_n	E_n
	(2mm)	(m2m)	mm2	D_m	(E_m)	(E_n)	D_n	E_m	(E_m)	(E_n)	E_n
	mmm	—	—	D_m	—	—	D_n	D_m	—	—	D_n
	mmm	mmm	mm2	D_m	—	—	D_n	E_m	—	—	E_n
	mmm	222	mmm	D_m	—	—	D_n	—	D_m	D_n	—
	mmm	mm2	mmm	D_m	—	—	D_n	—	E_m	E_n	—
Tetra-gonal	4	—	—	F_m	F_m	F_n	F_n	F_m	F_m	F_n	F_n
	4	4̄	4̄	F_m	F_m	F_n	F_n	G_m	G_m	G_n	G_n
	4̄	—	—	F_m	G_m	G_n	F_n	F_m	G_m	G_n	F_n
	4̄	4	4̄	F_m	G_m	G_n	F_n	G_m	F_m	F_n	G_n
	4/m	—	—	F_m	—	—	F_n	F_m	—	—	F_n
	4/m	4/m	4̄	F_m	—	—	F_n	G_m	—	—	G_n
	4/m	4	4/m	F_m	—	—	F_n	—	F_m	F_n	—
	4/m	4̄	4/m	F_m	—	—	F_n	—	G_m	G_n	—
	422	—	—	H_m	H_m	H_n	H_n	H_m	H_m	H_n	H_n

Tetragonal									
422	42m	42m	H_m	H_m	H_n	H_n	J_m	J_m	J_n	J_n
422	4mm	4mm	H_m	H_m	H_n	H_n	I_m	I_m	I_n	I_n
4mm	—	—	H_m	I_m	I_n	H_n	H_m	I_m	I_n	H_n
4mm	(4m2)	42m	H_m	I_m	I_n	H_n	J_m	(J_m)	(J_n)	J_n
4mm	422	4mm	H_m	I_m	I_n	H_n	I_m	H_m	H_n	I_n
42m	—	—	H_m	J_m	J_n	H_n	H_m	J_m	J_n	H_n
42m	422	42m	H_m	J_m	J_n	H_n	J_m	H_m	H_n	J_n
(4m2)	4mm	42m	H_m	(J_m)	(J_n)	H_n	J_m	I_m	I_n	J_n
42m	(42m)	4mm	H_m	J_m	J_n	H_n	I_m	(J_m)	(J_n)	I_n
4/mmm	—	—	H_m	—	—	H_n	H_m	—	—	H_n
4/mmm	4/mmm	42m	H_m	—	—	H_n	J_m	—	—	J_n
4/mmm	4/mmm	4mm	H_m	—	—	H_n	I_m	—	—	I_n
4/mmm	422	4/mmm	H_m	—	—	H_n	—	H_m	H_n	—
4/mmm	4mm	4/mmm	H_m	—	—	H_n	—	I_m	I_n	—
4/mmm	42m	4/mmm	H_m	—	—	H_n	—	J_m	J_n	—
Trigonal										
3	—	—	K_m	K_m	K_n	K_n	K_m	K_m	K_n	K_n
3	—	—	K_m	—	—	K_n	K_m	—	—	K_n
$\bar{3}$	3	$\bar{3}$	K_m	—	—	K_n	—	K_m	K_n	—

TABLE 7 (continued)

Crystal	Point group	$(\bar{6}2m)$	$(\bar{6}2m)$	P_m	P_m	P_n	P_n	(R_m)	(R_m)	(R_n)	(R_n)
Trigonal	32	—	—	L_m	L_m	L_n	L_n	L_m	L_m	L_n	L_n
	$3\underline{2}$	3m	3m	L_m	L_m	L_n	L_n	M_m	M_m	M_n	M_n
	3m	—	—	L_m	M_m	M_n	L_n	L_m	M_m	M_n	L_n
	$3\underline{m}$	32	3m	L_m	M_m	M_n	L_n	M_m	L_m	L_n	M_n
	$\bar{3}m$	—	—	L_m	—	—	L_n	L_m	—	—	L_n
	$\underline{\bar{3}m}$	$\bar{3}m$	3m	L_m	—	—	L_n	M_m	—	—	M_n
	$\underline{\bar{3}}\,m$	32	$\bar{3}m$	L_m	—	—	L_n	—	L_m	L_n	—
	$\underline{\bar{3}}\,\underline{m}$	3m	$\bar{3}m$	L_m	—	—	L_n	—	M_m	M_n	—
Hexagonal	6	—	—	N_m	N_m	N_n	N_n	N_m	N_m	N_n	N_n
	$\bar{6}$	$\bar{6}$	$\bar{6}$	N_m	N_m	N_n	N_n	O_m	O_m	O_n	O_n
	$\underline{6}$	—	—	N_m	O_m	O_n	N_n	N_m	O_m	O_n	N_n
	$\underline{\bar{6}}$	6	$\bar{6}$	N_m	O_m	O_n	N_n	O_m	N_m	N_n	O_n
	6/m	—	—	N_m	—	—	N_n	N_m	—	—	N_n
	$\underline{6}/\underline{m}$	6/m	$\bar{6}$	N_m	—	—	N_n	O_m	—	—	O_n
	$\underline{6}/m$	6	6/m	N_m	—	—	N_n	—	N_m	N_n	—
	$6/\underline{m}$	$\bar{6}$	6/m	N_m	—	—	N_n	—	O_m	O_n	—
	622	—	—	P_m	P_m	P_n	P_n	P_m	P_m	P_n	P_n
	$\underline{622}$	—	—	—	—	—	—	—	—	—	—

Hexa-gonal	$6\underline{22}$	6mm	6mm	P_m	P_m	F_n	P_n	Q_m	Q_m	Q_n	Q_n
	6mm	—	—	P_m	Q_m	Q_n	P_n	P_m	Q_m	Q_n	P_n
	$\underline{6}m\underline{m}$	$\bar{6}m2$	$(\bar{6}2m)$	P_m	Q_m	Q_n	P_n	(R_m)	R_m	R_n	(R_n)
	$6\underline{mm}$	622	6mm	P_m	Q_m	Q_n	P_n	Q_m	P_m	P_n	Q_n
	$\bar{6}m2$	—	—	P_m	R_m	R_n	P_n	P_m	R_m	R_n	P_n
	$(\bar{6}\underline{2m})$	622	$(\bar{6}2m)$	P_m	R_m	R_n	P_n	(R_m)	P_m	P_n	(R_n)
	$\bar{6}m\underline{2}$	6mm	$(\bar{6}2m)$	P_m	R_m	R_n	P_n	(R_m)	Q_m	Q_n	(R_n)
	$\bar{6}\underline{m2}$	$\bar{6}m2$	6mm	P_m	R_m	R_n	P_n	Q_m	R_m	R_n	Q_n
	6/mmm	—	—	P_m	—	—	P_n	P_m	—	—	P_n
	$\underline{6}/\underline{m}m\underline{m}$	6/mmm	$(\bar{6}2m)$	P_m	—	—	P_n	(R_m)	—	—	(R_n)
	$6/m\underline{mm}$	6/mmm	6mm	P_m	—	—	P_n	Q_m	—	—	Q_n
	$6/\underline{mmm}$	622	6/mmm	P_m	—	—	P_n	—	P_m	P_n	—
	$6/\underline{m}mm$	6mm	6/mmm	P_m	—	—	P_n	—	Q_m	Q_n	—
	$\underline{6}/m\underline{m}m$	$(\bar{6}2m)$	6/mmm	P_m	—	—	P_n	—	(R_m)	(R_n)	—
Cubic	23	—	—	S_m	S_m	S_n	S_n	S_m	S_m	S_n	S_n
	m3	—	—	S_m	—	—	S_n	S_m	—	—	S_n
	$\underline{m3}$	23	m3	S_m	—	—	S_n	—	S_m	S_n	—
	432	—	—	T_m	T_m	T_n	T_n	T_m	T_m	T_n	T_n

TABLE 7 (continued)

Cubic											
Cubic	432	$\bar{4}3m$	$\bar{4}3m$	T_m	T_m	T_n	T_n	U_m	U_m	U_n	U_n
	$\bar{4}3m$	—	—	T_m	U_m	U_n	T_n	T_m	U_m	U_n	T_n
	$\bar{4}3m$	432	$\bar{4}3m$	T_m	U_m	U_n	T_n	U_m	T_m	T_n	U_n
	m3m	—	—	T_m	—	—	T_n	T_m	—	—	T_n
	m3m	m3m	$\bar{4}3m$	T_m	—	—	T_n	U_m	—	—	U_n
	m3m	432	m3m	T_m	—	—	T_n	—	T_m	T_n	—
	m3m	$\bar{4}3m$	m3m	T_m	—	—	T_n	—	U_m	U_n	—

the various additional magnetic crystal classes could therefore be found by direct substitution of the appropriate generating matrices into equations (3.22) or (3.23). However, they could be more readily determined if it were possible to incorporate the (-1) occurring in equations (3.23) into the symmetry transformation equations for a set of *classical* symmetry operators. This may, in fact, be done since, as indicated below, the form of a c-tensor in a group $\mathcal{M}$ may be related to that of a tensor of the same rank in one of two classical groups $\mathcal{A}$ or $\mathcal{B}$. It is therefore possible to use the known results for the classical groups to predict the forms of property tensors in the additional magnetic groups.

Let the generating matrices of a particular additional magnetic point group $\mathcal{M}$ be denoted by $\sigma^{(\alpha)}$, $\sigma^{(\beta)}$, ..., $\sigma^{(\lambda)}$ and $\underline{\sigma}^{(\mu)}$. The group generated by $\sigma^{(\alpha)}, \sigma^{(\beta)}, ..., \sigma^{(\lambda)}$ and $-\sigma^{(\mu)}$ is (Lagrange's theorem)

$$\mathcal{A} = \mathcal{H} + (-\sigma^{(\mu)})\mathcal{H} = \mathcal{H} - R(R\sigma^{(\mu)})\mathcal{H}, \qquad (3.24)$$

that is, it is the group obtained from $\mathcal{M}$ by multiplying every $\underline{S}_t$ by $-R$. Now consider the symmetry transformation equations (either (3.22) or (3.23) for c-tensors) written out in full for all the symmetry matrices of $\mathcal{M}$, remembering that these may correspond to rotation axes of type n, $\bar{n}$, $\underline{n}$ or $\underline{\bar{n}}$. For polar tensors of odd rank and axial tensors of even rank, this set of equations is identical with the set of transformation equations obtained by employing every element of the group $\mathcal{A}$ in equations (3.22). The group $\mathcal{A}$ may be readily identified since its generating matrices are those shown in column 7 of Table 6 together with the additional generating matrix (of column 8) multiplied by $-R$. The groups $\mathcal{A}$ corresponding to the various additional magnetic groups $\mathcal{M}$ are listed in column 3 of Table 7. Similarly, it is possible (BIRSS [1962]) to construct a group $\mathcal{B}$ appropriate to polar tensors of even rank and axial tensors of odd rank. In this case, however, axial tensors in $\mathcal{M}$ must be related to polar tensors in $\mathcal{B}$ and vice versa. Specifically, the elements of $\mathcal{M}$ impose the same symmetry transformations on polar c-tensors of even rank as do the elements of $\mathscr{B}$ on axial tensors of even rank, and impose the same symmetry transformations on axial c-tensors of odd rank as do the elements of $\mathscr{B}$ on polar tensors of odd rank. The various groups $\mathscr{B}$ are listed in column 4 of Table 7.

Since each of the groups $\mathscr{A}$ and $\mathscr{B}$ can be identified with a classical crystallographic group ($\mathscr{G}$) – for which the form of the property tensors is known – the form of property tensors for all the magnetic groups may be readily ascertained from Table 4. The equalities between property tensors in the various magnetic crystal classes are displayed in columns 5 to 12 of Table 7, the occurrence of the same symbol in the various rows and columns of the table again indicating equality of the various property tensors. The actual form of the tensor (assumed to possess no intrinsic symmetry) which is represented by a given symbol may again be obtained from Tables 4b, c, d, e and f for tensors of ranks 0, 1, 2, 3 and 4 respectively.

The symbols for the (additional) magnetic group $\underline{2}\underline{m}m$ and its associated group $\mathscr{A}$ have been placed within brackets thus: ($\underline{2}\underline{m}m$) and (m2m). These, and the brackets around the symbols E_m and E_n representing the property tensors, indicate that the orientation of the reference axes is not the same as it is for the group mm2. In fact, $\mathscr{A}$ may be denoted by $\underset{m2m}{xyz}$ and $\mathscr{B}$ by $\underset{mm2}{xyz}$, where – as indicated by Table 6 – $\mathscr{G} = \underset{2mm}{xyz}$ and $\mathscr{M} = \underset{\underline{2}\underline{m}m}{xyz}$. Similarly, the groups $\bar{4}m2$ and $\bar{4}m\underline{2}$ are referred to axes that are rotated by an angle of $\frac{1}{4}\pi$ from those used for $\bar{4}2m$, whilst the axes for $\bar{6}2m$ and $\bar{6}\underline{2}\underline{m}$ differ by $\frac{1}{6}\pi$ from those used for $\bar{6}m2$.

§ 3.2. The Symmetry of Property Tensors
representing Transport Phenomena

As indicated above, transport effects merit special consideration because Neumann's principle cannot be applied in space-time, there being an intrinsically preferred direction of time. However, the symmetry of a crystal may be used to simplify the form of a property tensor representing a transport effect as indicated below.

Transport phenomena may be described in terms of equations (2.28) of Ch. 2, § 6. The J_i of (2.28) are, of course, the components of a c-tensor, whilst the X_i are the components of an i-tensor, so that L_{ij} is time-antisymmetric, and the application of Neumann's principle yields the erroneous result that all transport effects are prohibited for non-magnetic (i.e. time-symmetric) crystals. Because Neumann's principle cannot be applied in space-time, symmetry operators of the crystal of the form $\underline{S} = RS$ may not be used to simplify the form of the matrix L_{ij}. Symmetry operators which do not involve R may, of course, be employed in the usual way. For the non-magnetic groups $\mathscr{G}'$ and the magnetic groups $\mathscr{G}$, the form of the matrix L_{ij} is the same as would be deduced classically by substituting the generating matrices corresponding to the classical symmetry operators of the particular crystal class into equations (2.18). This is because there are no symmetry operators of the form $\underline{S}$ for the groups $\mathscr{G}$, whilst every symmetry operator of the form $\underline{S}$ is duplicated as S for the groups $\mathscr{G}'$. For the additional magnetic groups $\mathscr{M}$, only those symmetry operators denoted by S_h (in § 2) may be used in equations (2.18), so that the matrix L_{ij} displays (at least) the symmetry appropriate to the classical sub-group $\mathscr{H}$ †. For any particular additional magnetic group, the sub-group $\mathscr{H}$ may be immediately identified from Table 6.

To summarize, the form of the matrix L_{ij} characterizing a transport property may be obtained for a crystal of the point group $\mathscr{G}'$, $\mathscr{G}$ or $\mathscr{M}$ by ascertaining, from Table 4, that appropriate to a crystal of the (classical) point group $\mathscr{G}$, $\mathscr{G}$ or $\mathscr{H}$ respectively. Alternatively, columns 5 to 8 of Table 7 (i.e. those corresponding

† The severe reduction in symmetry effected by replacing the group $\mathscr{M}$ by the sub-group $\mathscr{H}$ may cause some misgivings and this point is discussed further in Ch. 5, § 1.1.

to static i-tensors) may be used, notwithstanding that L_{ij} is, in fact, time-antisymmetric. Hence the L_{ij} of (2.28) must be regarded as time-symmetric, i.e. as an i-matrix, if the concepts of space-time symmetry are to be applied in the same manner for both transport and static properties. Nevertheless, the forms of two otherwise identical tensors representing a transport and a static property respectively may differ in detail because of the different restrictions imposed by intrinsic symmetry.

For example, consider the resistivity tensor, ϱ_{ij}, defined by equation (1.2d) and the magnetic permeability tensor, μ_{ij}, defined by (1.27) for an antiferromagnetic material in a non-magnetic class. In general, the relation between B and H can be non-linear, and (1.27) must then be written in the form

$$B_i = \mu_{ij}H_j + P_{ijk}H_jH_k + \cdots. \tag{3.25}$$

Similarly, in the presence of a magnetic field, (1.2d) must be generalized to

$$E_i = \varrho_{ij}J_j + R_{ijk}J_jH_k + \cdots. \tag{3.26}$$

As stated in Ch. 2, § 6, it follows from the second law of thermo-dynamics that $\mu_{ij} = \mu_{ji}$. When (3.25) is used instead of (1.27), the reversibility of the order in which the free energy may be successively differentiated with respect to two components of the magnetic field leads, in addition, to the relations

$$P_{123} + P_{132} = P_{231} + P_{213} = P_{312} + P_{321}. \tag{3.27}$$

For a transport process, it follows from Onsager's theorem of irreversible thermodynamics that $L_{ij}(H) = L_{ji}(-H)$: in this case, therefore, the restrictions imposed by intrinsic symmetry comprise the equations $\varrho_{ij} = \varrho_{ji}$ and the relations

$$R_{ijk} = -R_{jik}. \tag{3.28}$$

It may be noted that, since the two field components are inter-changeable in $P_{ijk}H_jH_k$, intrinsic symmetry also imposes the restrictions $P_{ijk} = P_{ikj}$. There is no similar restriction on the R_{ijk} but, of course, this difference could have been anticipated immediately from the forms of equations (3.25) and (3.26).

§4. THE SYMMETRY OF PHYSICAL TENSORS

To utilize Tables 4 and 7 to determine the form of a property tensor representing a macroscopic static physical property of a crystal it is necessary to classify the property tensor under investigation as either an i-tensor (i.e. as time-symmetric) or a c-tensor (i.e. as time-antisymmetric). Just as the invariance of equation (1.25), defining the property tensor, under space-inversion leads to the 'product' rule for classifying a tensor as polar or axial, so the invariance of this equation under time-inversion enables the property tensor to be immediately classified as an i-tensor or a c-tensor provided the physical tensors are already so classified. Thus, if $e_{i_1i_2...i_m}$ and $i_{j_1j_2...j_n}$ are both i-tensors or both c-tensors then $d_{i_1i_2...i_mj_1j_2...j_n}$ is an i-tensor, whilst if one of the physical tensors is an i-tensor and the other a c-tensor then the property tensor is a c-tensor. This rule is therefore another 'product' rule, and it has an obvious extension to cases where two or more influences are acting on the crystal simultaneously.

The classification of physical tensors themselves as time-symmetric or time-antisymmetric can often be achieved from quantum-mechanical considerations as exemplified in § 1. Very often spin is suppressed in a quantum-mechanical formulation and the wave function of an electron is considered to be a scalar rather than a spinor. It might therefore be expected that most physical tensors are time-symmetric. However, an obvious exception is when magnetic quantities are involved. For example, since time-inversion reverses spin, it should also reverse magnetic moment, and a simple quantum-mechanical calculation [+] confirms this. The time-antisymmetry of magnetic moment suggests that the magnetic field vector, H, might also be a c-vector. Further, it is particularly important to determine whether H and the electric field

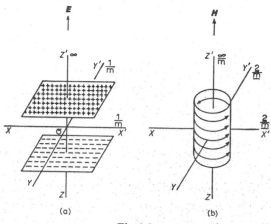

Fig. 3.2

vector, E, are i-vectors or c-vectors, since a crystal may be readily subjected to these influences, and E and H occur as physical tensors in the defining equations of many important property tensors.

One method of ascertaining whether field vectors such as E and H are time-symmetric or time-antisymmetric is by examining the symmetry of physical systems to which they are equivalent. For example, for the electric field vector, the equivalent physical system may be taken to be a pair of parallel plates (strictly, of infinite extent) carrying equal and opposite uniform densities of charge as shown in Fig. 3.2a. This system exhibits cylindrical

[+] $\langle \sigma_i \rangle = \psi^\dagger \sigma_i \psi$, where σ_i ($i = 1, 2, 3$) are the Pauli spin matrices (SEITZ [1940]) and $\psi^\dagger$ is the adjoint of ψ (i.e. the transpose, $[\psi_1^* \psi_2^*]$, of ψ^*). Thus $\langle \sigma_1 \rangle = \frac{1}{2}\hbar(\psi_1^*\psi_2 + \psi_2^*\psi_1)$, $\langle \sigma_2 \rangle = -\frac{1}{2}i\hbar(\psi_1^*\psi_2 - \psi_2^*\psi_1)$ and $\langle \sigma_3 \rangle = \frac{1}{2}\hbar(\psi_1^*\psi_1 - \psi_2^*\psi_2)$, so that all three components are reversed by the transformation (3.9), which changes ψ_1, ψ_1^*, ψ_2 and ψ_2^* to $\psi_2^*, \psi_2, -\psi_1^*$ and $-\psi_1$ respectively.

symmetry about the axis ZZ', *any* rotation about this axis being a symmetry operator. The axis ZZ' is therefore referred to as an infinity-fold axis (denoted by ∞). XX' and YY' are axes of type $\frac{1}{m}$, that is they are normals to reflection planes. The spatial symmetry of the system is thus characterized by the (full) international symbol $\infty \frac{1}{m} \frac{1}{m}$, and, since charge is time-symmetric, the system is unaltered by time-inversion, so that this symbol also characterizes the space-time symmetry. This situation may be contrasted with that which arises for a uniform magnetic field H. A uniform magnetic field may be represented by a cylindrical current sheet (strictly, of infinite length) as shown in Fig. 3.2b. ZZ' is an axis of type $\frac{\infty}{m}$, and this characterizes the spatial symmetry of the system completely. However, if it is remembered that time-inversion reverses the direction of current, it may be seen that XX' and YY' are also symmetry axes, of type $\frac{2}{m}$, so that the system is characterized by the international symbol $\frac{\infty}{m} \frac{2}{m} \frac{2}{m}$. To recapitulate, E is † a polar i-vector with symmetry $\infty \frac{1}{m} \frac{1}{m}$ and H is an axial c-vector with symmetry $\frac{\infty}{m} \frac{2}{m} \frac{2}{m}$. It may be observed, however, that this

---

† It may be noted that, if the operator R were identified with charge-reversal rather than time-inversion, E would be a polar c-vector with symmetry $\frac{\infty}{m} \frac{2}{m} \frac{2}{m}$ whilst H would still be an axial c-vector with symmetry $\frac{\infty}{m} \frac{2}{m} \frac{2}{m}$. It would then be possible, for example, to predict (NERONOVA and BELOV [1959, 1960]) which crystal classes exhibit pyroelectricity, and these classes would, in general, be denoted by different symbols from those resulting from the identification of R with time-inversion (vide Ch. 4, Table 8). However, such a classification would be of little value unless there were some method of ascertaining, *a priori*, the symmetry of crystals with respect to the charge-reversal operator and combinations of this operator with spatial symmetry operators. In practice this information would be obtained by studying the property tensors themselves, since neutron diffraction experiments reveal the magnetic, rather than the electrical, structure of a crystal. The advantage of a formulation in terms of time-inversion is that there is an *independent* method by which the symmetry of property tensors can be established.

method of classification succeeds only because the two equivalent systems are related to charge and current – two quantities whose behaviour under time-inversion has been previously investigated in § 1. This method is therefore only applicable when the behaviour under time-inversion of the physical quantities which form the equivalent system is already known.

Since the special theory of relativity provides a four-dimensional formulation of physics in which the fourth dimension, x_4, is related to time, it might be thought that the transformation $t \rightarrow -t$ would, when applied to the 4-tensors of this theory, reveal whether they were time-symmetric or time-antisymmetric. In fact, however, no more information can be obtained on this point by employing the four-dimensional formulation of the special theory of relativity than by employing the ordinary three-dimensional formulation. This important point is illustrated below in relation to the electric and magnetic field vectors and to Maxwell's equations, that is to equations (1.28).

There is a close similarity between the procedure adopted to determine whether tensors are polar or axial and that adopted to determine whether they are i-tensors or c-tensors. For example, under the *proper* rotation of the three spatial coordinate axes given by equation (2.9), all the vectors E, D, H, B and J of (1.28) transform according to equations (1.16), that is according to

$$d_i' = l_{ip}d_p \qquad (i, p = 1, 2, 3), \qquad (3.29a)$$

where the d_i denote the three components of any one of these vectors. However, for an *improper* rotation (i.e. one involving space-inversion) this equation must be modified to

$$d_i' = \pm l_{ip}d_p \qquad (i, p = 1, 2, 3), \qquad (3.29b)$$

the positive sign being taken for polar vectors and the negative sign for axial vectors. Which vectors are polar and which axial is deduced from the invariance of equations (1.28) under space-inversion.

To obtain a four-dimensional formulation of Maxwell's equations, a fourth coordinate x_4 – related in some way to time – must be added to the three spatial coordinates x_1, x_2, x_3. According to the special theory of relativity, the velocity of propagation of a light wave in free space is a universal constant, c, which is independent of the reference system. Thus, if a spherical light wave is emitted at time $t = 0$ from the origin, O, of a system of coordinates x_1, x_2, x_3, an observer located at the point x_1, x_2, x_3 will note the passage of the wave-front at the instant ct and deduce that the equation of a point on the wave-front is

$$x_1^2 + x_2^2 + x_3^2 - c^2t^2 = 0. \tag{3.30}$$

A second observer, however, who measures position and time with respect to a second reference frame x_1', x_2', x_3', the origin of which, O', moves at velocity v relative to O so as to keep x_3' parallel to x_3, notes that the equation of the wave-front in his system of coordinates is

$$x_1'^2 + x_2'^2 + x_3'^2 - c^2t'^2 = 0, \tag{3.31}$$

assuming that O' and O coincide at $t' = t = 0$. The quantity x_4 may therefore be identified with ict and the transformations which leave $x_1^2 + x_2^2 + x_3^2 + x_4^2$ invariant upon a change from the first to the second observer's frame of reference may be written in the well-known form

$$x_1' = x_1, \qquad\qquad x_2' = x_2,$$
$$x_3' = \frac{x_3 - vt}{\sqrt{(1 - v^2/c^2)}}, \qquad t' = \frac{t - vx_3/c^2}{\sqrt{(1 - v^2/c^2)}}. \tag{3.32}$$

These transformations have been named after Lorentz, who was the first to show that Maxwell's equations are invariant with respect to the change of variables defined by (3.32), but not in-variant under the Galilean transformation

$$x_1' = x_1, \qquad x_2' = x_2,$$
$$x_3' = x_3 - vt, \qquad t' = t. \tag{3.33}$$

Special relativity is primarily concerned with the *proper* Lorentz group of transformations, that is with the transformations obtained by combining those of the group of proper rotations (which preserve $x_1^2 + x_2^2 + x_3^2$ invariant and for which $t' = t$) with the transformations given by (3.32).

The four-dimensional form of Maxwell's equations is obtained (STRATTON [1941]) by replacing the 3-vectors E and B by the 4-tensor

$$[F_{ij}] = \begin{bmatrix} 0 & B_3 & -B_2 & -iE_1 \\ -B_3 & 0 & B_1 & -iE_2 \\ B_2 & -B_1 & 0 & -iE_3 \\ iE_1 & iE_2 & iE_3 & 0 \end{bmatrix}, \tag{3.34a}$$

the 3-vectors D and H by the 4-tensor

$$[G_{ij}] = \begin{bmatrix} 0 & H_3 & -H_2 & -iD_1 \\ -H_3 & 0 & H_1 & -iD_2 \\ H_2 & -H_1 & 0 & -iD_3 \\ iD_1 & iD_2 & iD_3 & 0 \end{bmatrix}, \tag{3.34b}$$

and the scalar ϱ and the 3-vector J by the 4-vector

$$[J_i] = [J_1/c \quad J_2/c \quad J_3/c \quad i\varrho]. \tag{3.34c}$$

It may then be readily verified that equations (1.28c) and (1.28d) may be expressed in the form

$$\frac{\partial F_{ij}}{\partial x_k} + \frac{\partial F_{ki}}{\partial x_j} + \frac{\partial F_{jk}}{\partial x_i} = 0, \tag{3.35a}$$

where i, j, k are any three of the four numbers 1, 2, 3, 4, and that equations (1.28a) and (1.28b) may be expressed in the form

$$\frac{\partial G_{ip}}{\partial x_p} = 4\pi J_i \qquad (i, p = 1, 2, 3, 4). \qquad (3.35b)$$

These 4-tensors transform as true (i.e. polar) tensors under the transformations of the proper Lorentz group – a group that specifically excludes the discrete transformations corresponding to space-inversion and time-inversion. However, it may be noted that the axial 3-vectors H and B are represented in the first three rows and columns of F_{ij} and G_{ij} in a form which would correspond, in three dimensions, to the correct representation of an axial 3-vector as an antisymmetrical polar 3-tensor of second rank. Such a representation in three dimensions would remove the need for a $\pm$ sign in equations (1.23) because the quantities under consideration would all be polar tensors so that (1.16) could always be used. It might therefore be anticipated that the 4-tensors F_{ij}, G_{ij} and J_i would also transform as polar tensors under the Lorentz group of transformations, which is defined as the group formed by augmenting the proper Lorentz group by the addition of the space-inversion operator C. If this operator, which is represented by the matrix

$$[C_{ij}] = \begin{bmatrix} -1 & 0 & 0 & 0 \\ 0 & -1 & 0 & 0 \\ 0 & 0 & -1 & 0 \\ 0 & 0 & 0 & 1 \end{bmatrix}, \qquad (3.36)$$

is substituted into the transformation law

$$F'_{ij} = C_{ip}C_{jq}F_{pq}, \qquad (3.37)$$

then F'_{ij} is the tensor

$$[F'_{ij}] = \begin{bmatrix} 0 & B_3 & -B_2 & iE_1 \\ -B_3 & 0 & B_1 & iE_2 \\ B_2 & -B_1 & 0 & iE_3 \\ -iE_1 & -iE_2 & -iE_3 & 0 \end{bmatrix}. \tag{3.38}$$

The transformation has therefore reversed the signs of E_1, E_2, E_3 whilst leaving those of B_1, B_2, B_3 unchanged. As this is the expected result of applying C, in three dimensions, to a polar E vector and an axial B vector, it may be seen that F_{ij} is a polar 4-tensor and that it would be incorrect to incorporate a minus sign into equation (3.37) when the Lorentz group replaces the proper Lorentz group. Similarly the transformation

$$G'_{ij} = C_{ip}C_{jq}G_{pq} \tag{3.39}$$

yields

$$[G'_{ij}] = \begin{bmatrix} 0 & H_3 & -H_2 & iD_1 \\ -H_3 & 0 & H_1 & iD_2 \\ H_2 & -H_1 & 0 & iD_3 \\ -iD_1 & -iD_2 & -iD_3 & 0 \end{bmatrix}, \tag{3.40}$$

and

$$J'_i = C_{ip}J_p \tag{3.41}$$

yields

$$[J'_i] = [-J_1/c \quad -J_2/c \quad -J_3/c \quad i\varrho], \tag{3.42}$$

in agreement with the representation in three dimensions of D and J as polar vectors, H as an axial vector and ϱ as a true scalar. Hence it would be incorrect to incorporate a minus sign into (3.39) or (3.41) when the Lorentz group replaces the proper Lorentz group.

When a further extension is made to the *extended* Lorentz group of transformations by augmenting the Lorentz group by the addition of the time-inversion operator R, it is found that it may again be necessary to introduce $\pm$ signs into the transformation laws. For the second-rank tensor F_{ij}, the substitution of

$$[R_{ij}] = \begin{bmatrix} 1 & 0 & 0 & 0 \\ 0 & 1 & 0 & 0 \\ 0 & 0 & 1 & 0 \\ 0 & 0 & 0 & -1 \end{bmatrix} \tag{3.43}$$

into

$$F'_{ij} = R_{ip}R_{jq}F_{pq} \tag{3.44}$$

yields the same tensor F'_{ij} as is given by (3.38), since $R^2 = C^2$. The transformation has therefore again reversed the signs of E_1, E_2, E_3 whilst leaving those of B_1, B_2, B_3 unchanged. However, it may be deduced from the invariance of equation (1.28c) under time-inversion that, because of the occurrence of the differential operator $\partial/\partial t$, either E must be an i-vector and B a c-vector, or E must be a c-vector and B an i-vector. From the considerations outlined above and in § 1 it is obvious that the former alternative is to be preferred, so that it is essential to incorporate a minus sign into (3.44). It is therefore necessary to incorporate a $\pm$ sign into the general transformation equation when the extended Lorentz group replaces the Lorentz group. Similarly it may readily be shown that the assumption that D is an i-vector, that H and J are c-vectors and that ϱ is an i-scalar (i.e. a true scalar) is the preferable alternative consistent with the invariance of (1.28a) and (1.28b) under time-inversion. This means that G_{ij} transforms as

$$G'_{ij} = -R_{ip}R_{jq}G_{pq}, \tag{3.45}$$

and that the current 4-vector J_i transforms as

$$J'_i = -R_{ip}J_p. \tag{3.46}$$

The presence of the minus signs in (3.45) and (3.46) again indicates that a $\pm$ sign must be incorporated into the transformation equations for general four-dimensional rotations in space-time. The fact that there must be minus signs either in both or in neither equations could, of course, have been deduced directly from the invariance of the 4-tensor equation (3.35b) under time-inversion.

It may therefore be concluded that the four-dimensional formulation of the special relativity theory facilitates the identification of the correct physical 4-tensor. However, this theory only admits transformations which leave the relation past–future invariant, and if transformations involving time-inversion are to be considered then the transformation equation for the 4-tensor must be modified by the inclusion of a $\pm$ sign. To decide whether physical tensors are i-tensors or c-tensors it is always necessary to refer to the invariance of fundamental physical laws involving these tensors under time-inversion. This can, of course, be done for either a three-dimensional or a four-dimensional formulation of these laws.

§ 5. NULL PROPERTY TENSORS: 'FORBIDDEN' EFFECTS

As indicated in Ch. 2, § 7, crystal symmetry does not impose nullity on any tensor in *all* crystal classes, so that there are no effects which are completely 'forbidden' from symmetry considerations. However, certain types of tensors are identically zero in certain classes of crystals, e.g. all c-tensors representing static properties are null in non-magnetic crystals. It is essential in what follows to distinguish clearly between a (classical) magnetic group, denoted by $\mathscr{G}$, and the corresponding non-magnetic group, denoted by $\mathscr{G}'$. Thus, for example, the magnetic group with the symmetry elements $1, 2_z, \pm 4_z$ is denoted by the (bold-face) symbol **4** whilst the non-magnetic group with the symmetry elements $1, 2_z, \pm 4_z, \underline{1}, \underline{2}_z, \pm \underline{4}_z$ is denoted by the symbol 4.

For the non-magnetic groups, $\mathscr{G}'$, and for *static* properties:

(a) all c-tensors are null,

(b) polar i-tensors of odd rank and axial i-tensors of even rank vanish identically for the centrosymmetrical groups.

The only further restrictions are those imposed on tensors of the first and second rank or as a result of particularization. Within the complete set, n, of the 32 non-magnetic crystal classes, the 11 centrosymmetrical classes comprise a sub-set, n_1, defined by

$$n_1 = (\bar{1}, 2/m, mmm, 4/m, 4/mmm, \bar{3},$$

$$\bar{3}m, 6/m, 6/mmm, m3, m3m). \qquad (3.47)$$

The magnetic groups, $\mathscr{M}'$, comprise the classical (magnetic) groups, $\mathscr{G}$, and the additional magnetic groups, $\mathscr{M}$. Within the complete set, m, of the 90 magnetic crystal classes there are two sub-sets, m_2 and m_3, which may be readily identified from Table 7. The members of m_2 are the 21 classes for which no symbol appears in columns 10 and 11 of Table 7, that is

$$m_2 = (\bar{1}, 2/\underline{m}, \underline{2/m}, \underline{mmm}, \underline{mmm}, 4/\underline{m}, \underline{4}/m, 4/\underline{mmm},$$

$$\underline{4}/mmm, 4/m\underline{mm}, \bar{3}, \bar{3}m, \bar{3}\underline{m}, 6/m, \underline{6}/m, 6/mmm,$$

$$\underline{6}/\underline{mmm}, 6/\underline{mmm}, m3, m3m, m3\underline{m}). \qquad (3.48)$$

The members of m_3 are the (different) 21 classes for which no symbol appears in columns 9 and 12 of Table 7, that is

$$m_3 = (\underline{\bar{1}}, 2/\underline{m}, \underline{2}/m, \underline{mmm}, mm\underline{m}, 4/\underline{m}, \underline{4}/m, 4/\underline{mmm},$$

$$4/\underline{m}mm, \underline{4}/\underline{mmm}, \underline{\bar{3}}, \underline{\bar{3}m}, \bar{3}\underline{m}, 6/\underline{m}, \underline{6}/m,$$

$$6/\underline{mmm}, 6/\underline{mmm}, \underline{6}/\underline{mmm}, \underline{m}3, \underline{m}3\underline{m}, \underline{m}3m). \qquad (3.49)$$

It may be seen from Table 6 that m_2 comprises all the magnetic crystal classes for which $\bar{1}$ is a symmetry operator, whilst m_3 comprises all the magnetic crystal classes for which $\underline{I} \equiv R\bar{I}$ is a symmetry operator. The two sets taken together form a set $m_1 = m_2 + m_3$, all the members of which are, or are derived from, the centrosymmetrical magnetic crystal classes corresponding to the set n_1. It follows from Table 7 that, for *static* properties:

(c) axial c-tensors of even rank and polar c-tensors of odd rank are null in the 21 magnetic crystal classes contained in the set m_2,

(d) polar c-tensors of even rank and axial c-tensors of odd rank are null in the 21 magnetic crystal classes contained in the set m_3,

(e) axial i-tensors of even rank and polar i-tensors of odd rank are null in the 42 magnetic crystal classes contained in the set $m_1 = m_2 + m_3$.

The detailed application of the restrictions (a), (b), (c), (d) and (e), given above, is considered in Chapters 4 and 5.

CHAPTER 4

THE MAGNETIC PROPERTIES
OF ANTIFERROMAGNETIC MATERIALS

§ 1. 'FORBIDDEN' EFFECTS AND OTHER STATIC PROPERTIES

An antiferromagnetic material may be readily allocated to its
correct magnetic or non-magnetic crystal class provided that a
complete specification is available of the antiferromagnetic array
of spin magnetic moments. For ferromagnetic and ferrimagnetic
crystals, however, the directions assumed by the spins (on which,
of course, the space-time symmetry depends) are strongly influenced by any magnetic field that may be applied to the crystal.
Such crystals therefore merit separate consideration and the magnetic properties of ferromagnetic and ferrimagnetic materials
are considered in detail in Chapter 5.

For tensors of high rank, symmetry requirements impose nullity
on all the components of a static property tensor only by virtue of
the restrictions (a), (b), (c), (d) and (e) of Ch. 3, § 5. However,
tensors of the third and lower ranks may vanish by virtue of
particularization imposed by intrinsic symmetry. For example,
consider the piezomagnetic effect, which is characterized by a
third-rank tensor. Piezomagnetism is associated with the presence,
in the thermodynamic potential, Φ, of terms involving products of
a stress component, T_{jk}, and a magnetic field component, H_i.
Thus Φ may be written in the form $\Phi = q_{ijk}H_iT_{jk}$, whence the
components of the magnetization vector are $I_i = -\partial\Phi/\partial H_i$

$= -q_{ijk}T_{jk}$. Alternatively, piezomagnetism may be defined directly by reference to equations of the form

$$I_i = Q_{ijk}T_{jk}. \tag{4.1}$$

Since the T_{jk} are the components of a second-rank polar i-tensor and the I_i are the components of an axial c-tensor of first rank, Q_{ijk} is an axial c-tensor of third rank. From restriction (a) of Ch. 3, § 5, non-magnetic crystals cannot exhibit piezomagnetism, whilst from (d), the piezomagnetic effect is, in addition, absent for the 21 magnetic crystal classes contained in the set m_3. Moreover, piezomagnetism is also absent for the magnetic crystal classes **432**, $\overline{\mathbf{4}}\mathbf{3m}$ and **m3m**. This is a consequence of particularization: the symmetry of the stress tensor ($T_{jk} = T_{kj}$)† ensures that the tensor Q_{ijk} is symmetrical in the last two of its three indices, so that T_3 of Table 4e vanishes identically. Thus the piezomagnetic effect may only be exhibited by crystals belonging to the remaining $(90 - 21 - 3) = 66$ magnetic classes contained in the set $m - m_3 - (\mathbf{432}, \overline{\mathbf{4}}\mathbf{3m}, \mathbf{m3m})$.

Even in the absence of intrinsic symmetry, tensors of ranks lower than the third may be null in crystal classes other than those indicated by the restrictions (a), (b), (c), (d) and (e) of Ch. 3, § 5. For example, consider the magnetoelectric effect, which is characterized by a second-rank tensor. The magnetoelectric effect is associated with the presence, in the thermodynamic potential, Φ, of terms involving products of a magnetic field component, H_i, and an electric field component, E_j. It may therefore be defined by an equation of the form $\Phi = q_{ij}H_iE_j$ or, more directly, by

$$I_i = Q_{ij}E_j. \tag{4.2}$$

Since the I_i are the components of an axial c-tensor of first rank and the E_j are the components of a polar i-tensor of first rank,

---

† The validity of assuming that the stress tensor is symmetrical is examined in Ch. 5, § 3.

Q_{ij} is an axial c-tensor of second rank. From restriction (a), non-magnetic crystals cannot exhibit the magnetoelectric effect; nor does the tensor Q_{ij} exhibit intrinsic symmetry. From (c), the magnetoelectric effect is absent for the 21 magnetic crystal classes contained in the set m_2. This leaves the $(90 - 21) = 69$ magnetic crystal classes contained in the set $m - m_2$; but inspection of Table 4d shows that O_2, R_2 and U_2 vanish identically and the number of classes in which the magnetoelectric effect is possible is thereby reduced from 69 to 58.

Even more prohibitive restrictions are imposed on first-rank tensors, i.e. vectors. For example, consider the pyromagnetic effect, which is characterized by a first-rank tensor, Q_i, defined by the equations

$$I_i = Q_i\theta, \qquad (4.3)$$

where θ is the difference between the temperature of the crystal and some reference temperature. The property tensor of pyromagnetism, Q_i, is thus an axial c-tensor of first rank. From restriction (a) of Ch. 3, § 5, non-magnetic crystals cannot exhibit pyromagnetism, whilst from (d) pyromagnetism is also absent for the 21 magnetic crystal classes contained in the set m_3. These restrictions are, in fact, the same as those imposed on the property tensor characterizing piezomagnetism. In addition, however, it may be seen from Table 4c that D_1, G_1, H_1, J_1, L_1, O_1, P_1, R_1, S_1, T_1 and U_1 all vanish identically. The number of classes in which pyromagnetism is possible is thereby reduced from 69 to 31. These 31 classes are also those for which crystals can display a spontaneous magnetic moment or for which crystals can be magnetized by uniform hydrostatic pressure, the property tensor being an axial c-tensor of first rank in both cases.

The property tensors considered above are all c-tensors characterizing static properties, namely the piezomagnetic, magnetoelectric and pyromagnetic effects. Static properties characterized by i-tensors may be dealt with in the same way as those characterized by c-tensors. In general, i-tensors do not represent 'forbidden' effects and the corresponding properties are well established classically, so that a consideration of space-time symmetry operators leads to less spectacular results. The only new feature that emerges is that a property may be exhibited both by nonmagnetic and magnetic crystals. For example, consider the pyroelectric effect, which is characterized by a first-rank tensor, Q_i^*, defined by the equations

$$P_i = Q_i^* \theta, \tag{4.4}$$

where the P_i are the components of the electrical polarization and θ is the difference between the temperature of the crystal and some reference temperature.

The P_i, like the E_i, are the components of a polar i-tensor of first rank, so that Q_i^* is also a polar i-tensor of first rank. Thus, from restriction (b), pyroelectricity may not be exhibited by the 11(centrosymmetrical)non-magnetic crystal classes contained in the set n_1, nor, from restriction (e), by the 42 magnetic crystal classes contained in the set m_1. This leaves the 21 non-magnetic classes contained in the set $n - n_1$ and the 48 magnetic classes contained in the set $m - m_1$. However, as before, D_1, G_1, H_1, J_1, L_1, O_1, P_1, R_1, S_1, T_1 and U_1 all vanish identically, whilst $B_1 = E_1 = F_1 = I_1 = K_1 = M_1 = N_1 = Q_1$, and the pyroelectric effect may only be exhibited by the 10 non-magnetic classes and the 21 magnetic classes listed in Table 8. The form of the pyroelectric tensor, for these classes, is one of three basic types and is given in the third column of Table 8. The classes listed in Table 8 are also those for which crystals can display a spontaneous electrical polarization or for which crystals can be polarized by uniform hydrostatic pressure, the property tensor being a polar i-tensor of first rank in both cases.

The realization that the 'forbidden' effects discussed above might be exhibited by crystals possessing ordered arrays of spin magnetic moments is quite recent and, consequently, there is not

an abundance of confirmatory experimental data. Certain experiments (described in §§ 2, 3 and 4) have, however, been performed to verify the existence of these effects in selected antiferromagnetic materials. Direct experimental confirmation of the
existence of 'forbidden' effects in antiferromagnetics is confined,

TABLE 8

Non-magnetic crystal classes	Magnetic crystal classes	Matrix representation of the property tensor, Q_i^*
1	1	$[Q_1^* \ Q_2^* \ Q_3^*]$
m	m, $\underline{m}$	$[Q_1^* \ Q_2^* \ 0]$
2, mm2, 4, 4mm, 3, 3m, 6, 6mm	2, $\underline{2}$, mm2, $\underline{mm}$2, ($\underline{2}$mm), 4, $\underline{4}$, 4mm, $\underline{4}$mm, 4$\underline{mm}$, 3, 3m, 3$\underline{m}$, 6, $\underline{6}$, 6mm, $\underline{6}$mm, 6$\underline{mm}$	$[0 \ 0 \ Q_3^*]$

at present, to those which are represented by tensors of the third,
second or first rank, in particular to piezomagnetism, the magnetoelectric effect, pyromagnetism and the property of exhibiting spontaneous magnetization.

§ 2. PYROMAGNETISM (PARASITIC FERROMAGNETISM)

The piezomagnetic effect can be investigated by applying uniform
hydrostatic pressure to a specimen, rather than more general systems of stresses, but then, of course, the experimental data may
be characterized by an axial c-tensor of first rather than third
rank. An axial c-vector also characterizes pyromagnetism and the
property of exhibiting spontaneous magnetization, and, as stated

in § 1, the number of classes in which pyromagnetism is possible is 31. These are the magnetic classes:

$$1, \underline{\bar{1}}, 2, \underline{2}, m, \underline{m}, 2/m, \underline{2}/\underline{m}, \underline{222}, mm2, \underline{2}mm,$$

$$\underline{mm}m, 4, \bar{4}, 4/m, 4\underline{22}, 4\underline{mm}, \bar{4}2\underline{m}, 4/m\underline{mm}, 3, \bar{3},$$

$$3\underline{2}, 3\underline{m}, \bar{3}\underline{m}, 6, \bar{6}, 6/m, 6\underline{22}, 6\underline{mm}, \bar{6}m\underline{2}, 6/m\underline{mm}.$$

The tensor Q_i of equation (4.3), characterizing the effect, has only three possible forms and these are the same as those characterizing the pyroelectric effect. In the magnetic classes 1 and $\bar{1}$, Q_i is of the type symbolized by A_1 and has three independent components Q_1, Q_2 and Q_3. Similarly, in the magnetic classes $\underline{2}$, $\underline{m}$ and $\underline{2}/\underline{m}$, Q_i is of the type symbolized by C_1 and has two independent components Q_1 and Q_2. In the remaining 26 classes in which pyromagnetism is possible, Q_i has only one non-vanishing component, Q_3. The property of pyromagnetism and the property of exhibiting spontaneous magnetization represent, in reality, the same physical phenomenon, for if a crystal exhibits spontaneous magnetization this magnetization will, in general, be temperature dependent, that is the crystal will be pyromagnetic. Certain antiferromagnetic crystals such as α-Fe_2O_3, $MnCO_3$, $CoCO_3$ and NiF_2 do, in fact, possess a small spontaneous magnetization in the absence of an applied magnetic field, and they are therefore said to exhibit weak (or parasitic) ferromagnetism. The smallness of the spontaneous magnetization indicates that the weak ferromagnetism may be attributed to a slight tilting or canting of the spins from the (antiparallel) alignment appropriate to a perfect antiferromagnetic arrangement. Whether a particular antiferromagnetic crystal can exhibit weak ferromagnetism is determined by its space-time symmetry (DZIALOSHINSKII [1957]).

For example, consider the two isomorphic antiferromagnetics α-Fe_2O_3 (haematite) and Cr_2O_3, both of which exhibit a corundum-type crystal structure, as shown in Fig. 4.1. The disposition

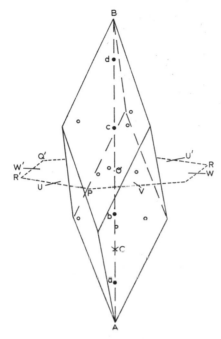

Fig. 4.1 a

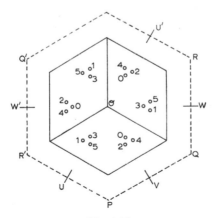

Fig. 4.1 b

of the oxygen ions, which are denoted by open circles, is indicated in Fig. 4.1a relative to a rhombohedral unit cell with centre at O. The metallic ions, Fe^{+++} or Cr^{+++}, are situated along the [111] axis, AB, at the points a, b, c and d (so that Aa = Ob = Oc = Bd). The exact location of the O^{--} ions (for haematite) may be more readily appreciated by referring to Fig. 4.1b which shows their positions relative to a succession of equally spaced (111) planes, the numbers indicating the perpendicular distance of the planes from A (towards B) in units of one-sixth of the distance AB. Classically, the crystal possesses a three-fold axis, AB, and three two-fold axes, OU, OV, OW. Also the point C, which divides the line AB so that AC = $\frac{1}{4}$AB, is a centre of symmetry. The appropriate classical point group is thus $\bar{3}m$ with symmetry elements 1, $\bar{1}$, $3(2_{\perp})$, $3(\bar{2}_{\perp})$, $\pm 3_z$, $\pm \bar{3}_z$.

For Cr_2O_3, the spins of the metallic ions form a simple anti-ferromagnetic arrangement, adjacent spins pointing in opposite directions: with reference to Fig. 4.1a the spins have the signature

$$a\uparrow \quad b\downarrow \quad c\uparrow \quad d\downarrow.$$

In α-Fe_2O_3, on the other hand, the spins of adjacent metallic ions are not always antiparallel, for they conform to the signature

$$a\uparrow \quad b\uparrow \quad c\downarrow \quad d\downarrow.$$

Whether weak ferromagnetism is possible or not depends not only on the signature of the spins but also on the absolute *orientation* of the spin directions relative to the crystal lattice.

In α-Fe_2O_3 at high temperatures (specifically, between about 250°K and 950°K) the spins lie in a symmetry plane, for example, the plane BOR† in Fig. 4.1a, and make a small angle with the (111) plane. Thus, for example, the spins at a and b may point

---

† For the point group $\bar{3}m$, the plane BOR is a mirror reflection plane although, as may be seen from Fig. 4.1b, it is actually an (axial) glide reflection plane for the complete space group of the crystal.

nearly parallel to OR whilst those at c and d may point nearly parallel to OR'. With this distribution of spins, the [111] direction is no longer a three-fold axis and the directions OU and OW are no longer two-fold axes. However, OV is still a two-fold axis and C is still a centre of symmetry, so that the appropriate magnetic point group is $2/m$, with symmetry elements $1, \bar{1}, 2_z, \bar{2}_z$. It was shown above that pyromagnetism is a possible effect for crystals with this magnetic point group, and this is in agreement with the experimental observation that haematite crystals exhibit weak ferromagnetism at high temperatures. Physically, the weak ferromagnetism is permissible because it is possible to change the directions of the spins in such a way as to make the sum of their magnetic moments over a unit cell non-zero whilst still preserving unchanged the symmetry of the original distribution. Thus, for example, the spins at a and b (which originally pointed nearly parallel to OR) and the spins at c and d (which originally pointed nearly parallel to OR') may both be rotated about the axis AB towards the direction OV without altering the symmetry of the crystal from that appropriate to the magnetic point group $2/m$. These rotations of the spins create a resultant magnetic moment for the unit cell in the direction OV, so that the crystal as a whole will exhibit a spontaneous magnetization, that is it will be weakly ferromagnetic. The direction of the spontaneous magnetization is in agreement with that predicted above. The requirement that the symmetry of the crystal is unaltered does not, of course, impose any limitations on the magnitude of the magnetic moment. For example, it is possible, whilst still preserving the symmetry $2/m$, to rotate the two sets of spins through 90° so that their directions coincide and the crystal exhibits pure ferromagnetism. That the spontaneous magnetization is, in fact, small may be deduced from Landau's thermodynamic theory of phase transitions of the second kind (DZIALOSHINSKII [1957]), which clarifies the intimate connection between antiferromagnetism and weak ferromagnetism.

In α-Fe_2O_3 at low temperatures (below about 250°K) the spins are arranged parallel and antiparallel to the [111] direction (AB). The appropriate magnetic point group is therefore $\bar{3}m$ with symmetry elements 1, $\bar{1}$, $3(2_\perp)$, $3(\bar{2}_\perp)$, $\pm 3_z$, $\pm \bar{3}_z$. Similarly, for Cr_2O_3, the spins are arranged parallel and antiparallel to the [111] direction: the signature of the spins is, however, different, and the appropriate magnetic point group is now $\underline{\bar{3}m}$ with symmetry elements 1, $3(2_\perp)$, $\pm 3_z$, $\underline{\bar{1}}$, $3(\underline{\bar{2}}_\perp)$, $\pm \underline{\bar{3}}_z$. As stated above, pyromagnetism is impossible for the magnetic point groups $\bar{3}m$ and $\underline{\bar{3}m}$, so

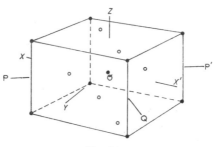

Fig. 4.2

that weak ferromagnetism cannot be exhibited by haematite at low temperatures or by chromic oxide. Physically, weak ferromagnetism is prohibited because any rotation of the spins away from parallelism or antiparallelism with the [111] direction lowers the symmetry of the crystal, since this direction is then no longer a three-fold axis of symmetry.

A similar situation obtains for the isomorphic antiferromagnetic difluorides MnF_2, FeF_2, CoF_2 and NiF_2, all of which exhibit a rutile-type crystal structure, as shown in Fig. 4.2. The disposition of the metallic ions, Mn^{++}, Fe^{++}, Co^{++} or Ni^{++}, which are denoted by closed circles, is indicated relative to a tetragonal unit cell with centre at O. The F^- ions, denoted by open circles, are all the same distance from the nearest metallic ion. Classically, the crystal possesses a four-fold axis, OZ, four two-fold axes, OX, OP, OY,

OQ, and a centre of symmetry, O. The appropriate classical point group is thus **4/mmm** with symmetry elements 1, $\bar{1}$, 2_x, 2_y, 2_z, 2_{xy}, 2_{-xy}, $\bar{2}_x$, $\bar{2}_y$, $\bar{2}_z$, $\bar{2}_{xy}$, $\bar{2}_{-xy}$, $\pm 4_z$, $\pm \bar{4}_z$.

For all four difluorides, the spins of all the metallic ions shown in Fig. 4.2, except that at O, are parallel to each other, and antiparallel to that at O. In MnF_2, FeF_2 and CoF_2 the spins are directed along the tetragonal axis, OZ, whilst for NiF_2 the spins are orientated parallel or antiparallel either to OX or to OY. Thus, for MnF_2, FeF_2 and CoF_2, the appropriate magnetic point group is **4/mmm** with symmetry elements 1, $\bar{1}$, 2_x, 2_y, 2_z, $\bar{2}_x$, $\bar{2}_y$, $\bar{2}_z$, $\underline{2}_{xy}$, $\underline{2}_{-xy}$, $\underline{\bar{2}}_{xy}$, $\underline{\bar{2}}_{-xy}$, $\pm \underline{4}_z$, $\pm \underline{\bar{4}}_z$, the x-,y- and z-axes being parallel to the directions OX, OY and OZ respectively. For NiF_2, the appropriate magnetic point group is **mmm** with symmetry elements 1, $\bar{1}$, 2_z, $\bar{2}_z$, $\underline{2}_x$, $\underline{2}_y$, $\underline{\bar{2}}_x$, $\underline{\bar{2}}_y$, the x-, y- and z-axes being parallel to the directions OZ, OX (the spin axis) and OY respectively. It was shown above that pyromagnetism is a possible effect for the magnetic point group **mmm** but not for the group **4/mmm**, and this is in agreement with the observation that NiF_2 exhibits weak ferromagnetism whilst MnF_2, FeF_2 and CoF_2 do not. Physically, the weak ferromagnetism is permissible in NiF_2 because it is possible to rotate the spins from, for example, parallelism with OX and OX' towards OY without changing the symmetry of the crystal. Weak ferromagnetism is prohibited for the other three difluorides because any rotation of the spins away from parallelism or antiparallelism with the tetragonal axis, OZ, lowers the symmetry of the crystal, since this direction is then no longer a four-fold axis of symmetry.

Similar considerations also hold for the isomorphic antiferromagnetic carbonates $MnCO_3$, $CoCO_3$ and $FeCO_3$. The symmetry of these crystals is described by the same space group as for α-Fe_2O_3 and Cr_2O_3 (D_{3d}^6 or $R\bar{3}2/c$), but there are only two metallic ions in the rhombohedral unit cell of Fig. 4.1a, situated at the mid-points of OB (i.e. at C) and of OA. Although the arrangement of the spins of these two ions is always antiparallel, weak ferromagnetism is not exhibited by $FeCO_3$, for which the spins are directed along the [111] axis, but is exhibited by $MnCO_3$ and $CoCO_3$, for which the spins are not directed along the [111] axis (BOROVIK-ROMANOV and ORLOVA [1956]).

§3. THE MAGNETOELECTRIC EFFECT

The magnetoelectric effect is characterized by the second-rank axial c-tensor Q_{ij} of equations (4.2) and, as stated in §1, the number of crystal classes in which the effect is possible is 58. Moreover, inspection of Table 4d reveals that $F_2 = K_2 = N_2$, $H_2 = L_2 = P_2, I_2 = M_2 = Q_2$ and $S_2 = T_2$, so that the number of possible forms of the tensor Q_{ij} is (further) reduced from 18 to 11. Table 9 lists the 58 magnetic crystal classes which can exhibit the magnetoelectric effect and also displays the form of the magnetoelectric tensor, Q_{ij}, for each of these classes. The occurrence of brackets around some of the symbols representing the crystal classes is associated with the rotations of axes discussed in Ch. 3, § 3.1.

The magnetoelectric effect was first observed experimentally by ASTROV [1960], who subjected an unorientated single crystal of Cr_2O_3 to an alternating electric field and detected the resultant variation in its magnetization. Astrov verified that the effect was linear in the applied electric field and investigated its temperature dependence in the neighbourhood of the Néel point (307°K). The form of the tensor characterizing the magnetoelectric effect in Cr_2O_3, which is that appropriate to the magnetic point group $\bar{3}\underline{m}$, may be obtained from Table 9. It is

$$[Q_{ij}] = \begin{bmatrix} Q_{11} & 0 & 0 \\ 0 & Q_{11} & 0 \\ 0 & 0 & Q_{33} \end{bmatrix}, \tag{4.5}$$

TABLE 9

Magnetic crystal class	Matrix representation of the property tensor, Q_{ij}
1, $\bar{1}$	$\begin{bmatrix} Q_{11} & Q_{12} & Q_{13} \\ Q_{21} & Q_{22} & Q_{23} \\ Q_{31} & Q_{32} & Q_{33} \end{bmatrix}$
2, $\underline{m}$, $2/\underline{m}$	$\begin{bmatrix} Q_{11} & Q_{12} & 0 \\ Q_{21} & Q_{22} & 0 \\ 0 & 0 & Q_{33} \end{bmatrix}$
$\underline{2}$, m, $\underline{2}/m$	$\begin{bmatrix} 0 & 0 & Q_{13} \\ 0 & 0 & Q_{23} \\ Q_{31} & Q_{32} & 0 \end{bmatrix}$
222, $\underline{mm}2$, $\underline{mmm}$	$\begin{bmatrix} Q_{11} & 0 & 0 \\ 0 & Q_{22} & 0 \\ 0 & 0 & Q_{33} \end{bmatrix}$
$\underline{22}2$, mm2, $(2\underline{mm})$, $mm\underline{m}$	$\begin{bmatrix} 0 & Q_{12} & 0 \\ Q_{21} & 0 & 0 \\ 0 & 0 & 0 \end{bmatrix}$
4, $\bar{4}$, $4/\underline{m}$, 3, $\underline{\bar{3}}$, 6, $\underline{\bar{6}}$, $6/\underline{m}$	$\begin{bmatrix} Q_{11} & Q_{12} & 0 \\ -Q_{12} & Q_{11} & 0 \\ 0 & 0 & Q_{33} \end{bmatrix}$
$\underline{4}$, $\bar{4}$, $\underline{4}/\underline{m}$	$\begin{bmatrix} Q_{11} & Q_{12} & 0 \\ Q_{12} & -Q_{11} & 0 \\ 0 & 0 & 0 \end{bmatrix}$

TABLE 9 (continued)

Magnetic crystal class	Matrix representation of the property tensor, Q_{ij}
422, 4$\underline{mm}$, $\bar{4}$2$\underline{m}$, 4/$\underline{mmm}$, 32, 3$\underline{m}$, $\bar{3}\underline{m}$, 622, 6$\underline{mm}$, ($\bar{6}$2$\underline{m}$), 6/$\underline{mmm}$	$\begin{bmatrix} Q_{11} & 0 & 0 \\ 0 & Q_{11} & 0 \\ 0 & 0 & Q_{33} \end{bmatrix}$
4$\underline{2}$2, ($\underline{4}$mm), $\bar{4}$2m, ($\bar{4}$2$\underline{m}$), $\underline{4}$/mmm	$\begin{bmatrix} Q_{11} & 0 & 0 \\ 0 & -Q_{11} & 0 \\ 0 & 0 & 0 \end{bmatrix}$
4$\underline{2}$2, 4mm, ($\bar{4}$m$\underline{2}$), 4/$\underline{mmm}$, 3$\underline{2}$, 3m, $\bar{3}$m, 6$\underline{2}$2, 6mm, $\bar{6}$m2, 6/$\underline{mmm}$	$\begin{bmatrix} 0 & Q_{12} & 0 \\ -Q_{12} & 0 & 0 \\ 0 & 0 & 0 \end{bmatrix}$
23, $\underline{m}$3, 432, $\bar{4}$3$\underline{m}$, $\underline{m}$3$\underline{m}$	$\begin{bmatrix} Q_{11} & 0 & 0 \\ 0 & Q_{11} & 0 \\ 0 & 0 & Q_{11} \end{bmatrix}$

so that equations (4.2) reduce to

$$I_1 = Q_{11}E_1,$$
$$I_2 = Q_{11}E_2, \qquad\qquad (4.6)$$
$$I_3 = Q_{33}E_3.$$

That the equations governing the magnetoelectric effect in Cr_2O_3 are indeed of this form was first verified by FOLEN, RADO and STALDER [1961] who applied a 1000 c/sec alternating electric field across two single-crystal disks in turn, the surfaces of the disks being perpendicular, respectively, to directions such as AB and

OW of Fig. 4.1a. A search coil of 10000 turns was used to detect the resultant changes in the magnetization of the specimens, measurements being made in a vacuum (to prevent electrical breakdown) and at various temperatures. Fig. 4.3 shows the observed temperature dependence of the magnitudes of the apparent values of the two quantities $\alpha_\perp = 4\pi Q_{11}$ and $\alpha_{//} = 4\pi Q_{33}$

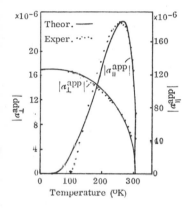

Fig. 4.3

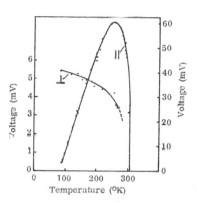

Fig. 4.4

(these differ from the real values of $\alpha_\perp$ and $\alpha_{//}$ because the crystals are subject to their own demagnetizing field even although the applied magnetic field is zero). Fig. 4.3 also shows theoretical curves for $\alpha_\perp$ and $\alpha_{//}$ derived by assuming that they are proportional to the product of the appropriate magnetic susceptibility and the zero-field sub-lattice magnetization, as calculated from the Néel–Van Vleck molecular field theory.

The first observations of the inverse effect, in which an electrical polarization is produced by an applied magnetic field, were made– with the same Cr_2O_3 crystals – by RADO and FOLEN [1962]. Fig. 4.4 shows the temperature dependence of the voltage induced across the disks when a magnetic field was applied in the same direction. The temperature dependence of the direct and inverse magnetoelectric effects is observed to be the same, as must, of course, be the case since both effects derive from the same terms (of the form H_iE_j) in the thermodynamic potential. In Cr_2O_3, both effects are strongly sensitive to magnetic annealing from a temperature just above the Néel point.

§ 4. THE PIEZOMAGNETIC EFFECT

The piezomagnetic effect is characterized by the third-rank axial c-tensor Q_{ijk} of equations (4.1), and, as stated in § 1, the number of crystal classes in which the effect is possible is 66. Table 10 lists these 66 magnetic crystal classes and also displays the form of the piezomagnetic tensor appropriate to each class. The piezomagnetic tensors, Q_{ijk}, are each of a type symbolized by one of the 20 symbols A_3, B_3, C_3, ..., R_3, S_3 and U_3. However, inspection of Table 4e shows that $F_3 = N_3$, $H_3 = P_3$, $I_3 = Q_3$ and $S_3 = U_3$, so that only 16 types of piezomagnetic tensor are possible. Since the stress tensor, T_{jk}, is symmetrical, it has only six independent components and a considerable simplification may be effected by replacing the full tensor notation with a new (matrix) notation using a single suffix running from one to six, according to the following scheme,

Old notation	T_{11}	T_{22}	T_{33}	T_{23}, T_{32}	T_{31}, T_{13}	T_{12}, T_{21}
New notation	T_1	T_2	T_3	T_4	T_5	T_6

Equations (4.1) may then be written in the form

$$I_i = Q_{iA}T_A, \tag{4.7}$$

where $i = 1, 2, 3$ and $A = 1, 2, 3, 4, 5, 6$. This is the notation adopted in Table 10, where one of the 16 different types of piezomagnetic tensor is associated with each of the 66 magnetic groups

TABLE 10   141

Magnetic crystal class	Matrix representation of the property tensor, Q_{ijk}					
1, $\bar{1}$	Q_{11}	Q_{12}	Q_{13}	Q_{14}	Q_{15}	Q_{16}
	Q_{21}	Q_{22}	Q_{23}	Q_{24}	Q_{25}	Q_{26}
	Q_{31}	Q_{32}	Q_{33}	Q_{34}	Q_{35}	Q_{36}
2, m, 2/m	0	0	0	Q_{14}	Q_{15}	0
	0	0	0	Q_{24}	Q_{25}	0
	Q_{31}	Q_{32}	Q_{33}	0	0	Q_{36}
$\underline{2}$, $\underline{m}$, $2/\underline{m}$	Q_{11}	Q_{12}	Q_{13}	0	0	Q_{16}
	Q_{21}	Q_{22}	Q_{23}	0	0	Q_{26}
	0	0	0	Q_{34}	Q_{35}	0
222, mm2, mmm	0	0	0	Q_{14}	0	0
	0	0	0	0	Q_{25}	0
	0	0	0	0	0	Q_{36}
$\underline{222}$, $\underline{mm}2$, $(\underline{2mm})$, $\underline{mmm}$	0	0	0	0	Q_{15}	0
	0	0	0	Q_{24}	0	0
	Q_{31}	Q_{32}	Q_{33}	0	0	0
4, $\bar{4}$, 4/m, 6, $\bar{6}$, 6/m	0	0	0	Q_{14}	Q_{15}	0
	0	0	0	Q_{15}	$-Q_{14}$	0
	Q_{31}	Q_{31}	Q_{33}	0	0	0
$\underline{4}$, $\underline{\bar{4}}$, $\underline{4}/m$	0	0	0	Q_{14}	Q_{15}	0
	0	0	0	$-Q_{15}$	Q_{14}	0
	Q_{31}	$-Q_{31}$	0	0	0	Q_{36}
422, 4mm, $\bar{4}$2m, 4/mmm, 622, 6mm, $\bar{6}$m2, 6/mmm	0	0	0	Q_{14}	0	0
	0	0	0	0	$-Q_{14}$	0
	0	0	0	0	0	0

Table 10 (continued)

Magnetic crystal class	Matrix representation of the property tensor, Q_{ijk}					
$\underline{4}2\underline{2}$, $\underline{4}$mm, $\bar{4}2$m, ($\bar{4}$m$\underline{2}$), $\underline{4}$/mm$\underline{m}$	0	0	0	Q_{14}	0	0
	0	0	0	0	Q_{14}	0
	0	0	0	0	0	Q_{36}
422, 4$\underline{\text{mm}}$, $\bar{4}$2m, 4/mm$\underline{m}$, 6$\underline{2}\underline{2}$, 6$\underline{\text{mm}}$, $\bar{6}$m$\underline{2}$, 6/mm$\underline{m}$	0	0	0	0	Q_{15}	0
	0	0	0	Q_{15}	0	0
	Q_{31}	Q_{31}	Q_{33}	0	0	0
3, $\bar{3}$	Q_{11}	$-Q_{11}$	0	Q_{14}	Q_{15}	$-2Q_{22}$
	$-Q_{22}$	Q_{22}	0	Q_{15}	$-Q_{14}$	$-2Q_{11}$
	Q_{31}	Q_{31}	Q_{33}	0	0	0
32, 3m, $\bar{3}$m	0	0	0	Q_{14}	0	$-2Q_{22}$
	$-Q_{22}$	Q_{22}	0	0	$-Q_{14}$	0
	0	0	0	0	0	0
3$\underline{2}$, 3$\underline{m}$, $\bar{3}\underline{m}$	Q_{11}	$-Q_{11}$	0	0	Q_{15}	0
	0	0	0	Q_{15}	0	$-2Q_{11}$
	Q_{31}	Q_{31}	Q_{33}	0	0	0
$\underline{6}$, $\bar{\underline{6}}$, $\underline{6}$/m	Q_{11}	$-Q_{11}$	0	0	0	$-2Q_{22}$
	$-Q_{22}$	Q_{22}	0	0	0	$-2Q_{11}$
	0	0	0	0	0	0
($\underline{6}2\underline{2}$), ($\underline{6}$mm), ($\bar{6}2\underline{m}$), ($\bar{6}m\underline{2}$), ($\underline{6}$/mm$\underline{m}$)	0	0	0	0	0	$-2Q_{22}$
	$-Q_{22}$	Q_{22}	0	0	0	0
	0	0	0	0	0	0
23, m3, $\underline{4}3\underline{2}$, $\bar{4}3\underline{m}$, m3$\underline{m}$	0	0	0	Q_{14}	0	0
	0	0	0	0	Q_{14}	0
	0	0	0	0	0	Q_{14}

in which piezomagnetism is possible. None of the symbols representing the crystal classes appears in brackets in this case and it is therefore unnecessary to consider the rotations of axes discussed in Ch. 3, § 3.1.

The piezomagnetic effect was first observed experimentally by BOROVIK-ROMANOV [1959, 1960] in measurements on single crystals of CoF_2 and MnF_2. Since these antiferromagnetic difluorides belong to the magnetic crystal class $\underline{4/mmm}$, the matrix characterizing the piezomagnetic effect (Table 10) is

$$[Q_{iA}] = \begin{bmatrix} 0 & 0 & 0 & Q_{14} & 0 & 0 \\ 0 & 0 & 0 & 0 & Q_{14} & 0 \\ 0 & 0 & 0 & 0 & 0 & Q_{36} \end{bmatrix}, \qquad (4.8)$$

where the x_1-, x_2- and x_3-axes are, respectively, directions such as OX, OY and OZ in Fig. 4.2. Equations (4.7) therefore reduce to

$$I_1 = Q_{14}T_{23},$$

$$I_2 = Q_{14}T_{31}, \qquad (4.9)$$

$$I_3 = Q_{36}T_{12}.$$

The piezomagnetic moment was revealed by the presence of a shift in the magnetization curve, parallel to the magnetization axis, on the application of pressure. A specially constructed magnetic torsion balance was used in which a press containing the specimen was suspended from vertical wires, measurements being made at liquid-hydrogen temperature (20.4°K). In the first experiments (BOROVIK-ROMANOV [1959]) pressure was applied to single-crystal parallelepipeds of CoF_2 and MnF_2 in a direction such as that of the bisector of the angle XOZ of Fig. 4.2. For a value of the resultant shear stress, T_{31}, of 500 kg cm^{-2}, a magnetization, $I_2 = Q_{14}T_{31}$, of about 1 gauss was observed for CoF_2, the effect being about one hundred times smaller in MnF_2. In the later experiments, BOROVIK-ROMANOV [1960] also obtained values for the constant Q_{36} by applying pressure to a second specimen in a direction such as OP of Fig. 4.2. The values obtained for the piezomagnetic coefficients, in units of gauss $kg^{-1}cm^2$ and at 20.4°K, were $Q_{14} = 2.1 \times 10^{-3}$, $Q_{36} = 0.8 \times 10^{-3}$ and $Q_{14} \simeq 10^{-5}$, $Q_{36} = 0$, for CoF_2 and MnF_2 respectively.

More recently, these experiments have been extended to the antiferromagnetic carbonate $FeCO_3$ (BOROVIK-ROMANOV, ALEK-SANJAN and RUDASHEVSKIJ [1962]) which belongs to the magnetic crystal class $\bar{3}m$. The matrix characterizing the piezomagnetic effect (Table 10) is

$$[Q_{\iota A}] = \begin{bmatrix} 0 & 0 & 0 & Q_{14} & 0 & -2Q_{22} \\ -Q_{22} & Q_{22} & 0 & 0 & -Q_{14} & 0 \\ 0 & 0 & 0 & 0 & 0 & 0 \end{bmatrix}, \quad (4.10)$$

so that equations (4.7) reduce to

$$I_1 = Q_{14}T_{23} - 2Q_{22}T_{12},$$
$$I_2 = Q_{22}(T_{22} - T_{11}) - Q_{14}T_{31}, \quad (4.11)$$
$$I_3 = 0.$$

Q_{11} was too small to be measured, whilst Q_{14} was observed to be finite only if the specimen was cooled to liquid-hydrogen temperature under pressure; when cooled without the application of pressure the effect was smaller, presumably because of the presence of antiferromagnetic domains. These authors also investigated the piezomagnetic effect in CoF_2 produced by pressure which pulsated at frequencies between 10 and 200 kc/sec, generated ultrasonically by a barium-titanate transducer. The temperature dependence of the piezomagnetic magnetization, I, measured in arbitrary units, is shown in Fig. 4.5, for temperatures up to the Néel point, 38.2°K.

A tensor that is closely related, in the symmetry it exhibits, to the piezomagnetic tensor is the tensor P_{ijk} of equations (3.25). The tensor P_{ijk}, like the Q_{ijk} of (4.1), is an axial c-tensor of third rank which has only six independent components since the last

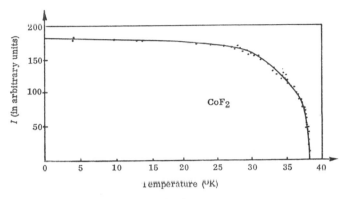

Fig. 4.5

pair of indices are interchangeable. Consequently, the tensor P_{ijk} may also be represented by matrix coefficients P_{iA}, where $i = 1$, 2, 3 and $A = 1, 2, 3, 4, 5, 6$. An antiferromagnetic that does not exhibit weak ferromagnetism must belong to one of the 59 classes obtained by excluding from the totality of the 90 magnetic classes the 31 magnetic classes, listed in § 2, in which pyromagnetism is possible. Since piezomagnetic crystals are, by definition, pyromagnetic, these 59 magnetic classes contain $(66 - 31) = 35$ magnetic classes in which piezomagnetism is possible. However, the corresponding number in which the tensor P_{iA} may be non-zero is not 35 but 27 because of the additional restrictions imposed by intrinsic symmetry, namely equations (3.27). These equations may be written in the form $P_{14} = P_{25} = P_{36}$, and it may be readily verified, from Table 10, that they cause the matrix P_{iA} to vanish for the eight magnetic crystal classes **422**, **4mm**, **$\overline{4}$2m**, **4/mmm**, **622**, **6mm**, **$\overline{6}$m2** and **6/mmm**.

CHAPTER 5

THE MAGNETIC PROPERTIES OF FERROMAGNETIC
AND FERRIMAGNETIC MATERIALS

§ 1. THE DEPENDENCE OF THE SPACE-TIME SYMMETRY ON PHYSICAL INFLUENCES

It was stated in Ch. 4, § 1, that ferromagnetic and ferrimagnetic crystals merit separate consideration because, for these materials, the directions assumed by the spins depend strongly on any magnetic field that may be applied to the crystal. Consider, for example, a (body-centred cubic) single crystal of iron, whose classical symmetry is that appropriate to the point group **m3m**. If the crystal is subjected to a magnetic field which is large enough to saturate it so that all the spins are aligned parallel to the same cube-edge, or ⟨100⟩ direction, then the appropriate magnetic point group is **4/mmm**. Similarly the magnetic point groups **mmm** and **3̄m** are those appropriate respectively to saturation parallel to a cube-face diagonal, or ⟨110⟩ direction, and to a cube-body diagonal, or ⟨111⟩ direction. For directions other than these three principal directions of crystallographic symmetry, the appropriate magnetic point group is **2/m** when the magnetization is perpendicular to a cube-edge or to a cube-face diagonal (i.e. for ⟨hkO⟩ or ⟨hhk⟩ directions) and is **1̄** otherwise (i.e. for ⟨hkl⟩ directions). The space-time symmetry of the crystal thus depends on the direction in which the saturating magnetic field is applied. Further, in the demagnetized state, the crystal is subdivided into a number of domains each of which is magnetized to saturation parallel to a

146

cube edge. In the *ideal* demagnetized state the domain magnetization vectors are equally distributed over the six $\langle 100 \rangle$ directions. As far as its space-time symmetry is concerned the demagnetized crystal is therefore not one crystal but many, which nevertheless possess a certain degree of order, analogous to that exhibited by a polysynthetic twinned crystal rather than by a polycrystal.

This situation may be contrasted with that obtaining for antiferromagnetic crystals, for which the existence of weak ferromagnetism is governed by the *requirement* that the space-time symmetry of the crystal is not altered by the associated rotation of spins. For antiferromagnetics, this symmetry is not influenced by the physical tensor, or tensors, which constitute the influence applied to the crystal, and the space-time symmetry of the crystal may be used to make predictions about property tensors in the manner indicated in the preceding chapters. For ferromagnetics and ferrimagnetics, however, the space-time symmetry of the crystal is often not independent of the physical influences applied to the crystal. It is convenient to consider separately the cases in which the symmetry is dependent on the physical influences and those in which it is independent of these influences.

§ 1.1. *Independence*

When the directions assumed by the spins are completely independent of the physical influences applied to the crystal, then the space-time symmetry of the crystal is unaltered by changes in the tensor or tensors which constitute the influence $i_{j_1 j_2 \ldots j_n}$ of equation (1.25). This implies, of course, that the crystal (assumed to be appreciably larger than 'single-domain size') is at least partially demagnetized. Under these circumstances the space-time symmetry of the ferromagnetic or ferrimagnetic crystal can be used to make predictions about property tensors in exactly the same manner as for antiferromagnetic materials. Unfortunately, however, the demagnetized crystal normally consists of a number of domains and, although each domain can be allocated to its appropriate space-time point group, the crystal as a whole cannot necessarily be allocated to any one of them. This can – depending on the exact distribution of domains – lead to a severe reduction in the symmetry exhibited by the crystal, so that the multidomain crystal is of far lower symmetry than that obtained classically by ignoring the presence of ordered arrays of spin magnetic moments. Unsatisfactory as this may be, the situation cannot, in fact, be alleviated by symmetry arguments, but only from physical considerations, which often permit an equation of the form (1.25) to be set up under the implicit assumption that the *classical* symmetry operators shall be used to simplify the form of the property tensor $d_{i_1 i_2 \ldots i_m j_1 j_2 \ldots j_n}$.

For example, it might be suspected that the thermal conductivity of a demagnetized cubic ferrite crystal exhibits cubic symmetry rather than the lower (space-time) symmetry appropriate to the multidomain crystal. The higher symmetry is not, of course, *precluded* by considerations of space-time symmetry, but it would obviously be advantageous if its existence could be verified. This may be done experimentally by ascertaining that measurements of the thermal conductivity of such a crystal exhibit cubic symmetry within the limits of accuracy of the experimental data, or theoretically by affirming that the phonon–magnon interaction is zero. In either case a *physical* argument is being used, and the latter procedure emphasizes that such arguments are essentially approximate – the experimental measurements do not distinguish between zero interaction and a negligibly small interaction, either of which would have been permitted from a consideration of space-time symmetry rather than classical symmetry. Subject to this limitation, however, it is permissible to formulate a law of thermal conductivity (Fourier's law) in the form of equation (1.25) and to stipulate that (only) the *classical* symmetry operators shall be used to simplify the form of the property tensor appearing in this equation. In a similar way, the severe reduction in the symmetry exhibited by transport phenomena in antiferromagnetic crystals effected by replacing the group $\mathscr{M}$ by the sub-group $\mathscr{H}$ as indicated in Ch. 3, § 3.2 may be alleviated if physical considerations operate to permit the classical point group $\mathscr{G}$ to be used.

The stipulation that (only) the classical symmetry operators shall be used to simplify the form of the property tensor appearing in (1.25) constitutes an implicit restriction that is not entirely without precedent. The existence of an equation of the form of (1.25) itself implies that physical arguments have been used to exclude certain physical influences from consideration. It may be, of course, that these influences are excluded because they are not applied to the crystal – a modification of (1.25) to include them being necessary if they were. But it is very difficult to preclude the application of some physical influences (e.g. gravitational fields), and the absence of such influences from equation (1.25) constitutes a restriction which has been validated physically, either by direct experiment or by theoretical arguments at a microscopic level. Apart from physical influences there are further factors, such as the geometrical shape of the specimen, which are excluded in formulating (1.25). The geometry of the specimen introduces additional symmetry features and there are obviously some physical phenomena where the shape of the specimen is important (an example is discussed in § 3). However, the exclusion of any reference to the shape of the specimen in equation (1.25) constitutes an implicit restriction which can only be justified from physical considerations, for example by direct experiment.

§ 1.2. *Dependence*

When the directions assumed by the spins are dependent on the physical influences applied to the crystal, then the space-time symmetry of the crystal is not unaltered by (all) changes in the tensor or tensors which constitute the influence $i_{j_1 j_2 \ldots j_n}$ of equation (1.25). However, symmetry arguments may still be used when the distribution of spins is completely determined by the external influence. For example, consider a crystal magnetized to saturation in an external field H, a particular property being defined by equation (1.25). In this case the spin distribution is not determined by the crystal but solely by the influence $i_{j_1 j_2 \ldots j_n}$: thus, if the crystal is rotated, the spins do not rotate with it unless the influence is altered. The description of the spin distribution can, in fact, be removed from the description of the physical crystal, and the distribution of spins can be regarded as an additional influence, the resulting physical effect being uniquely determined by the spin distribution and by the original influences acting on the crystal. This means that the geometrical description of the crystal of classical crystallography regains its validity provided that an appropriate specification of the spin distribution is incorporated into the influences acting on the crystal. Since the crystal is magnetically saturated the effect will often be independent of the magnitude of H, but the direction of H must still be taken into account. This may be accomplished, in general, by assuming that the influence acting on the crystal is a linear combination of terms of the form $i_{j_1 j_2 \ldots j_{n-1}}$, $i_{j_1 j_2 \ldots j_{n-1}} \alpha_{j_n}$, $i_{j_1 j_2 \ldots j_{n-1}} \alpha_{j_n} \alpha_{j_{n+1}}$ and so on, where the α_j are the direction cosines of the magnetization vector, parallel to which the spins are aligned at saturation. That saturation properties are, in fact, governed by considerations of classical symmetry, the space-time symmetry of the crystal being effectively suppressed, is demonstrated below, using an argument which may advantageously be compared with that used in Ch. 1, § 6.

Consider two identical *non-magnetic* crystals, c and C, for which σ is a classical symmetry matrix corresponding to a *proper* rotation. Let the orientations of c and C differ by the spatial rotation corresponding to σ, and let two exactly similar sets of coordinates or frames of reference, γ and Γ, be orientated in such a way that they also differ only by this rotation, the sense of the rotation being such that c is in the same relationship relative to γ

as C is to Γ. In the frame of reference γ, a particular property of crystal c may be described by a property tensor $d_{i_1i_2...i_mj_1j_2...j_n}$, whilst, relative to Γ, it may be described by a tensor $d'_{i_1i_2...i_mj_1j_2...j_n}$. Similarly, the same property of crystal C may be represented by tensors $D_{i_1i_2...i_mj_1j_2...j_n}$ and $D'_{i_1i_2...i_mj_1j_2...j_n}$ relative to the frames of reference γ and Γ respectively.

Now, in any one frame of reference, the property tensors for the crystals c and C must be the same, because σ is a symmetry matrix for the crystals, whilst c and C differ in orientation by the spatial rotation corresponding to σ but are otherwise identical. Hence,

$$d_{i_1i_2...i_mj_1j_2...j_n} = D_{i_1i_2...i_mj_1j_2...j_n}$$

and

$$d'_{i_1i_2...i_mj_1j_2...j_n} = D'_{i_1i_2...i_mj_1j_2...j_n}.$$

Further, since free space is isotropic, the property tensor can depend only on the relative orientation of the crystal and the frame of reference, and not on their absolute orientations in space. Thus

$$d_{i_1i_2...i_mj_1j_2...j_n} = D'_{i_1i_2...i_mj_1j_2...j_n},$$

since c is in the same relationship relative to γ as C is to Γ. It therefore follows that

$$d'_{i_1i_2...i_mj_1j_2...j_n} = d_{i_1i_2...i_mj_1j_2...j_n},$$

so that $d_{i_1i_2...i_mj_1j_2...j_n}$ may be substituted for $d'_{i_1i_2...i_mj_1j_2...j_n}$ into the known relationship

$$d'_{i_1i_2...i_mj_1j_2...j_n} = \sigma_{i_1p_1}\sigma_{i_2p_2} \cdots \sigma_{i_mp_m}\sigma_{j_1q_1}\sigma_{j_2q_2} \cdots \sigma_{j_nq_n} d_{p_1p_2...p_mq_1q_2...q_n}$$

$$(5.1)$$

to give equation (2.18a). This is the desired result since it allows the symmetry matrix σ to be used to simplify the form of the property tensor.

For a ferromagnetic or ferrimagnetic crystal similar considerations apply but it is now necessary to consider in which directions the spins are pointing. However, at saturation, and in any
one frame of reference, the same effect must be produced in
crystals c and C if identical influences $i_{j_1 j_2 \ldots j_{n-1}}$, $i_{j_1 j_2 \ldots j_{n-1} \alpha_{j_n}}$,
$i_{j_1 j_2 \ldots j_{n-1} \alpha_{j_n} \alpha_{j_{n+1}}}$, and so on, are applied to them. This is because
σ is a classical symmetry matrix (i.e. one obtained by neglecting
spin) and because the spin directions – being determined by the
influences – are the same in both crystals. Therefore, since the
same influences produce the same effect,

$$d_{i_1 i_2 \ldots i_m j_1 j_2 \ldots j_n} = D_{i_1 i_2 \ldots i_m j_1 j_2 \ldots j_n}$$

and

$$d'_{i_1 i_2 \ldots i_m j_1 j_2 \ldots j_n} = D'_{i_1 i_2 \ldots i_m j_1 j_2 \ldots j_n},$$

whilst, as before,

$$d_{i_1 i_2 \ldots i_m j_1 j_2 \ldots j_n} = D'_{i_1 i_2 \ldots i_m j_1 j_2 \ldots j_n},$$

since c is in the same relationship relative to γ as C is to $\varGamma$.

The arguments advanced above can also be repeated for impro-
per rotations, for which the result $d'_{i_1 i_2 \ldots i_m j_1 j_2 \ldots j_n} = d_{i_1 i_2 \ldots i_m j_1 j_2 \ldots j_n}$
leads to equation (2.18b), so that *all* the classical symmetry
operators may be employed to simplify the form of a property
tensor for a saturated crystal. However, this does not exhaust the
limitations imposed by symmetry considerations. When the specification of the spin distribution has been incorporated into the
influences acting on the crystal as indicated above, then the time-
inversion operator, R, may also be used as a symmetry operator
for the, effectively spin-less, crystal. The assumption that there is
no preferred direction in time – which is valid for static properties – then leads to all c-tensors being identically zero. The application of the concepts of classical symmetry to simplify the forms
of tensors characterizing the properties of saturated ferromagnetic

or ferrimagnetic crystals is an essentially straightforward matter and a few specific examples suffice to demonstrate the procedure employed. Two static properties are considered in detail in § 2 and § 3 and a transport phenomenon in § 4. The fact that magnetic properties are formulated with reference to a saturated crystal does not necessarily preclude a description of magnetic properties below saturation, for at every stage of the magnetization process the crystal is subdivided into a number of domains each magnetized to the same saturation value. Thus the magnetic behaviour of a single crystal below saturation may often be determined (as illustrated below) by taking a suitable average over a number of saturated domains.

§ 2. THE MAGNETOCRYSTALLINE ANISOTROPY

Measurements of bulk magnetization as a function of applied magnetic field for a ferromagnetic of ferrimagnetic single crystal reveal that much smaller fields are needed to magnetize the crystal in some directions – the easy directions – than in others. Hence it follows that there are forces tending to turn the spontaneous magnetization of an individual domain into these easy directions so that the energy of the system depends on the direction assumed by the domain magnetization relative to the crystal axes. It is therefore customary to assume that the free energy of the crystal contains a component which depends only on the direction of the spontaneous magnetization and which is a minimum when this is parallel or antiparallel to an easy direction. This component is called the magnetocrystalline anisotropy energy.

For a saturated crystal (i.e. a single domain) the magnetocrystalline anisotropy energy density, V, may be formally expressed as a series expansion thus,

$$V = b_i' \alpha_i + b_{ij}' \alpha_i \alpha_j + b_{ijk}' \alpha_i \alpha_j \alpha_k + b_{ijkl}' \alpha_i \alpha_j \alpha_k \alpha_l$$
$$+ b_{ijklm}' \alpha_i \alpha_j \alpha_k \alpha_l \alpha_m + \cdots, \tag{5.2a}$$

where the α_i are the direction cosines of the magnetization relative to one of the sets of rectangular cartesian systems of coordinate axes identified in Ch.2, §1.4. It is possible, in principle, to expand V indefinitely in ascending powers of the α_i but higher order terms tend to make V oscillate rapidly with the angular orientation of the direction of magnetization. Since this is contrary to experiment, it is reasonable to expect the coefficients of such terms to be small. In practice the direction assumed by the magnetization vector of a particular domain is, in general, influenced by the geometrical shape of the crystal. Consequently (5.2a) may be applied directly to a saturated crystal in the form of a sphere but for other shapes the geometry of the specimen must be allowed for by adding a further term (the demagnetizing energy) to the free energy.

When reduced to unit magnitude, the magnetization vector has components α_i, which therefore represent the components of an axial c-vector. The energy density V is a true (i.e. polar) scalar so that the property tensors b'_i, b'_{ijk}, b'_{ijklm}, ..., of odd rank, are axial c-tensors whilst the property tensors b'_{ij}, b'_{ijkl}, ..., of even rank, are polar i-tensors. However, as stated in § 1.2, the time-inversion operator, R, is a symmetry operator for the, effectively spin-less, crystal when the specification of the spin distribution has been incorporated into the influences acting on the crystal – as it has in the formulation of (5.2a). The assumption that there is no preferred direction in time, which is valid as magnetocrystalline anisotropy is a static property, then leads to all c-tensors being identically zero so that the property tensors b'_i, b'_{ijk}, b'_{ijklm}, ..., of odd rank, are null and (5.2a) may be written in the form

$$V = b'_{ij}\alpha_i\alpha_j + b'_{ijkl}\alpha_i\alpha_j\alpha_k\alpha_l + b'_{ijklmn}\alpha_i\alpha_j\alpha_k\alpha_l\alpha_m\alpha_n + \ldots. \quad (5.2b)$$

The form of the tensors b'_{ij}, b'_{ijkl}, b'_{ijklmn}, ... is dictated entirely by the requirements of crystal and intrinsic symmetry as illustrated, for cubic and hexagonal crystals, in § 2.1 and § 2.2.

§ 2.1. *Anisotropy in Cubic Crystals*

Most ferromagnetic metals and their alloys are cubic and may be allocated, classically, to the crystal class **m3m**. The forms of general polar tensors of second and fourth rank in this crystal class may be obtained immediately from Table 4, and the relations between the non-zero components of these tensors may be written, using the compact notation introduced in Ch. 2, § 4, in the form

$$xx = yy = zz, \tag{5.3a}$$

$$xxxx = yyyy = zzzz, \tag{5.3b}$$
$$xxyy(6) = xxzz = yyzz = zzyy = zzxx = yyxx.$$

It follows directly from (5.3a) that $b'_{11} = b'_{22} = b'_{33}$ and that

$$b'_{ij}\alpha_i\alpha_j = b'_{11}(\alpha_1^2 + \alpha_2^2 + \alpha_3^2). \tag{5.4}$$

Similarly, after allowing for the particularization imposed by intrinsic symmetry, (5.3b) leads to

$$b'_{ijkl}\alpha_i\alpha_j\alpha_k\alpha_l = b'_{1111}(\alpha_1^4 + \alpha_2^4 + \alpha_3^4)$$
$$+ 6b'_{1122}(\alpha_1^2\alpha_2^2 + \alpha_2^2\alpha_3^2 + \alpha_3^2\alpha_1^2), \tag{5.5}$$

the factor 6 arising from the multiplicity implicit in the second set of relations of (5.3b). By introducing an operator $S(\ )$ which denotes the sum of the three quantities obtained by cyclic permutation of suffixes on the expression within the brackets, these equations may be written in the form

$$b'_{ij}\alpha_i\alpha_j = b'_{11}S(\alpha_1^2),$$

$$b'_{ijkl}\alpha_i\alpha_j\alpha_k\alpha_l = b'_{1111}S(\alpha_1^4) + 6b'_{1122}S(\alpha_1^2\alpha_2^2). \tag{5.6}$$

For general sixth-rank polar tensors the relations corresponding to (5.3a) and (5.3b) are (FIESCHI and FUMI [1953])

$$xxxxxx = yyyyyy = zzzzzz,$$

$$xxxxyy(15) = xxxxzz = yyyyzz = zzzzyy = zzzzxx$$

$$= yyyyxx,$$ (5.3c)

$$xxyyzz(90) = xxzzyy = yyzzxx = zzyyxx = zzxxyy$$

$$= yyxxzz.$$

Thus, after allowing for particularization,

$$b'_{ijklmn}\alpha_i\alpha_j\alpha_k\alpha_l\alpha_m\alpha_n = b'_{111111}S(\alpha_1^6) + 15b'_{111122}S(\alpha_1^4\alpha_2^2 + \alpha_1^2\alpha_2^4)$$

$$+ 90b'_{112233}\alpha_1^2\alpha_2^2\alpha_3^2.$$ (5.7)

However, since the three direction cosines are connected by the equation $\alpha_1^2 + \alpha_2^2 + \alpha_3^2 = 1$, further relationships may be obtained by equating integral powers of $S(\alpha_1^2)$ to unity. A number of these relationships is collected in Table 11, the two quantities $S(\alpha_1^2\alpha_2^2)$ and $\alpha_1^2\alpha_2^2\alpha_3^2$ being, for simplicity, denoted by s and p respectively. Equation (5.2b) may therefore be written, to sixth order in the α_i, in the form

$$V = K_0 + K_1S(\alpha_1^2\alpha_2^2) + K_2\alpha_1^2\alpha_2^2\alpha_3^2,$$ (5.8)

where

$$K_0 = b'_{11} + b'_{1111} + b'_{111111},$$

$$K_1 = 6b'_{1122} - 2b'_{1111} - 3b'_{111111} + 15b'_{111122},$$ (5.9)

$$K_2 = 3b'_{111111} - 45b'_{111122} + 90b'_{112233}.$$

The coefficients K_1 and K_2 are called the first and second anisotropy constants and, for cubic crystals, the experimental data can usually be analysed without recourse to anisotropy constants

TABLE 11

$S(\alpha_1^2) = 1$
$S(\alpha_1^2\alpha_2^2) = s$ $S(\alpha_1^4) = 1 - 2s$
$S(\alpha_1^2\alpha_2^2\alpha_3^2) = 3p$ $S(\alpha_1^4\alpha_2^2 + \alpha_1^2\alpha_2^4) = s - 3p$ $S(\alpha_1^6) = 1 - 3s + 3p$
$S(\alpha_1^4\alpha_2^2\alpha_3^2) = p$ $S(\alpha_1^4\alpha_2^4) = s^2 - 2p$ $S(\alpha_1^6\alpha_2^2 + \alpha_1^2\alpha_2^6) = s - p - 2s^2$ $S(\alpha_1^8) = 1 - 4s + 4p + 2s^2$
$S(\alpha_1^4\alpha_2^4\alpha_3^2) = sp$ $S(\alpha_1^6\alpha_2^2\alpha_3^2) = p - 2sp$ $S(\alpha_1^6\alpha_2^4 + \alpha_1^4\alpha_2^6) = s^2 - 2p - sp$ $S(\alpha_1^8\alpha_2^2 + \alpha_1^2\alpha_2^8) = s - p - 3s^2 + 5sp$ $S(\alpha_1^{10}) = 1 - 5s + 5p + 5s^2 - 5sp$
$S(\alpha_1^4\alpha_2^4\alpha_3^4) = 3p^2$ $S(\alpha_1^6\alpha_2^4\alpha_3^2 + \alpha_1^4\alpha_2^6\alpha_3^2) = sp - 3p^2$ $S(\alpha_1^8\alpha_2^2\alpha_3^2) = p - 3sp + 3p^2$ $S(\alpha_1^{10}\alpha_2^2 + \alpha_1^2\alpha_2^{10}) = s - p - 4s^2 + 7sp - 3p^2 + 2s^3$ $S(\alpha_1^8\alpha_2^4 + \alpha_1^4\alpha_2^8) = s^2 - 2p + 4sp - 3p^2 - 2s^3$ $S(\alpha_1^6\alpha_2^6) = s^3 - 3sp + 3p^2$ $S(\alpha_1^{12}) = 1 - 6s + 6p + 9s^2 - 12sp + 3p^2 - 2s^3$

of higher order. To this approximation, the values of V appropriate to magnetization parallel to the three principal crystallographic directions, [100], [110] and [111], are respectively 0, $\frac{1}{4}K_1$ and $\frac{1}{3}K_1 + \frac{1}{27}K_2$, and the following results may therefore be deduced. For $K_2 > 0$, the easy directions are $\langle 100 \rangle$ directions if $K_1 > 0$ (as in iron), are $\langle 110 \rangle$ directions if $0 > K_1 > -\frac{4}{9}K_2$ and are $\langle 111 \rangle$ directions if $K_1 < -\frac{4}{9}K_2$ (as in nickel). For $K_2 < 0$, the easy directions are $\langle 100 \rangle$ directions if $K_1 > -\frac{1}{9}K_2$ and are $\langle 111 \rangle$ directions if $K_1 < -\frac{1}{9}K_2$ (as in Fe_3O_4 and numerous ferrites).

§ 2.2. Anisotropy in Hexagonal Crystals

For the classical crystal class **6/mmm**, to which the ferromagnetic metals cobalt and gadolinium belong, the forms of general polar tensors may be obtained from Table 4 for second-rank and fourth-rank tensors and from the work of FIESCHI and FUMI [1953] for sixth-rank tensors. Thus, in the notation introduced in Ch. 2, § 4,

$$xx = yy,$$
$$zz = zz, \tag{5.10a}$$

$$xxxx = xxyy + xyxy + yxxy = yyyy,$$
$$xxyy(6) = yyxx,$$
$$xxzz(6) = yyzz, \tag{5.10b}$$
$$zzzz = zzzz,$$

$$xxyyxx = -2xxxxxx + 3yyyyyy - xxyxxy - xxyxyx$$
$$- xyyxxx - yxyxxx,$$

$$yyxxxx = xxxxyy + xxxyxy + xxxyyx - xyyxxx - yxyxxx,$$

$$xxyyyy = xxxxxx - yyyyyy + xxxxxy + xxxyxy + xxxyyx$$
$$- xyyxxx - yxyxxx,$$

$$yyxxyy = -xxxxxx + 2yyyyyy - xxyxxy - xxyxyx$$
$$- xyyxxx - yxyxxx,$$

$$yyyyxx(\oplus 9) = xxxxxx - yyyyyy + xxxxyy,$$

$$xyxxxy = -2xxxxxx + 3yyyyyy - xxxxyy - xxyxxy$$
$$- xxyxyx - xyxxyx - xyyxxx + yxxyxx,$$

$$yxxxxy = -xxxyxy + xxyxyx + xyxxyx + xyyxxx$$
$$- yxxyxx$$

$$yxxxyx = -2xxxxxx + 3yyyyyy - xxxxyy - xxxyyx$$
$$- xxyxyx - xyxxyx,$$

$$xyyyxy = -xxxxxx + 2yyyyyy - xxxxyy - xxxyyx$$
$$- xxyxyx - xyxxyx, \tag{5.10c}$$

$$xyyyyx = xxxxxx - yyyyyy - xxxyxy + xxyxyx$$
$$+ xyxxyx + xyyxxx - yxxyxx,$$

$$yxyyyx = -xxxxxx + 2yyyyyy - xxxxyy - xxyxxy$$
$$xxyxyx - xyxxyx - xyyxxx + yxxyxx,$$

$$xyxyxx = -xxxyxy - xxxyyx + xxyxxy + xxyxyx$$
$$+ xyyxxx - yxxyxx + yxyxxx,$$

$$yxyxyy = xxxxxx - yyyyyy - xxxyxy - xxxyyx$$
$$+ xxyxxy + xxyxyx + xyyxxx - yxxyxx$$
$$+ yxyxxx,$$

$$xxxxzz(xxxx:15) = xxyyzz + xyxyzz + xyyxzz,$$

$$yyyyzz(yyyy:15) = xxyyzz + xyxyzz + xyyxzz,$$

$$yyxxzz(90) = xxyyzz,$$

$$yyzzzz(15) = xxzzzz,$$

$$zzzzzz = zzzzzz.$$

As before, a notation of the type $yyxxzz(90)$ denotes the 90 quantities that are distinct unrestricted permutations of the quantity $yyxxzz$. Notations of the type $(xxxx:15)$ indicate the 15 equations obtained by permutating the corresponding equation in (5.10c) subject to the condition that the *order* of the first four indices of each of its terms is unchanged. The notation $(\oplus 9)$ indicates a set of nine permutations on each term of the equation in (5.10c), the permutations on $yyyyxx$, for example, being $yyyyxx$, $yyxyxy$, $yyxyyx$, $yyyxxy$, $yyyxyx$, $yxyyxx$, $xyxyyy$, $xyyxyy$, $yxxyyy$.

After allowing for the simplifying effect of intrinsic symmetry, equations (5.10a) lead to

$$b'_{ij}\alpha_i\alpha_j = b'_{11}(\alpha_1^2 + \alpha_2^2) + b'_{33}\alpha_3^2, \tag{5.11}$$

equations (5.10b) to

$$b'_{ijkl}\alpha_i\alpha_j\alpha_k\alpha_l = 3b'_{1122}(\alpha_1^2 + \alpha_2^2)^2 + 6b'_{1133}(\alpha_1^2 + \alpha_2^2)\alpha_3^2$$
$$+ b'_{3333}\alpha_3^4, \tag{5.12}$$

and equations (5.10c) to

$$\begin{aligned}
b'_{ijklmn}\alpha_i\alpha_j\alpha_k\alpha_l\alpha_m\alpha_n &= b'_{111111}\alpha_1^6 + b'_{222222}\alpha_2^6 \\
&+ 3(3b'_{222222} - 2b'_{111111})\alpha_1^4\alpha_2^2 \\
&+ 3(3b'_{111111} - 2b'_{222222})\alpha_1^2\alpha_2^4 \\
&+ 45b'_{112233}(\alpha_1^4 + \alpha_2^4)\alpha_3^2 \\
&+ 90b'_{112233}\alpha_1^2\alpha_2^2\alpha_3^2 \\
&+ 15b'_{113333}(\alpha_1^2 + \alpha_2^2)\alpha_3^4 + b'_{333333}\alpha_3^6. \quad (5.13)
\end{aligned}$$

However, integral powers of $S(\alpha_1^2)$ may again be equated to unity, so that equation (5.2b) may be written, to sixth order in the α_i, in the form

$$\begin{aligned}
V &= K_0 + K_1(\alpha_1^2 + \alpha_2^2) + K_2(\alpha_1^2 + \alpha_2^2)^2 + K_3(\alpha_1^2 + \alpha_2^2)^3 \\
&+ K_4(\alpha_1^2 - \alpha_2^2)(\alpha_1^4 - 14\alpha_1^2\alpha_2^2 + \alpha_2^4) + \cdots, \quad (5.14)
\end{aligned}$$

where

$$K_0 = b'_{33} + b'_{3333} + b'_{333333},$$

$$K_1 = b'_{11} - b'_{33} + 6b'_{1133} - 2b'_{3333} + 15b'_{113333} - 3b'_{333333},$$

$$K_2 = 3b'_{1122} - 6b'_{1133} + b'_{3333} + 45b'_{112233} - 30b'_{113333}$$

$$+ 3b'_{333333}, \tag{5.15}$$

$$K_3 = \tfrac{1}{2}(b'_{222222} - b'_{111111}) + b'_{113333} - 45b'_{112233}$$

$$- b'_{333333},$$

$$K_4 = \tfrac{1}{2}(b'_{111111} - b'_{222222}).$$

Experimental measurements of magnetocrystalline anisotropy can usually be analysed by retaining only the first and second anisotropy constants, K_1 and K_2, and neglecting the constants of higher order. The resulting expression for V is actually of cylindrical rather than hexagonal symmetry since it depends only on the angle, θ, between the magnetization and the (hexagonal) x_3-axis: thus, since

$$\sin^2\theta = 1 - \cos^2\theta = 1 - \alpha_3^2 = \alpha_1^2 + \alpha_2^2, \tag{5.16}$$

equation (5.14) may be written, to fourth order in the α_i, in the form

$$V = K_0 + K_1 \sin^2\theta + K_2 \sin^4\theta. \tag{5.17}$$

To this approximation, the following results may be deduced. For $K_1 > 0$, the easy directions are parallel and antiparallel to the hexagonal axis if $K_2 > -K_1$ (as in cobalt) and perpendicular thereto if $K_2 < -K_1$. For $K_1 < 0$, the easy directions are perpendicular to the hexagonal axis if $K_2 < -\tfrac{1}{2}K_1$ and at an angle $\sin^{-1}\sqrt{(-K_1/2K_2)}$ thereto, forming two cones of easy directions, if $K_2 > -\tfrac{1}{2}K_1$ (as in the mixed ferrite $Ba_2Co_2Fe_{12}O_{22}$).

§ 2.3. *Formulation in Terms of Surface Spherical Harmonics*

Equation (5.2b) is a very simple form of series expansion of V in ascending powers of the α_l, but it is frequently not the most suitable form for such an expansion. For some applications the most convenient series expansion for V is in terms of surface spherical harmonics, $Y_{n,m}(\theta, \phi)$, of degree n. Such an application is considered in § 2.4 where the temperature dependence of anisotropy is discussed: the greater utility of the functions $Y_{n,m}(\theta, \phi)$ is mainly associated with the fact that they are orthogonal, that is that the integral

$$I = \int_0^{2\pi} \int_0^{\pi} Y_{n,m}(\theta, \phi)\, Y_{n',m'}(\theta, \phi) \sin\theta\, \mathrm{d}\theta\, \mathrm{d}\phi \qquad (5.18)$$

vanishes unless $n = n'$ and $m = m'$.

For hexagonal crystals, experimental measurements of magnetocrystalline anisotropy are often completely consistent with equation (5.17), and the anisotropy constants K_3, K_4 and those of higher order may be neglected. Equation (5.17) represents uniaxial anisotropy, characterized by the fact that the anisotropy energy, $V = V(\theta)$, depends only on the angle, θ, between the bulk magnetization vector and the single axis of easy magnetization. One representation of uniaxial anisotropy would be to expand V as a Fourier series in $\cos n\theta$, terms in $\sin n\theta$ being absent since, from (5.2b), $V(\theta) = V(\theta + \pi)$. However, to facilitate the extension of this discussion to more general cases, it is convenient to express $V(\theta)$ in the form

$$V(\theta) = k_0 P_0(\alpha_3) + k_2 P_2(\alpha_3) + k_4 P_4(\alpha_3) + \cdots, \qquad (5.19)$$

where $\alpha_3 = \cos\theta$ and the $P_n(\alpha_3)$ are the Legendre polynomials,

$$P_n(\alpha_3) = \frac{1}{2^n n!} \frac{\mathrm{d}^n}{\mathrm{d}\alpha_3^n} (\alpha_3^2 - 1)^n. \qquad (5.20)$$

Because anisotropy is even in the magnetization, polynomials of odd degree are not involved. The quantities k_n are the anisotropy *coefficients*, and it may be noted that the suffix n indicates the degree of the Legendre polynomial with which the coefficient is associated. These coefficients should not be confused with the anisotropy *constants*, K_1, K_2, ..., which are used in the analysis of experimental data. Equation (5.19) is not as simple an expansion of $V(\theta)$ in ascending powers of the α_i as is (5.2b), for, in general, each $P_n(\alpha_3)$ contains terms in α_3 to the power $n-2, n-4, n-6, ...$; thus, for example,

$$
\begin{aligned}
P_0(\alpha_3) &= 1, \\
P_2(\alpha_3) &= \tfrac{1}{2}(3\alpha_3^2 - 1), \\
P_4(\alpha_3) &= \tfrac{1}{8}(35\alpha_3^4 - 30\alpha_3^2 + 3), \\
P_6(\alpha_3) &= \tfrac{1}{16}(231\alpha_3^6 - 315\alpha_3^4 + 105\alpha_3^2 - 5).
\end{aligned}
\tag{5.21}
$$

When a crystal exhibits more than one axis of easy magnetization, the anisotropy energy must be a function, $V = V(\theta, \phi)$, of polar and azimuthal angles, θ and ϕ, characterizing the direction of bulk magnetization. Since $V(\theta, \phi)$ is a continuous function of θ and ϕ, it may be expanded as a unique and uniformly convergent series in which the terms are surface spherical harmonics of positive integral degree. The anisotropy may therefore be written in the form

$$
V(\theta, \phi) = \sum_{n=0}^{\infty} Y_n(\theta, \phi) \qquad (0 < \theta < \pi,\ 0 < \phi < 2\pi), \tag{5.22}
$$

the most general surface harmonic of positive integral degree n being expressible in terms of $(2n+1)$ linearly independent surface harmonics of degree n thus (MacRobert [1927])

$$
Y_n(\theta, \phi) = k_n' P_n(\cos \theta)
$$
$$
+ \sum_{m=1}^{n} (k_{nm}'' \cos m\phi + k_{nm}''' \sin m\phi)\, P_n^m(\cos \theta), \tag{5.23}
$$

where $P_n^m(\cos \theta)$ is the (Ferrers's) associated Legendre function of the first kind,

$$P_n^m(\cos \theta) = \sin^m\theta \, \frac{d^m}{d(\cos \theta)^m} \, P_n(\cos \theta). \qquad (5.24)$$

Equation (5.23) may be written in the more compact form

$$Y_n(\theta, \phi) = \sum_{m=-n}^{n} k_{n,m} Y_{n,m}, \qquad (5.25)$$

where

$$Y_{n,m} = \cos m\phi \, P_n^m(\cos \theta) \quad \text{for} \quad m > 0,$$
$$Y_{n,m} = P_n(\cos \theta) \quad\quad\quad \text{for} \quad m = 0, \qquad (5.26)$$
$$Y_{n,m} = \sin |m|\phi \, P_n^{|m|}(\cos \theta) \quad \text{for} \quad m < 0,$$

so that

$$V(\theta, \phi) = \sum_{n=0}^{\infty} Y_{2n}(\theta, \phi) = \sum_{n=0}^{\infty} \sum_{m=-2n}^{2n} k_{2n,m} Y_{2n,m}, \qquad (5.27)$$

harmonics of odd degree again being absent because $V(\theta, \phi) = V(\pi - \theta, \pi + \phi)$.

If the x_3-axis is assumed to be the polar axis and the polar and azimuthal angles θ and ϕ are related to the direction cosines α_i by the equations

$$\alpha_1 = \sin \theta \cos \phi,$$
$$\alpha_2 = \sin \theta \sin \phi, \qquad (5.28)$$
$$\alpha_3 = \cos \theta,$$

then the zonal harmonics $Y_{n,0}$ and the tesseral harmonics $Y_{n,m}$ may be expressed in terms of the α_i as illustrated below.

$$Y_{0,0} = P_0 = 1. \qquad (5.29a)$$

$$Y_{1,0} = P_1 = \alpha_3,$$
$$Y_{1,1} = \cos \phi \, P_1^1 = \alpha_1, \qquad (5.29b)$$
$$Y_{1,-1} = \sin \phi \, P_1^1 = \alpha_2.$$

$$Y_{2,0} \;\; = P_2 \qquad\qquad = \tfrac{1}{2}(3\alpha_3^2 - 1),$$

$$Y_{2,1} \;\; = \cos\phi\, P_2^1 \;\; = 3\alpha_3\alpha_1,$$

$$Y_{2,-1} = \sin\phi\, P_2^1 \;\; = 3\alpha_2\alpha_3, \tag{5.29c}$$

$$Y_{2,2} \;\; = \cos 2\phi\, P_2^2 = 3(\alpha_1^2 - \alpha_2^2),$$

$$Y_{2,-2} = \sin 2\phi\, P_2^2 = 3(2\alpha_1\alpha_2).$$

$$Y_{3,0} \;\; = P_3 \qquad\qquad = \tfrac{1}{2}\alpha_3(5\alpha_3^2 - 3),$$

$$Y_{3,1} \;\; = \cos\phi\, P_3^1 \;\; = \tfrac{3}{2}\alpha_1(5\alpha_3^2 - 1),$$

$$Y_{3,-1} = \sin\phi\, P_3^1 \;\; = \tfrac{3}{2}\alpha_2(5\alpha_3^2 - 1),$$

$$Y_{3,2} \;\; = \cos 2\phi\, P_3^2 = 15\alpha_3(\alpha_1^2 - \alpha_2^2), \tag{5.29d}$$

$$Y_{3,-2} = \sin 2\phi\, P_3^2 = 15\alpha_3(2\alpha_1\alpha_2),$$

$$Y_{3,3} \;\; = \cos 3\phi\, P_3^3 = 15\alpha_1(\alpha_1^2 - 3\alpha_2^2),$$

$$Y_{3,-3} = \sin 3\phi\, P_3^3 = 15\alpha_2(3\alpha_1^2 - \alpha_2^2).$$

$$Y_{4,0} \;\; = P_4 \qquad\qquad = \tfrac{1}{8}(35\alpha_3^4 - 30\alpha_3^2 + 3),$$

$$Y_{4,1} \;\; = \cos\phi\, P_4^1 \;\; = \tfrac{5}{2}\alpha_3\alpha_1(7\alpha_3^2 - 3),$$

$$Y_{4,-1} = \sin\phi\, P_4^1 \;\; = \tfrac{5}{2}\alpha_2\alpha_3(7\alpha_3^2 - 3),$$

$$Y_{4,2} \;\; = \cos 2\phi\, P_4^2 = \tfrac{15}{2}(\alpha_1^2 - \alpha_2^2)(7\alpha_3^2 - 1),$$

$$Y_{4,-2} = \sin 2\phi\, P_4^2 = \tfrac{15}{2}(2\alpha_1\alpha_2)(7\alpha_3^2 - 1), \tag{5.29e}$$

$$Y_{4,3} \;\; = \cos 3\phi\, P_4^3 = 105\alpha_3\alpha_1(\alpha_1^2 - 3\alpha_2^2),$$

$$Y_{4,-3} = \sin 3\phi\, P_4^3 = 105\alpha_2\alpha_3(3\alpha_1^2 - \alpha_2^2),$$

$$Y_{4,4} \;\; = \cos 4\phi\, P_4^4 = 105(\alpha_1^4 + \alpha_2^4 - 6\alpha_1^2\alpha_2^2),$$

$$Y_{4,-4} = \sin 4\phi\, P_4^4 = 105(4\alpha_1\alpha_2)(\alpha_1^2 - \alpha_2^2).$$

$$Y_{5,0} = P_5 = \tfrac{1}{8}\alpha_3(63\alpha_3^4 - 70\alpha_3^2 + 15),$$

$$Y_{5,1} = \cos\phi\, P_5^1 = \tfrac{15}{8}\alpha_1(21\alpha_3^4 - 14\alpha_3^2 + 1),$$

$$Y_{5,-1} = \sin\phi\, P_5^1 = \tfrac{15}{8}\alpha_2(21\alpha_3^4 - 14\alpha_3^2 + 1),$$

$$Y_{5,2} = \cos 2\phi\, P_5^2 = \tfrac{105}{2}\alpha_3(\alpha_1^2 - \alpha_2^2)(3\alpha_3^2 - 1),$$

$$Y_{5,-2} = \sin 2\phi\, P_5^2 = \tfrac{105}{2}\alpha_3(2\alpha_1\alpha_2)(3\alpha_3^2 - 1),$$

$$Y_{5,3} = \cos 3\phi\, P_5^3 = \tfrac{105}{2}\alpha_1(\alpha_1^2 - 3\alpha_2^2)(9\alpha_3^2 - 1), \qquad (5.29f)$$

$$Y_{5,-3} = \sin 3\phi\, P_5^3 = \tfrac{105}{2}\alpha_2(3\alpha_1^2 - \alpha_2^2)(9\alpha_3^2 - 1),$$

$$Y_{5,4} = \cos 4\phi\, P_5^4 = 945\alpha_3(\alpha_1^4 + \alpha_2^4 - 6\alpha_1^2\alpha_2^2),$$

$$Y_{5,-4} = \sin 4\phi\, P_5^4 = 945\alpha_3(4\alpha_1\alpha_2)(\alpha_1^2 - \alpha_2^2),$$

$$Y_{5,5} = \cos 5\phi\, P_5^5 = 945\alpha_1(\alpha_2^4 - 3\alpha_1^4 - 2\alpha_1^2\alpha_2^2),$$

$$Y_{5,-5} = \sin 5\phi\, P_5^5 = 945\alpha_2(5\alpha_1^4 + \alpha_2^4 - 10\alpha_1^2\alpha_2^2).$$

$$Y_{6,0} = P_6 = \tfrac{1}{16}(231\alpha_3^6 - 315\alpha_3^4 + 105\alpha_3^2 - 5),$$

$$Y_{6,1} = \cos\phi\, P_6^1 = \tfrac{21}{8}\alpha_3\alpha_1(33\alpha_3^4 - 30\alpha_3^2 + 5),$$

$$Y_{6,-1} = \sin\phi\, P_6^1 = \tfrac{21}{8}\alpha_2\alpha_3(33\alpha_3^4 - 30\alpha_3^2 + 5),$$

$$Y_{6,2} = \cos 2\phi\, P_6^2 = \tfrac{105}{8}(\alpha_1^2 - \alpha_2^2)(33\alpha_3^4 - 18\alpha_3^2 + 1),$$

$$Y_{6,-2} = \sin 2\phi\, P_6^2 = \tfrac{105}{8}(2\alpha_1\alpha_2)(33\alpha_3^4 - 18\alpha_3^2 + 1),$$

$$Y_{6,3} = \cos 3\phi\, P_6^3 = \tfrac{315}{2}\alpha_3\alpha_1(\alpha_1^2 - 3\alpha_2^2)(11\alpha_3^2 - 3),$$

$$Y_{6,-3} = \sin 3\phi\, P_6^3 = \tfrac{315}{2}\alpha_2\alpha_3(3\alpha_1^2 - \alpha_2^2)(11\alpha_3^2 - 3), \qquad (5.29g)$$

$$Y_{6,4} = \cos 4\phi\, P_6^4 = \tfrac{945}{2}(\alpha_1^4 + \alpha_2^4 - 6\alpha_1^2\alpha_2^2)(11\alpha_3^2 - 1),$$

$$Y_{6,-4} = \sin 4\phi\, P_6^4 = \tfrac{945}{2}(4\alpha_1\alpha_2)(\alpha_1^2 - \alpha_2^2)(11\alpha_3^2 - 1),$$

$$Y_{6,5} = \cos 5\phi\, P_6^5 = 10\,395\alpha_3\alpha_1(\alpha_2^4 - 3\alpha_1^4 - 2\alpha_1^2\alpha_2^2),$$

$$Y_{6,-5} = \sin 5\phi\, P_6^5 = 10\,395\alpha_2\alpha_3(5\alpha_1^4 + \alpha_2^4 - 10\alpha_1^2\alpha_2^2),$$

$$Y_{6,6} = \cos 6\phi\, P_6^6 = 10\,395(\alpha_1^2 - \alpha_2^2)(\alpha_1^4 - 14\alpha_1^2\alpha_2^2 + \alpha_2^4),$$

$$Y_{6,-6} = \sin 6\phi\, P_6^6 = 10\,395(2\alpha_1\alpha_2)(3\alpha_1^2 - \alpha_2^2)(\alpha_1^2 - 3\alpha_2^2).$$

By using these expressions it may readily be shown that the form of equation (5.27) which corresponds to (5.8), for cubic crystals, is

$$V = K_0 + \tfrac{1}{105}(21K_1 + K_2)Y_{0,0} - \tfrac{1}{55}(11K_1 + K_2)Y_{4,0}$$
$$- \tfrac{1}{9240}(11K_1 + K_2)Y_{4,4} + \tfrac{2}{231}K_2 Y_{6,0} - \tfrac{1}{41580}K_2 Y_{6,4},$$
$$(5.30)$$

whilst that which corresponds to (5.14), for hexagonal crystals, is

$$V = K_0 + \tfrac{2}{105}(35K_1 + 28K_2 + 24K_3)Y_{0,0}$$
$$- \tfrac{2}{21}(7K_1 + 8K_2 + 8K_3)Y_{2,0} + \tfrac{8}{385}(11K_2 + 18K_3)Y_{4,0}$$
$$- \tfrac{16}{231}K_3 Y_{6,0} + \tfrac{1}{10395}K_4 Y_{6,6}.$$
$$(5.31)$$

§ 2.4. *The Temperature Dependence of Magnetocrystalline Anisotropy*

For a ferromagnetic or ferrimagnetic crystal the spontaneous magnetization, $I_s(T)$, at temperature T has a smaller value than at the absolute zero because the individual spins are not aligned exactly parallel to the magnetization vector but have an angular spread about this direction. The distribution of spins about the direction of magnetization will determine the value of the reduced spontaneous magnetization $\zeta = \zeta(T) = I_s(T)/I_s(0)$ at that temperature. However, the distribution of spins also determines the bulk anisotropy $V(T)$ at temperature T, since the total anisotropy energy is the sum of the energies required to put each spin in place so as to conform to the given spin distribution. An individual spin may therefore be regarded as being a local unit which carries with it an anisotropy energy having the same angular dependence as $V(0)$, and the observed anisotropy energy density $V(T)$ may be obtained by averaging $V(0)$ over the directions of all the spins†. In

---

† The localized model is used here since band theory does not, at present, provide reliable estimates of the temperature dependence of magnetocrystalline anisotropy.

the limit of no correlation between neighbouring spins, the calculation of anisotropy proceeds either classically, each spin being orientated independently by the molecular field, or quantummechanically, each spin being independently quantized in the molecular field. Classically, the energy of a spin, of magnetic moment p, which makes an angle θ' with the molecular field H' is $-p \cdot H' = -pH' \cos \theta'$, and the angular distribution of the spins, at temperature T, is assumed to be specified by a Boltzmann distribution function $w = C \exp p \cdot H'/kT$. Thus, if θ' and ϕ' are the polar and azimuthal angles of an individual spin with respect to axes *fixed relative to the direction of bulk magnetization*, the probability that a spin will be specified by angles lying within the range from θ' to $\theta' + d\theta'$ and ϕ' to $\phi' + d\phi'$ is $w \sin \theta' \, d\theta' \, d\phi'$. The constant C may therefore be obtained from the normalization condition

$$\int_0^{2\pi} \int_0^{\pi} w \sin \theta' \, d\theta' \, d\phi' = 1. \tag{5.32}$$

Now consider a crystal which exhibits uniaxial anisotropy at the absolute zero of temperature, so that, from (5.19),

$$V(0) = \sum_{n=0}^{\infty} k_{2n}(0) \, P_{2n}(\cos \theta), \tag{5.33}$$

where θ is the angle between the bulk magnetization and the main crystallographic axis, Ox_3. At temperature T, the spins sample the anisotropy in various directions and the bulk anisotropy energy density is therefore

$$V(T) = \int_0^{2\pi} \int_0^{\pi} \left[\sum_{n=0}^{\infty} k_{2n}(0) \, P_{2n}(\cos \Theta) \right] w \sin \theta' \, d\theta' \, d\phi', \tag{5.34}$$

where Θ is the angle made by an individual spin with the axis Ox_3.

To evaluate this integral it is necessary to express the $P_{2n}(\cos \Theta)$ in terms of the angles θ' and ϕ', that is to transform these harmonics to axes which are fixed relative to the direction of bulk magnetization rather than to the crystal lattice. The orientation of a set of axes Ox_i' (of which Ox_3' corresponds to the direction of bulk magnetization) with respect to the crystallographic axes Ox_i

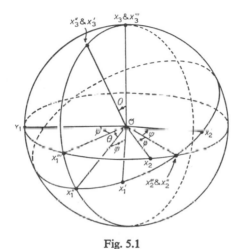

Fig. 5.1

may be conveniently specified by the Euler angles θ, ϕ and ψ as shown in Fig. 5.1. It may be seen from Fig. 5.1 that the axes Ox_i may be made to coincide with the axes Ox_i' first by rotating the axes Ox_i about Ox_3 through an angle ϕ until they coincide with the axes Ox_i''', secondly by rotating the axes Ox_i''' about Ox_2''' through an angle θ until they coincide with the axes Ox_i'' and finally by rotating the axes Ox_i'' about Ox_3'' through an angle ψ until they coincide with the axes Ox_i'. It may be readily verified from equation (2.9) that

$$x_i' = l_{ip}' x_p'', \qquad x_i'' = l_{ip}'' x_p''', \qquad x_i''' = l_{ip}''' x_p, \qquad (5.35)$$

where

$$[l'_{ij}] = \begin{bmatrix} \cos\psi & \sin\psi & 0 \\ -\sin\psi & \cos\psi & 0 \\ 0 & 0 & 1 \end{bmatrix},$$

$$[l''_{ij}] = \begin{bmatrix} \cos\theta & 0 & -\sin\theta \\ 0 & 1 & 0 \\ \sin\theta & 0 & \cos\theta \end{bmatrix}, \tag{5.36}$$

$$[l'''_{ij}] = \begin{bmatrix} \cos\phi & \sin\phi & 0 \\ -\sin\phi & \cos\phi & 0 \\ 0 & 0 & 1 \end{bmatrix}.$$

Thus

$$x'_i = l'_{ij} l''_{jk} l'''_{kl} x_l \tag{5.37}$$

or

$$x'_i = l_{ip} x_p, \tag{5.38}$$

where, by matrix multiplication,

$$[l_{ip}] = \begin{bmatrix} \begin{Bmatrix} \cos\psi\cos\theta\cos\phi \\ -\sin\psi\sin\phi \end{Bmatrix} & \begin{Bmatrix} \cos\psi\cos\theta\sin\phi \\ +\sin\psi\cos\phi \end{Bmatrix} & -\cos\psi\sin\theta \\ \begin{Bmatrix} -\sin\psi\cos\theta\cos\phi \\ -\cos\psi\sin\phi \end{Bmatrix} & \begin{Bmatrix} -\sin\psi\cos\theta\sin\phi \\ +\cos\psi\cos\phi \end{Bmatrix} & \sin\psi\sin\theta \\ \sin\theta\cos\phi & \sin\theta\sin\phi & \cos\theta \end{bmatrix}. \tag{5.39}$$

The harmonic $P_{2n}(\cos\Theta)$ – having the direction Ox_3 as axis – may now be expressed as a sum of zonal and tesseral harmonics referred to the direction of bulk magnetization as axis by means of the addition theorem (MacRobert [1927])

$$P_{2n}(\cos \Theta) = P_{2n}(\cos \theta') P_{2n}(\cos \theta)$$

$$+ \sum_{s=1}^{2n} 2 \frac{(2n - s)!}{(2n + s)!} P_{2n}^s(\cos \theta') P_{2n}^s(\cos \theta) \cos s(\phi' + \psi),$$
$$(5.40)$$

the polar and azimuthal angles of the direction Ox_3 relative to the axes Ox_i' being θ and $2\pi - \psi$ respectively. However, on inserting this expression into (5.34), the terms under the summation sign will vanish when averaged over all directions of spin to obtain the bulk anisotropy, $V(T)$, because w is a function of θ' only and

$$\int_0^{2\pi} \cos m\phi' \, d\phi' = \int_0^{2\pi} \sin m\phi' \, d\phi' = 0 \qquad (m = 1, 2, 3, ..., n).$$
$$(5.41)$$

Hence

$$V(T) = 2\pi \int_0^\pi \left[\sum_{n=0}^\infty k_{2n}(0) P_{2n}(\cos \theta') P_{2n}(\cos \theta) \right] C e^{a \cos \theta'} \sin \theta' \, d\theta'$$

$$= 2\pi \int_{-1}^{+1} \left[\sum_{n=0}^\infty k_{2n}(0) P_{2n}(\cos \theta) P_{2n}(x) \right] C e^{ax} \, dx, \qquad (5.42)$$

where $a = pH'/kT$ and $x = \cos \theta'$.

The integrals in (5.42) may be expressed (Morse and Feshbach [1953]) in terms of Bessel functions of imaginary argument thus:

$$\int_{-1}^{+1} P_{2n}(x) e^{ax} \, dx = \sqrt{\frac{2\pi}{a}} I_{2n+\frac{1}{2}}(a). \qquad (5.43)$$

Since $P_0(x) \equiv 1$, the constant C may also be obtained from this equation for, from (5.32),

$$\int_{-1}^{+1} C e^{ax} \, dx = C \sqrt{\frac{2\pi}{a}} I_{\frac{1}{2}}(a) = \frac{2C}{a} \sinh a = \frac{1}{2\pi}. \qquad (5.44)$$

Hence,

$$V(T) = \frac{\sum\limits_{n=0}^{\infty} k_{2n}(0) \, P_{2n}(\cos\theta) \, I_{2n+\frac{1}{2}}(a)}{I_{\frac{1}{2}}(a)}, \qquad (5.45)$$

which may be written in a similar form to equation (5.33), giving the anisotropy energy density at the absolute zero, as follows

$$V(T) = \sum_{n=0}^{\infty} k_{2n}(T) \, P_{2n}(\cos\theta), \qquad (5.46)$$

where

$$k_{2n}(T) = k_{2n}(0) \, \frac{I_{2n+\frac{1}{2}}(a)}{I_{\frac{1}{2}}(a)} . \qquad (5.47)$$

It may also be noted that, since $P_1(x) \equiv \cos\theta'$, the reduced magnetization is

$$\zeta = \zeta(T) = \frac{I_{\frac{3}{2}}(a)}{I_{\frac{1}{2}}(a)}, \qquad (5.48)$$

and, since

$$I_{\frac{3}{2}}(a) = \sqrt{\frac{2}{\pi a}} \left[\cosh a - \frac{\sinh a}{a} \right], \qquad (5.49)$$

the reduced magnetization is given by the familiar Langevin function

$$\zeta = L(a) = \coth a - \frac{1}{a}. \qquad (5.50)$$

The functions $I_{2n+\frac{1}{2}}(a)$ may be expressed (McLachlan [1955]) in series form thus:

$$I_{2n+\frac{1}{2}}(a) = \sqrt{\frac{1}{2\pi a}} \left[e^a \sum_{r=0}^{2n} \frac{(-1)^r \, (2n+r)!}{r! \, (2n-r)! \, (2a)^r} \right.$$
$$\left. + (-1)^{2n+1} e^{-a} \sum_{r=0}^{2n} \frac{(2n+r)!}{r! \, (2n-r)! \, (2a)^r} \right]. \qquad (5.51)$$

At low temperatures, that is for large values of a, it is permissible to neglect e^{-a} and the second and higher powers of $1/a$, so that

$$I_{2n+\frac{1}{2}}(a) = \sqrt{\frac{1}{2\pi a}}\, e^a \left[1 - n(2n+1)\frac{1}{a}\right]. \tag{5.52}$$

Thus

$$I_{\frac{3}{2}}(a) = \sqrt{\frac{1}{2\pi a}}\, e^a \left[1 - \frac{1}{a}\right] \tag{5.53}$$

and

$$I_{\frac{1}{2}}(a) = \sqrt{\frac{1}{2\pi a}}\, e^a, \tag{5.54}$$

so that, to this approximation,

$$\frac{I_{2n+\frac{1}{2}}(a)}{I_{\frac{1}{2}}(a)} = \left|\frac{I_{\frac{3}{2}}(a)}{I_{\frac{1}{2}}(a)}\right|^{n(2n+1)} = \zeta^{n(2n+1)}. \tag{5.55}$$

Substitution of this equation into (5.47) gives a relationship between the anisotropy coefficients appropriate to temperature T and those appropriate to the absolute zero, namely

$$\frac{k_{2n}(T)}{k_{2n}(0)} = \zeta^{n(2n+1)}. \tag{5.56}$$

If a crystal exhibits more than one axis of easy magnetization, the anisotropy at the absolute zero of temperature is given by an expression of the form (5.27), that is by

$$V(0) = \sum_{n=0}^{\infty}\left[k_{2n,0}(0)\, P_{2n}(\cos\theta)\right.$$

$$\left. + \sum_{m=1}^{2n}\left(k_{2n,m}(0)\cos m\phi + k_{2n,-m}(0)\sin m\phi\right) P_{2n}^{m}(\cos\theta)\right], \tag{5.57}$$

rather than by (5.33). The bulk anisotropy at temperature T is therefore

$$
V(T) = \int_0^{2\pi}\!\!\int_0^{\pi} \left\{ \sum_{n=0}^{\infty} \left[k_{2n,0}(0)\, P_{2n}(\cos \Theta) \right.\right.
$$

$$
\left.\left. + \sum_{m=1}^{2n} \big(k_{2n,\,m}(0) \cos m\Phi + k_{2n,-m}(0) \sin m\Phi\big)\, P_{2n}^{m}(\cos \Theta) \right] \right\}
$$

$$
\times\, w \sin \theta'\, d\theta'\, d\phi', \tag{5.58}
$$

where Θ and Φ are the polar and azimuthal angles of an individual spin relative to the crystallographic axes, Ox_i. This integral can be evaluated if the $P_{2n}(\cos \Theta)$, $\cos m\Phi$, $\sin m\Phi$ and $P_{2n}^{m}(\cos \Theta)$ can be expressed in terms of the angles θ' and ϕ' by using addition theorems analogous to (5.40). However, it may be observed that, if this is done, so that

$$
k_{2n,0}(0)\, P_{2n}(\cos \Theta) + \sum_{m=1}^{2n} \big[k_{2n,\,m}(0) \cos m\Phi
$$

$$
+ k_{2n,-m}(0) \sin m\Phi\big]\, P_{2n}^{m}(\cos \Theta) = A_{2n}(\theta, \phi, \psi)\, P_{2n}(\cos \theta')
$$

$$
+ \sum_{m=1}^{2n} \big[B_{2n}(\theta, \phi, \psi) \cos m\phi' + C_{2n}(\theta, \phi, \psi) \sin m\phi'\big]\, P_{2n}^{m}(\cos \theta'),
$$

$$
\tag{5.59}
$$

the terms involving $B_{2n}(\theta, \phi, \psi)$ and $C_{2n}(\theta, \phi, \psi)$ will disappear in the subsequent integration with respect to ϕ' indicated in (5.58), because of (5.41). It is therefore only necessary to evaluate the coefficient $A_{2n}(\theta, \phi, \psi)$ and this may be readily achieved by noting that, in the limit as $\theta' \to 0$, then $\Theta \to \theta, \Phi \to \phi$ and the right-hand side of (5.59) approaches $A_{2n}(\theta, \phi, \psi)$, whence

$$
A_{2n}(\theta, \phi, \psi) = k_{2n,0}(0)\, P_{2n}(\cos \theta) + \sum_{m=1}^{2n} \big(k_{2n,\,m}(0) \cos m\phi
$$

$$
+ k_{2n,-m}(0) \sin m\phi\big)\, P_{2n}^{m}(\cos \theta). \tag{5.60}
$$

Thus,

$$V(T) = 2\pi \int_0^\pi \left[\sum_{n=0}^\infty A_{2n}(\theta, \phi, \psi) \, P_{2n}(\cos \theta') \right] C e^{a\cos\theta'} \sin \theta' \, d\theta', \tag{5.61}$$

where $a = pH'/kT$, so that, as before,

$$V(T) = \frac{\displaystyle\sum_{n=0}^\infty A_{2n}(\theta, \phi, \psi) \, I_{2n+\frac{1}{2}}(a)}{I_{\frac{1}{2}}(a)} = \sum_{n=0}^\infty \zeta^{n(2n+1)} A_{2n}(\theta, \phi, \psi). \tag{5.62}$$

If the value for $A_{2n}(\theta, \phi, \psi)$ from (5.60) is substituted into this equation and the resulting expression compared with (5.57), it may be seen that, for low temperatures, the anisotropy coefficients at temperature T again depend on $\zeta^{n(2n+1)}$ and are related to those at the absolute zero by the relations

$$\frac{k_{2n,\,m}(T)}{k_{2n,\,m}(0)} = \zeta^{n(2n+1)}. \tag{5.63}$$

The above discussion has assumed that there is no correlation between neighbouring spins, each spin being orientated independently by the molecular field. In the limit of complete correlation the local unit of magnetization over which the averaging is performed is considered to be a region in which the spins are all pointing in the same direction. The calculation of the temperature dependence of the anisotropy then proceeds exactly as before, except that a different form is usually assumed for the weighting factor w which specifies the angular distribution of the regions of parallel spins. Thus ZENER [1954] assumes that the local fluctuations in the direction of magnetization may be specified by a random walk distribution function $w = w(\theta', \tau)$, where θ' is again the angle made with the bulk magnetization vector and τ is a parameter which specifies the spread of the distribution. The function $w = w(\theta', \tau)$ therefore satisfies the differential equation

$$\frac{\partial w}{\partial \tau} = \frac{1}{\sin \theta'} \frac{\partial}{\partial \theta'} \left[\sin \theta' \frac{\partial w}{\partial \theta'} \right], \tag{5.64}$$

appropriate to a random walk on a spherical surface. Equation (5.64) is satisfied by $w = e^{-k(k+1)\tau} P_k(\cos \theta')$, so that the most general solution for w, subject to the boundary condition that w approaches a delta function about $\theta' = 0$ as τ tends to zero and to the normalization condition (5.32), is

$$w = \sum_{k=0}^{\infty} \frac{2k+1}{4\pi} e^{-k(k+1)\tau} P_k(\cos \theta'). \qquad (5.65)$$

Since w is a function only of θ' and τ, and is independent of ϕ', equation (5.58) reduces, with $x = \cos \theta'$, to

$$V(T) = 2\pi \int_{-1}^{+1} \sum_{n=0}^{\infty} \left[A_{2n}(\theta, \phi, \psi) P_{2n}(x) \right] w \, dx. \qquad (5.66)$$

But, for $2n \neq k$,

$$\int_{-1}^{+1} P_{2n}(x) P_k(x) \, dx = 0, \qquad (5.67)$$

whilst

$$\int_{-1}^{+1} \left[P_{2n}(x) \right]^2 dx = \frac{2}{4n+1}. \qquad (5.68)$$

Thus

$$V(T) = \sum_{n=0}^{\infty} A_{2n}(\theta, \phi, \psi) e^{-2n(2n+1)\tau}. \qquad (5.69)$$

Similarly, the reduced magnetization is given by

$$\zeta = \zeta(T) = 2\pi \int_{-1}^{+1} xw \, dx = e^{-2\tau}, \qquad (5.70)$$

so that

$$V(T) = \sum_{n=0}^{\infty} A_{2n}(\theta, \phi, \psi) \zeta^{n(2n+1)}, \qquad (5.71)$$

and the anisotropy coefficients at temperature T are again related to those at the absolute zero by (5.63). In this case, however, the validity of equation (5.63) is not, theoretically, limited to low temperatures.

The temperature dependence of the anisotropy coefficients $k_{2n, m}$ must, of course, be distinguished from that of the anisotropy constants, $K_1, K_2, \ldots$, which are used in the analysis of experimental data. Thus, the relations (5.63), when applied to equation (5.30), give, for cubic crystals,

$$K_1(T) + \tfrac{1}{11}K_2(T) = [K_1(0) + \tfrac{1}{11}K_2(0)]\,\zeta^{10},$$
$$K_2(T) = K_2(0)\,\zeta^{21}, \tag{5.72}$$

so that

$$K_1(T) = [K_1(0) + \tfrac{1}{11}K_2(0)]\,\zeta^{10} - \tfrac{1}{11}K_2(0)\,\zeta^{21},$$
$$K_2(T) = K_2(0)\,\zeta^{21}, \tag{5.73}$$

and, when applied to equation (5.31), give, for hexagonal crystals,

$$K_1(T) + \tfrac{8}{7}K_2(T) + \tfrac{8}{7}K_3(T) = [K_1(0) + \tfrac{8}{7}K_2(0) + \tfrac{8}{7}K_3(0)]\,\zeta^3,$$
$$K_2(T) + \tfrac{18}{11}K_3(T) = [K_2(0) + \tfrac{10}{11}K_3(0)]\,\zeta^{10},$$
$$K_3(T) = K_3(0)\,\zeta^{21}, \tag{5.74}$$
$$K_4(T) = K_4(0)\,\zeta^{21},$$

so that

$$K_1(T) = [K_1(0) + \tfrac{8}{7}K_2(0) + \tfrac{8}{7}K_3(0)]\,\zeta^3$$
$$\qquad - [\tfrac{8}{7}K_2(0) + \tfrac{144}{77}K_3(0)]\,\zeta^{10} + \tfrac{8}{11}K_3(0)\,\zeta^{21},$$
$$K_2(T) = [K_2(0) + \tfrac{18}{11}K_3(0)]\,\zeta^{10} - \tfrac{18}{11}K_3(0)\,\zeta^{21}, \tag{5.75}$$
$$K_3(T) = K_3(0)\,\zeta^{21},$$
$$K_4(T) = K_4(0)\,\zeta^{21}.$$

It may be noted that no attempt has been made to calculate the temperature dependence of the coefficients of $Y_{0,0}$ in (5.30) and (5.31). These coefficients – in which K_0 may be included – have a different physical significance from those of the other surface harmonics. This is because the angular-dependent part of $V(T)$

arises from the existence of mutual forces between an individual spin and the crystalline lattice whereas the constant part depends primarily on the average angle that one spin makes with another, that is on spin–spin alignment rather than spin–lattice alignment. Since exchange forces and the exchange energy depend strongly on the degree of spin–spin alignment, it is clear that the temperature dependence of the angular-independent part of $V(T)$ cannot be predicted from a theory that is derived by averaging the energies corresponding to all the individual spin–lattice couplings. To maintain that the coefficients of $Y_{0,0}$ vary as ζ^0 is merely to state, incorrectly, that the energy of an individual spin depends only upon its orientation relative to the crystalline lattice and not upon the orientation of its neighbours.

Unfortunately, neither (5.73) nor (5.75) can be said to be conspicuously in agreement with experimental measurements of the temperature dependence of anisotropy. For iron, $K_1(T)$ varies more nearly as the sixth power of ζ (GRAHAM [1958]), whilst for nickel the variation with ζ is much more rapid than ζ^{10} and is as rapid as ζ^{20} at low temperatures. Recent measurements on the hexagonal materials cobalt (BARNIER, PAUTHENET and RIMET [1961]) and gadolinium (GRAHAM [1962]; CORNER, ROE and TAYLOR [1962]) reveal a lack of agreement with (5.75), in general, although, for cobalt, these equations do predict the correct values of $K_1(T)$ below 120°K and of $K_2(T)$ below 220°K. However, for *cubic* cobalt RODBELL [1962] has found that $K_1(T)$ varies as ζ^{10} and $K_2(T)$ as a much higher power of ζ. That the model used to derive (5.73) and (5.75) is probably not itself seriously in error is indicated by the fact that it predicts a temperature dependence of magnetoelastic coupling constants (discussed in § 3.4) which is in good agreement with experiment for nickel (LEE and BIRSS [1961]; CALLEN and CALLEN [1963]) and for yttrium iron garnet (CLARK, DeSAVAGE, COLEMAN and CALLEN [1963]). One possible explanation of the discrepancies is that the higher-order anisotropy constants – being associated with progressively higher powers of ζ – have a more significant effect in (5.73) and (5.75) than in (5.30) and (5.31): this seems, for example, to be the case for gadolinium (CORNER, ROE and TAYLOR [1962]). The assumption that the distribution function w depends on θ' but not on ϕ' would appear to be justified by the small magnitude of anisotropy forces in comparison with exchange forces, although it must be conceded that some dependence on ϕ' is to be expected for $\theta' = \theta$ (i.e. when an easy direction is a generator of the cone of semi-vertical angle θ'). However, perhaps the most obvious objection to equations (5.73) and (5.75) is that the averaging process used in their derivation is one appropriate to constant lattice strain whereas the experimental data customarily refer to constant stress.

In comparing $V(T)$ with $V(0)$ it must be remembered that the corresponding states of strain of the crystalline lattice differ first because thermal expansion introduces an isotropic volume strain and secondly because of magnetostriction (discussed in § 3). The normal thermal expansion is supplemented by a change in magnetostriction with temperature to give a deformation of the lattice which is principally an isotropic volume strain, $\omega = \omega(T)$, but is partly an anisotropic deformation that depends on the direction of magnetization. The effect of this is to modify the left-hand side of (5.63) in a way which is considered, in § 3.4, after magnetostriction has been discussed. The corresponding modification to the right-hand side of (5.63) may, however, be made immediately since it is observed experimentally† that the magnitude of the saturation magnetization depends on ω but not on the direction of the magnetization relative to the crystallographic axes. It is therefore possible to express the spontaneous magnetization, $I_s(T, \omega)$, at temperature T and volume strain ω approximately in the form

$$I_s(T, \omega) = I_s(T, 0) + \frac{\partial I_s(T, \omega)}{\partial \omega}\, \omega, \qquad (5.76)$$

† There is a possibility that this may not be true for a material (like ludlamite) with a low Curie point and a large anisotropy (CALLEN and CALLEN [1960]).

where $\omega(0) = 0$. Since the averaging process is really appropriate to constant strain, the quantity observed experimentally, $\zeta = I_s(T, \omega)/I_s(0, 0)$, should be replaced in (5.63) by either $I_s(T, \omega)/I_s(0, \omega)$ or $I_s(T, 0)/I_s(0, 0)$, that is by

$$\zeta' = \zeta - \frac{1}{I_s(0, 0)} \frac{\partial I_s(T, \omega)}{\partial \omega} \omega. \qquad (5.77)$$

§ 2.5. Magnetization below Saturation

As stated in § 1.2, the fact that magnetic properties are formulated with reference to a saturated crystal does not necessarily preclude a description of magnetic properties below saturation, for at every stage of the magnetization process the crystal is subdivided into a number of domains each magnetized to the same saturation value. Thus the expressions for V given by (5.8) and (5.17) may be used to deduce the magnetization of a crystal below saturation provided that the detailed distribution of the domains is known as a function of the applied magnetic field. This knowledge is usually available only in high fields – that is in the region of domain vector rotation – so that detailed agreement with experiment cannot be expected in lower fields.

The simplest cases arise when the magnetic field is applied longitudinally to long rod-shaped crystals cut parallel to a principal crystallographic direction, for the field and the magnetization are then co-directional. When a field H is applied to such a crystal an extra term $-I_s \cdot H$ must be added to the free energy, and the equilibrium direction of domain magnetization is such as to minimize the sum $V - I_s \cdot H$. Calculations of magnetization curves by this method were first performed by AKULOV [1929, 1931] and by GANS and CZERLINSKI [1932]: the results, which may be found in any detailed treatment of the theory of magnetization curves (e.g. STONER [1950]; BOZORTH [1951]; STEWART [1954]), are in excellent agreement with experiment. For directions of applied magnetic field other than those of the principal crystallo-

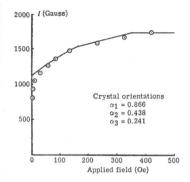

Fig. 5.2. Magnetization, *I*, for a long rod as calculated by LAWTON and STEWART [1948] and as measured by SIZOO [1929], the orientation of the rod being given by the direction cosines α_1, α_2, α_3.

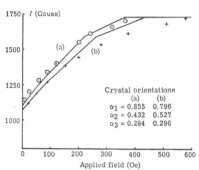

Fig. 5.3. Magnetization, *I*, for long rods as calculated by LAWTON and STEWART [1948] and as measured by KAYA [1933], the orientation of the rods being given by the direction cosines α_1, α_2, α_3.

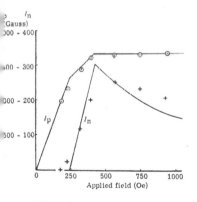

Fig. 5.4. The parallel, I_p, and normal, I_n, components of magnetization for a (001) oblate spheroid as calculated by LAWTON and STEWART [1948] and as measured by HONDA and KAYA [1926] for $\bar{\theta} = 25°$.

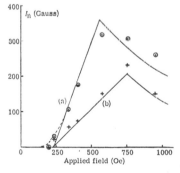

Fig. 5.5. The normal component of magnetization, I_n, for a (001) oblate spheroid as calculated by LAWTON and STEWART [1948] and as measured by HONDA and KAYA [1926] for (a) $\bar{\theta} = 15°$ and (b) $\bar{\theta} = 5°$.

graphic directions, few calculations of magnetization curves have been published. However, for iron crystals of certain shapes, the basic processes of magnetization are known from the work of LAWTON and STEWART [1948] and LAWTON [1949]. The former publication deals with an oblate spheroid for which the equatorial plane is a (001) crystallographic plane and also with a long crystalline rod of arbitrary orientation, whilst the latter paper is concerned with a (110) oblate spheroid. Their calculated curves of magnetization versus applied field for these three cases are all in reasonable agreement with experiment: some typical results are shown in Figs. 5.2 to 5.5. ($\bar{\theta}$ is the angle that the applied field makes with a $\langle 110 \rangle$ axis; I_p and I_n are respectively the components of the bulk magnetization parallel and normal to the field.)

§ 3. MAGNETOSTRICTION

It is observed experimentally that a change in the magnetic state of a ferromagnetic or ferrimagnetic single crystal is, in general, accompanied by a magnetostrictive deformation. However, at every stage of the magnetization process the crystal is subdivided into a number of domains each magnetized to the same saturation value, I_s, so that if the local magnetostriction were to depend only on the *magnitude* of the local magnetization no deformation would accompany a rearrangement of these domains. It is therefore necessary to assume that the magnetostrictive strain which accompanies the magnetization to saturation of an elementary region of the body is anisotropic and depends on the orientation of the magnetization vector with respect to the crystallographic axes associated with this region. The magnetostrictive deformation of the body as a whole, i.e. the bulk magnetostriction, is thus explained by postulating that in each domain the establishment of the spontaneous magnetization is accompanied by the appearance of an anisotropic deformation of the domain and this deformation is referred to as the spontaneous magnetostriction.

Whatever the state of magnetization of the crystal, the observed bulk magnetostriction may be interpreted in terms of the spontaneous magnetostriction of each domain, but this interpretation is both simple and unambiguous only when the crystal is magnetized as a single domain. This situation may be produced without the use of very intense applied fields provided that the magnetic field acting within the body is uniform throughout the volume of the crystal. Thus, if the specimen is situated in a uniform external magnetic field, the demagnetizing field must also be uniform and for this condition to be satisfied the crystal boundary must be a complete surface of the second degree. The only case in which such a body is of finite dimensions is when it is ellipsoidal in shape. The use of such a specimen ensures that the strain components are the same at every point in the body and this limitation greatly simplifies the determination of the form of the spontaneous magnetostriction. A further simplification is afforded by the fact that the purely anisotropic part of the spontaneous magnetostriction is small, the associated lattice strain usually being considerably less than one part per thousand.

Although the observed saturation magnetostriction of single-crystal ellipsoids usually agrees closely with that calculated by using theoretical expressions for the spontaneous magnetostriction, there is often a small difference between these quantities which indicates that the deformation of the crystal does not arise wholly as a direct result of the occurrence of the spontaneous magnetization. The explanation of this effect is to be found in the interaction of the demagnetizing field with the spontaneous magnetization. Since the demagnetizing energy depends upon the shape of the specimen, it may be decreased by a deformation of the body. It is thus to be expected that the strain dependence of the demagnetizing energy will give rise to an additional lattice strain and this phenomenon is known as the form effect. The contribution of this effect to the magnetostriction is usually small – considerably less than 10^{-6} – and in what follows the form effect will be ignored.

The method adopted to obtain a formal expression for the spontaneous magnetostriction is to represent the associated lattice strain in terms of successively increasing powers of the direction cosines, α_i, of the spontaneous magnetization referred to one of the sets of rectangular cartesian coordinate axes identified in Ch. 2, § 1.4. In order to describe the deformation of the crystal, an arbitrary point, P, defined in the undeformed lattice by the coordinates x_i may be assumed to undergo a displacement u_i. For small strains, the displacement of a neighbouring point $x_i + \Delta x_i$ is $u_i + \Delta u_i$ where

$$\Delta u_i = \frac{\partial u_i}{\partial x_j} \Delta x_j. \tag{5.78}$$

The strain tensor $e_{ij} = \partial u_i / \partial x_j$ may be separated into its symmetrical and antisymmetrical parts, the latter representing a rotation of the crystal as a whole without any deformation of the lattice. The former is the symmetrical strain tensor $E_{ij} = \frac{1}{2}(e_{ij} + e_{ji})$ which characterizes a pure deformation and represents the distortion of the crystal in the neighbourhood of the point P. For a homogeneous strain the components e_{ij} are constants of the crystal which do not depend upon position so that the lattice strain in the direction of the element Δx_i, as measured by any of the more usual mechanical methods, is

$$\lambda = \Delta u_i \, \Delta x_i / \Delta x_j \, \Delta x_j. \tag{5.79}$$

Introducing the direction cosines of the measuring direction, $\beta_i = \Delta x_i / \sqrt{(\Delta x_j \, \Delta x_j)}$, the strain in the direction $\boldsymbol{\beta}$ associated with magnetization in the direction $\boldsymbol{\alpha}$, becomes

$$\lambda = e_{ij}\beta_i\beta_j = E_{ij}\beta_i\beta_j, \tag{5.80}$$

where the E_{ij} are functions only of the α_i. If the lattice strain is investigated by means of a strain gauge cemented to the crystal then the gauge accommodates itself to the true deformation of

the lattice. Thus the relative orientation of the measuring direction and the crystal lattice is preserved and the corresponding
quantity that is measured is $\lambda = \sqrt{(\Delta u_i \, \Delta u_i / \Delta x_j \, \Delta x_j)}$, which differs
from $e_{ij}\beta_i\beta_j$ only by negligible terms involving products of the e_{ij}.

Since the magnetostrictive deformation of the crystal is opposed
by purely elastic forces the equilibrium deformation of the crystal
may be found by minimizing the sum of the magnetic and elastic
energies with respect to the components of strain, e_{ij}. The existence of the spontaneous magnetostriction indicates that the magnetic energy, V', must be strain dependent. Since, however, the
deformation of a crystal arising from the presence of the spontaneous magnetostriction is small, the dependence of the magnetic
energy on the state of strain of the lattice may conveniently be
introduced by expanding V' as a Maclaurin series in the e_{ij}, thus

$$V' = V^0 + V^0_{ij}e_{ij} + \tfrac{1}{2}V^0_{ijkl}e_{ij}e_{kl} + \cdots. \qquad (5.81)$$

The zero superscript on the quantities V^0, V^0_{ij}, V^0_{ijkl}, indicates that
they have been numerically evaluated relative to the undeformed
crystal lattice: at any one temperature, they are therefore fixed,
strain-independent coefficients which can be functions only of the
direction cosines, α_i, of the direction of the spontaneous magnetization. The undeformed crystal lattice, which defines the state of
zero strain, is one in which the magnetic interactions have been
annihilated. This state, in which there are no magnetic interactions to deform the crystal, is not, of course, realizable experimentally but it is shown in § 3.3 that there are in fact several
ways of estimating the lattice deformation associated with the
destruction of the spontaneous magnetization. In practice, however, it is rarely necessary to define this hypothetical initial state
more exactly since, due to the presence of the spontaneous
magnetostriction, experimental measurements of strain always refer to two or more *deformed* states of the crystal and interest is
centred mainly in the lattice strain which accompanies a variation

in the direction in which the crystal is magnetized to saturation. Since V^0 and the V^0_{ij} are functions of the α_i only, they may be expressed in the forms

$$V^0 = b_{ij}\alpha_i\alpha_j + b_{ijkl}\alpha_i\alpha_j\alpha_k\alpha_i + b_{ijklmn}\alpha_i\alpha_j\alpha_k\alpha_l\alpha_m\alpha_n + \cdots,$$
(5.82a)

$$V^0_{ij} = c_{ij} + c_{klij}\alpha_k\alpha_i + c_{klmnij}\alpha_k\alpha_i\alpha_m\alpha_n + \cdots,$$
(5.82b)

tensors of odd rank again being absent, as in equation (5.2b), because they are c-tensors and the spontaneous magnetostriction is a static property. The first term in (5.81), V^0, is the anisotropy at zero strain, and crystal symmetry imposes the same restrictions on the tensors b_{ij}, b_{ijkl}, b_{ijklmn}, ... as it does on the tensors b'_{ij}, b'_{ijkl}, b'_{ijklmn}, ... of (5.2b). The two sets of tensors may not, however, be identified for (5.82a) refers to the anisotropy at zero strain whilst (5.2b) refers not even to constant strain but to constant stress. The relationship between the anisotropy at zero strain and the anisotropy at zero stress is discussed in § 3.3. The second term in (5.81), $V^0_{ij}e_{ij}$, arises from the interaction between magnetic anisotropy and strain: it is referred to as the magnetoelastic energy density. The third term, $V^0_{ijkl}e_{ij}e_{kl}$ may be regarded as an additional contribution to the elastic energy density $\frac{1}{2}C_{ijkl}e_{ij}e_{kl}$ (see equation (5.84), below) which incorporates the effect upon the crystal symmetry of the deformation of the lattice. This arises because the distortion of the body due to the spontaneous magnetostriction results in the crystalline lattice having a lower symmetry than the original undeformed crystal and the term $V^0_{ijkl}e_{ij}e_{kl}$ introduces the required additional constants which are, of course, small compared with the C_{ijkl}. Effects of this type, which arise when elastic strains alter the symmetry of a structure, have been called morphic effects by MUELLER [1940] and the corresponding energy is usually referred to as morphic energy.

According to the classical theory of elasticity (Love [1944]) a linear relation exists between the components of stress and strain which may either be written in the form

$$T_{ij} = C_{ijkl}e_{kl} \tag{5.83a}$$

or in the reciprocal form

$$e_{ij} = S_{ijkl}T_{kl}, \tag{5.83b}$$

where the C_{ijkl} are the elastic stiffness constants and the S_{ijkl} the elastic compliance moduli. The elastic energy density, U, is therefore given by

$$U = \int T_{ij}\,de_{ij} = \int (C_{ijkl}e_{kl})\,de_{ij} = \tfrac{1}{2}C_{ijkl}e_{ij}e_{kl}. \tag{5.84}$$

Any homogeneous strain may, of course, be analysed into a pure strain and a rotation, the latter being ignored in formulating the stress–strain relationships: in addition it is assumed that the tractive forces acting on elements of area in the solid are so related that no torques tending to rotate the volume elements of the crystal are present. Provided that these assumptions are made, the generalized Hooke's law (5.83) is simplified by the relations $T_{ij} = T_{ji}$ and $e_{ij} = e_{ji} = E_{ij}$. Recent work by Laval [1951a, b, 1954a, b] has, however, cast doubt on the validity of these relations when either the static or the dynamic properties of crystals are under consideration. Le Corre [1953a, b, c, 1954a, b, 1955] has extended and developed Laval's approach and has given the complete schemes of the elastic coefficients for all the crystal classes. This work has been confirmed by Raman and Viswanathan [1955] and it now appears that cubic crystals such as iron and nickel might be characterized by four independent elastic coefficients whilst eight coefficients might be necessary to describe the elastic properties of hexagonal crystals such as cobalt and gadolinium. Although it has been suggested (Joel and Wooster [1958]) that, in crystals subject to mechanical strains only, these numbers may be reduced to three and six respectively, it may nevertheless be maintained that the methods of the classical theory of elasticity are not applicable to the general case of heterogeneous strain. Furthermore, since only infinitesimal strains are considered in the developments mentioned above, the consequential modifications that must be made to the classical theory are of a different nature from those encountered when the deformation of the body is considered to be finite. If the classical approach is to be used to evaluate the spontaneous magnetostriction then it may be necessary to ensure that, in addition to the deformation being small, it is also the same at every point in the body, for it is only in this case that the relations $T_{ij} = T_{ji}$ and $e_{ij} = E_{ij}$ regain their validity. However, as shown in §§ 3.1 and 3.2, the forms of the expressions for the spontaneous magnetostriction do not depend on the assumption that $e_{ij} = E_{ij}$, and the formulation of V' and U in terms of the e_{ij} given by (5.78) and (5.84) may therefore be retained.

Remembering that V^0, V_{ij}^0 and V_{ijkl}^0 are functions only of the α_i (and that, because of particularization, $V_{ijkl}^0 = V_{klij}^0$), the equilibrium components of strain, e_{kl}^*, may be found by partial differentiation of $(U + V')$ with respect to all the strain components, i.e. with respect to all the e_{ij}, in turn, thus

$$\left[\frac{\partial (U + V')}{\partial e_{ij}} \right]_{\text{equilibrium}} = C_{ijkl} e_{kl}^* + V_{ij}^0 + V_{ijkl}^0 e_{kl}^* = 0. \quad (5.85)$$

It may be seen that the coefficients V_{ijkl}^0 of the morphic energy terms enter equations (5.85) only together with the elastic constants C_{ijkl}, as coefficients of the e_{kl}^*. Since the C_{ijkl} do not, in general, all vanish for any of the minimal equations, V_{ijkl}^0 may be neglected in favour of C_{ijkl} and equations (5.85) become

$$V_{ij}^0 = - C_{ijkl} e_{kl}^*. \quad (5.86a)$$

Upon inverting this equation and putting $g_{ijkl} = -S_{ijkl}$,

$$e_{ij}^* = g_{ijkl}V_{kl}^0, \qquad (5.86b)$$

whilst, from (5.80),

$$\lambda = g_{ijkl}\beta_i\beta_j V_{kl}^0. \qquad (5.87)$$

§ 3.1. The Spontaneous Magnetostriction in Cubic Crystals

For the classical crystal class **m3m**, the forms of general polar tensors of second, fourth and sixth ranks may be obtained immediately from equations (5.3). The elastic tensors C_{ijkl}, S_{ijkl} and g_{ijkl} may not be further simplified by the presence of intrinsic symmetry and the forms of all these tensors may be displayed by setting out the suffixes of the non-vanishing components in the following scheme:

e_{kl} \ e_{ij}	e_{11}	e_{22}	e_{33}	e_{23}	e_{32}	e_{31}	e_{13}	e_{12}	e_{21}
e_{11}	1111	1122	1122						
e_{22}	1122	1111	1122						
e_{33}	1122	1122	1111						
e_{23}				2323	2332				
e_{32}				2332	2323				
e_{31}						2323	2332		
e_{13}						2332	2323		
e_{12}								2323	2332
e_{21}								2332	2323

$$(5.88)$$

After allowing for the simplifying effects of intrinsic symmetry, the magnetoelastic tensors c_{ij}, c_{klij}, c_{klmnij} may be particularized into forms which may be displayed in a similar way as follows:

e_{ij}	e_{11}	e_{22}	e_{33}	e_{23}	e_{32}	e_{31}	e_{13}	e_{12}	e_{21}
	11	11	11						

$$(5.89)$$

$\alpha_k\alpha_l$ \\ e_{ij}	e_{11}	e_{22}	e_{33}	e_{23}	e_{32}	e_{31}	e_{13}	e_{12}	e_{21}
α_1^2	1111	1122	1122						
α_2^2	1122	1111	1122						
α_3^2	1122	1122	1111						
$\alpha_2\alpha_3$				2323	2323				
$\alpha_3\alpha_1$						2323	2323		
$\alpha_1\alpha_2$								2323	2323

$$(5.90)$$

$\alpha_k\alpha_l\alpha_m\alpha_n$ \\ e_{ij}	e_{11}	e_{22}	e_{33}	e_{23}	e_{32}	e_{31}	e_{13}	e_{12}	e_{21}
α_1^4	111111	111122	111122						
α_2^4	111122	111111	111122						
α_3^4	111122	111122	111111						
$\alpha_2^2\alpha_3^2$	112233	112211	112211						
$\alpha_3^2\alpha_1^2$	112211	112233	112211						
$\alpha_1^2\alpha_2^2$	112211	112211	112233						
$\alpha_1^2\alpha_2\alpha_3$				112323	112323				
$\alpha_2^2\alpha_3\alpha_1$						112323	112323		
$\alpha_3^2\alpha_1\alpha_2$								112323	112323
$\alpha_3^3\alpha_3$				111212	111221				
$\alpha_3^3\alpha_1$						111212	111221		
$\alpha_1^3\alpha_2$								111212	111221
$\alpha_3^3\alpha_2$				111221	111212				
$\alpha_1^3\alpha_3$						111221	111212		
$\alpha_2^3\alpha_1$								111221	111212

$$(5.91)$$

The spontaneous magnetostriction is given by equation (5.87), so that, by using the values of g_{ijkl} obtained from (5.88), λ may be written in the form

$$\lambda = \beta_1^2[g_{1111}V_{11}^0 + g_{1122}(V_{22}^0 + V_{33}^0)]$$

$$+ \beta_2^2[g_{1111}V_{22}^0 + g_{1122}(V_{33}^0 + V_{11}^0)]$$

$$+ \beta_3^2[g_{1111}V_{33}^0 + g_{1122}(V_{11}^0 + V_{22}^0)]$$

$$+ \beta_2\beta_3(g_{2323} + g_{2332})(V_{23}^0 + V_{32}^0)$$

$$+ \beta_3\beta_1(g_{2323} + g_{2332})(V_{31}^0 + V_{13}^0)$$

$$+ \beta_1\beta_2(g_{2323} + g_{2332})(V_{12}^0 + V_{21}^0). \qquad (5.92)$$

The V_{ij}^0 are given, to a fourth order in the α_i, by

$$V_{ij}^0 = c_{ij} + c_{klij}\alpha_k\alpha_l + c_{klmnij}\alpha_k\alpha_l\alpha_m\alpha_n, \qquad (5.93)$$

from which it follows, by using (5.89), (5.90), (5.91) and the relation $S(\alpha_1^2) = 1$, that

$$V_{11}^0 = L_0 + L_1\alpha_1^2 + L_2\alpha_1^4 + L_3\alpha_2^2\alpha_3^2,$$

$$V_{22}^0 = L_0 + L_1\alpha_2^2 + L_2\alpha_2^4 + L_3\alpha_3^2\alpha_1^2,$$

$$V_{33}^0 = L_0 + L_1\alpha_3^2 + L_2\alpha_3^4 + L_3\alpha_1^2\alpha_2^2,$$

$$V_{23}^0 + V_{32}^0 = \alpha_2\alpha_3(M_0 + M_1\alpha_1^2),$$

$$V_{31}^0 + V_{13}^0 = \alpha_3\alpha_1(M_0 + M_1\alpha_2^2),$$

$$V_{12}^0 + V_{21}^0 = \alpha_1\alpha_2(M_0 + M_1\alpha_3^2),$$

$$(5.94)$$

where the coefficients L_0, L_1, L_2, L_3, M_0, M_1 are called the magnetoelastic coupling constants and are given by

$$
\begin{aligned}
L_0 &= c'_{11} + c'_{1122} + c'_{111122}, \\
L_1 &= c'_{1111} - c'_{1122} - 2c'_{111122} + c'_{112211}, \\
L_2 &= c'_{111111} + c'_{111122} - c'_{112211}, \\
L_3 &= c'_{112233} - 2c'_{111122}, \\
M_0 &= 2c'_{2323} + c'_{111212} + c'_{111221}, \\
M_1 &= 2c'_{112323} - c'_{111212} - c'_{111221},
\end{aligned}
\tag{5.95}
$$

and where the primed magnetoelastic coefficients correspond to the schemes of subscripts set out in (5.89), (5.90) and (5.91) and to the summations implied therein. Because of the multiplicity involved in some of the functions of the α_t, the primed coefficients are contracted (matrix) forms of the corresponding components of the magnetoelastic tensors: thus, for example, $c'_{2323} = 2c_{2323}$, since $\alpha_2\alpha_3$ appears twice in $c_{klij}\alpha_k\alpha_l e_{ij}$ but only once in the summation implicit in (5.90). If equations (5.92) and (5.94) are combined, the spontaneous magnetostriction may be written in the form

$$
\begin{aligned}
\lambda = B_0 &+ B_1 S(\alpha_1^2\beta_1^2) + B_2 S(\alpha_1\alpha_2\beta_1\beta_2) + B_3 S(\alpha_1^2\alpha_2^2) \\
&+ B_4 S(\alpha_1^4\beta_1^2) + B_5 S(\alpha_1\alpha_2\alpha_3^2\beta_1\beta_2),
\end{aligned}
\tag{5.96}
$$

where the saturation magnetostriction constants $B_0, \ldots B_5$ are related to the magnetoelastic coupling constants by the equations

$$
\begin{aligned}
B_0 &= -L_0 S_{11} - (2L_0 + L_1 + L_2)\, S_{12}, \\
B_1 &= -(L_1 - L_3)(S_{11} - S_{12}), \\
B_2 &= -M_0 S_{44}, \\
B_3 &= -L_3 S_{11} + 2L_2 S_{12}, \\
B_4 &= -(L_2 + L_3)(S_{11} - S_{12}), \\
B_5 &= -M_1 S_{44},
\end{aligned}
\tag{5.97}
$$

and where

$$S_{11} = -g_{1111}, \qquad S_{12} = -g_{1122},$$
$$S_{44} = -(g_{2323} + g_{2332}). \tag{5.98}$$

Experimental values, for cubic crystals, of the constants S_{11}, S_{12}, S_{44}, of the magnetoelastic coupling constants, and of the saturation magnetostriction constants are presented in § 3.3.

§ 3.2. The Spontaneous Magnetostriction in Hexagonal Crystals

For the classical crystal class **6/mmm**, the forms of general polar tensors of second, fourth and sixth ranks may be obtained immediately from equations (5.10). After allowing for the simplifying effects of intrinsic symmetry, the elastic tensors C_{ijkl}, S_{ijkl} and g_{ijkl} may be particularized into a form which may be displayed by setting out the suffixes of the non-vanishing components in the following scheme:

e_{kl} \\ e_{ij}	e_{11}	e_{22}	e_{33}	e_{23}	e_{32}	e_{31}	e_{13}	e_{12}	e_{21}
e_{11}	1111	1122	1133						
e_{22}	1122	1111	1133						
e_{33}	1133	1133	3333						
e_{23}				2323	2332				
e_{32}				2332	3232				
e_{31}						3232	2332		
e_{13}						2332	2323		
e_{12}								1212	1221
e_{21}								1221	1212

$$\tag{5.99a}$$

where, if d_{ijkl} denotes any of these tensors,

$$d_{1111} = d_{1122} + d_{1212} + d_{1221}. \tag{5.99b}$$

The components of the magnetoelastic tensors c_{ij}, c_{klij}, c_{klmnij} may be displayed in a similar way, as follows:

e_{ij}	e_{11}	e_{22}	e_{33}	e_{23}	e_{32}	e_{31}	e_{13}	e_{12}	e_{21}
	11	11	33						

$$(5.100)$$

$\alpha_k\alpha_l$ \ e_{ij}	e_{11}	e_{22}	e_{33}	e_{23}	e_{32}	e_{31}	e_{13}	e_{12}	e_{21}
α_1^2	1111	1122	1133						
α_2^2	1122	1111	1133						
α_3^2	3311	3311	3333						
$\alpha_2\alpha_3$				2323	2332				
$\alpha_3\alpha_1$						2332	2323		
$\alpha_1\alpha_2$								1212	1212

$$(5.101a)$$

$\alpha_k\alpha_l\alpha_m\alpha_n$ \ e_{ij}	e_{11}	e_{22}	e_{33}	e_{23}	e_{32}	e_{31}	e_{13}	e_{12}	e_{21}
α_1^4	111111	111122	111133						
α_2^4	222211	222222	111133						
α_3^4	333311	333311	333333						
$\alpha_2^2\alpha_3^2$	223311	223322	223333						
$\alpha_3^2\alpha_1^2$	223322	223311	223333						
$\alpha_1^2\alpha_2^2$	112211	112222	112233						
$\alpha_1^2\alpha_2\alpha_3$				112323	112332				
$\alpha_2^2\alpha_3\alpha_1$						112332	112323		
$\alpha_3^2\alpha_1\alpha_2$								331212	331212
$\alpha_2^3\alpha_3$				112323	112332				
$\alpha_3^3\alpha_1$						333131	333113		
$\alpha_1^3\alpha_2$								111212	111212
$\alpha_3^3\alpha_2$				333113	333131				
$\alpha_1^3\alpha_3$						112332	112323		
$\alpha_2^3\alpha_1$								222121	222121

$$(5.102a)$$

where
$$c'_{1111} = c'_{1122} + c'_{1212}, \qquad (5.101b)$$
and
$$c'_{111122} = 2c'_{111111} - 3c'_{222222} + c'_{112211},$$

$$c'_{112233} = 2c'_{111133},$$

$$c'_{222211} = 3c'_{111111} - 4c'_{222222} + c'_{112211},$$

$$c'_{223322} = c'_{223311} + c'_{331212}, \qquad (5.102b)$$

$$c'_{112222} = 6c'_{111111} - 6c'_{222222} + c'_{112211},$$

$$c'_{111212} = -4c'_{111111} + 6c'_{222222} - c'_{112211},$$

$$c'_{222121} = 2c'_{222222} - c'_{112211}.$$

As in § 3.1, the primes indicate that, because of the multiplicity involved in some of the functions of the α_i, the coefficients c'_{ijkl} and c'_{ijklmn} are contracted (matrix) coefficients rather than the individual components of the tensors c_{ijkl} and c_{ijklmn}. For hexagonal crystals, the relations between the non-vanishing components are altered when contracted coefficients are employed. For example, the equation $c_{111133} = 3c_{112233}$ derived from (5.10) becomes $2c'_{111133} = c'_{112233}$ in (5.102b) because the multiplicity of $\alpha_1^2\alpha_2^2$ is six. Similarly the apparent omission from (5.101b) of a factor two, as compared with (5.99b), corresponds to a multiplicity of two for the function $\alpha_1\alpha_2$.

The values of the coefficients g_{ijkl} obtained from (5.99), when substituted into (5.87), give, for the spontaneous magnetostriction,

$$
\begin{aligned}
\lambda = & \ \beta_1^2(g_{1111}V^0_{11} + g_{1122}V^0_{22} + g_{1133}V^0_{33}) \\
& + \beta_2^2(g_{1111}V^0_{22} + g_{1122}V^0_{11} + g_{1133}V^0_{33}) \\
& + \beta_3^2[g_{1133}(V^0_{11} + V^0_{22}) + g_{3333}V^0_{33}] \\
& + \beta_2\beta_3[g_{2323}V^0_{23} + g_{2332}(V^0_{23} + V^0_{32}) + g_{3232}V^0_{32}] \\
& + \beta_3\beta_1[g_{2323}V^0_{13} + g_{2332}(V^0_{13} + V^0_{31}) + g_{3232}V^0_{31}] \\
& + \beta_1\beta_2(g_{1111} - g_{1122})(V^0_{12} + V^0_{21}). \qquad (5.103)
\end{aligned}
$$

The V_{ij}^0 are again given, to a fourth order in the α_i, by equation (5.93), from which it follows, by using (5.100), (5.101), (5.102) and the relation $S(\alpha_1^2) = 1$, that

$$V_{11}^0 = L_0 + (L_1 - L_3)\,\alpha_1^2 + L_2\alpha_2^2 + 4L_3\alpha_1^2\alpha_2^2 + L_4\alpha_2^2\alpha_3^2$$
$$+ (L_5 + L_3)\,\alpha_3^2\alpha_1^2,$$

$$V_{22}^0 = L_0 + (L_2 + L_3)\,\alpha_1^2 + L_1\alpha_2^2 - 4L_3\alpha_1^2\alpha_2^2 + L_5\alpha_2^2\alpha_3^2$$
$$+ (L_4 - L_3)\,\alpha_3^2\alpha_1^2,$$

$$V_{33}^0 = M_0 + M_1(\alpha_1^2 + \alpha_2^2) + M_2(\alpha_1^2 + \alpha_2^2)\,\alpha_3^2, \qquad (5.104)$$

$$V_{23}^0 = \alpha_2\alpha_3(N_0' + N_1'\alpha_3^2), \qquad V_{32}^0 = \alpha_2\alpha_3(N_0'' + N_1''\alpha_3^2),$$

$$V_{31}^0 = \alpha_3\alpha_1(N_0'' + N_1''\alpha_3^2), \qquad V_{13}^0 = \alpha_3\alpha_1(N_0' + N_1'\alpha_3^2),$$

$$V_{12}^0 = V_{21}^0 = \alpha_1\alpha_2[(L_1 - L_2 - L_3) - (L_4 - L_5 - L_3)\,\alpha_3^2$$
$$+ 2L_3(\alpha_1^2 - \alpha_2^2)],$$

where the magnetoelastic coupling constants are given by

$$L_0 = c_{11}' + c_{3311}' + c_{333311}',$$

$$L_1 = c_{1111}' - c_{3311}' + c_{222222}' - c_{333311}',$$

$$L_2 = c_{1122}' - c_{3311}' + 3c_{111111}' - 4c_{222222}' + c_{112211}'$$
$$- c_{333311}',$$

$$L_3 = -c_{111111}' + c_{222222}',$$

$$L_4 = -3c_{111111}' + 4c_{222222}' - c_{112211}' - c_{333311}' + c_{223311}',$$

$$L_5 = -c_{222222}' - c_{333311}' + c_{223311}' + c_{331212}', \qquad (5.105)$$

$$M_0 = c_{33}' + c_{3333}' + c_{333333}',$$

$$M_1 = -c_{3333}' + c_{1133}' - c_{333333}' + c_{111133}',$$

$$M_2 = -c_{333333}' - c_{111133}' + c_{223333}',$$

$$N_0' = c_{2323}' + c_{112323}', \qquad N_0'' = c_{2332}' + c_{112332}',$$

$$N_1' = -c_{112323}' + c_{333113}', \qquad N_1'' = -c_{112332}' + c_{333131}',$$

and where the primed magnetoelastic coefficients correspond to the schemes of subscripts set out in (5.100), (5.101a) and (5.102a) and to the summations implied therein. If equations (5.103) and (5.104) are combined, the spontaneous magnetostriction may be written in the form

$$
\begin{aligned}
\lambda = Q_0 &+ Q_1\beta_3^2 \\
&+ (Q_2 + Q_3\alpha_3^2)(1 - \alpha_3^2) \\
&+ (Q_4 + Q_5\alpha_3^2)(1 - \alpha_3^2)\beta_3^2 \\
&+ (Q_6 + Q_7\alpha_3^2)(\alpha_1\beta_1 + \alpha_2\beta_2)\alpha_3\beta_3 \\
&+ (Q_8 + Q_9\alpha_3^2)(\alpha_1\beta_1 + \alpha_2\beta_2)^2 \\
&+ Q_{10}(2\alpha_1\alpha_2\beta_1 + \alpha_1^2\beta_2 - \alpha_2^2\beta_2)^2,
\end{aligned} \tag{5.106}
$$

where the saturation magnetostriction constants $Q_0, \ldots Q_{10}$ are related to the magnetoelastic coupling constants by the equations

$$
\begin{aligned}
Q_0 &= -L_0(S_{11} + S_{12}) - M_0 S_{13}, \\
Q_1 &= -L_0(2S_{13} - S_{11} - S_{12}) + M_0(S_{13} - S_{33}), \\
Q_2 &= -L_1 S_{12} - L_2 S_{11} - M_1 S_{13}, \\
Q_3 &= -L_4 S_{11} - L_5 S_{12} - M_2 S_{13}, \\
Q_4 &= L_1(S_{12} - S_{13}) + L_2(S_{11} - S_{13}) + M_1(S_{13} - S_{33}), \\
Q_5 &= L_4(S_{11} - S_{13}) + L_5(S_{12} - S_{13}) \\
&\quad + M_2(S_{13} - S_{33}), \\
Q_6 &= -N_0' S_{44}' - N_0'' S_{44}'', \\
Q_7 &= -N_1' S_{44}' - N_1'' S_{44}'', \\
Q_8 &= -(L_1 - L_2 - L_3)(S_{11} - S_{12}), \\
Q_9 &= -(L_3 - L_4 + L_5)(S_{11} - S_{12}), \\
Q_{10} &= -L_3(S_{11} - S_{12}),
\end{aligned} \tag{5.107}
$$

and

$$S_{11} = -g_{1111}, \qquad S_{33} = -g_{3333},$$

$$S_{12} = -g_{1122}, \qquad S'_{44} = -(g_{2323} + g_{2332}), \qquad (5.108)$$

$$S_{13} = -g_{1133}, \qquad S''_{44} = -(g_{2332} + g_{3232}).$$

Experimental values, for hexagonal crystals, of the constants S_{11}, S_{12}, S_{13}, ..., of the magnetoelastic coupling constants, and of the saturation magnetostriction constants are presented in § 3.3.

§ 3.3. *The Difference between the Anisotropy at Zero Strain and at Zero Stress*

At zero strain $e_{ij} = 0$, and, from (5.81), the sum of the elastic and magnetic energy densities reduces to

$$U + V' = V^0. \qquad (5.109)$$

At zero stress the strain components e_{ij} will have their equilibrium values e^*_{ij} given by (5.86), so that

$$U + V' = -\tfrac{1}{2}V^0_{ij}e^*_{ij} + V^0 + V^0_{ij}e^*_{ij}$$
$$= V^0 + \tfrac{1}{2}V^0_{ij}e^*_{ij}. \qquad (5.110)$$

To a close approximation this also represents the anisotropy energy density measured at atmospheric pressure, that is the V of § 2, so that

$$V = V^0 + \tfrac{1}{2}V^0_{ij}e^*_{ij}. \qquad (5.111)$$

The observed anisotropy energy density is thus composed of two parts, an intrinsic part appropriate to zero lattice strain and a magnetoelastic contribution of magnitude

$$\tfrac{1}{2}V^0_{ij}e^*_{ij} = -\tfrac{1}{2}C_{ijkl}e^*_{ij}e^*_{kl} = -\tfrac{1}{2}S_{ijkl}V^0_{ij}V^0_{kl}. \qquad (5.112)$$

For cubic and hexagonal crystals, the values of the equilibrium strains, e^*_{ij}, may be found in terms of the saturation magnetostriction constants from (5.80) and from equations (5.96) and

(5.106). (For example, e_{11}^* is the value of λ when $\beta_1 = 1, \beta_2 = \beta_3 = 0$; e_{12}^* is obtained from the value of λ when $\beta_1 = \beta_2 = 1/\sqrt{2}$, $\beta_3 = 0$, and so on.) Since (5.96) and (5.106) are both symmetrical in the β_i, it follows that $e_{ij}^* = e_{ji}^*$, so that either strain component may be replaced by the corresponding component $E_{ij}^* = \frac{1}{2}(e_{ij}^* + e_{ji}^*)$ of the symmetrical strain tensor. In what follows it will be assumed that the strain tensor is symmetrical and a considerable simplification may then be effected by replacing the full tensor notation with a new (matrix) notation using a single suffix running from one to six, according to the following scheme,

Old notation	E_{11}	E_{22}	E_{33}	E_{23}, E_{32}	E_{31}, E_{13}	E_{12}, E_{21}
New notation	E_1	E_2	E_3	$\frac{1}{2}E_4$	$\frac{1}{2}E_5$	$\frac{1}{2}E_6$

The factors of $\frac{1}{2}$ are necessary if the elastic energy is to be written in a compact form as the sum of similar terms, that is if full advantage is to be taken of the summation convention. It may be noted in passing that E_4, E_5, E_6, as defined above, are equal to the 'engineering' shear strain components. In a similar way the function V_{ij}^0 and the elastic stiffness constants C_{ijkl} may be replaced by V_A^0 and C_{AB}, where the pairs of suffixes ij and kl have been replaced respectively by the suffixes A and B, running from one to six. In both cases, however, no factors of $\frac{1}{2}$ are necessary, and the strain energy density may be expressed in the form

$$U = \frac{1}{2}C_{AB}E_A E_B \qquad (A, B = 1, 2, 3, 4, 5, 6). \qquad (5.113)$$

In this notation the magnetoelastic contribution to the anisotropy energy density is

$$\frac{1}{2}V_A^0 E_A^* = -\frac{1}{2}C_{AB}E_A^* E_B^* = -\frac{1}{2}S_{AB}V_A^0 V_B^0, \qquad (5.114)$$

where the coefficients S_{AB} form a matrix which is reciprocal to that formed by the coefficients C_{AB}.

For cubic crystals the symmetry relations between the elastic compliance moduli simplify the form of $V_A^0 E_A^*$ and

$$V_A^0 E_A^* = -S_{11}(V_1^{0\,2} + V_2^{0\,2} + V_3^{0\,2}) - 2S_{12}(V_1^0 V_2^0 + V_2^0 V_3^0 + V_3^0 V_1^0)$$
$$- S_{44}(V_4^{0\,2} + V_5^{0\,2} + V_6^{0\,2}), \tag{5.115}$$

whilst the V_A^0 are given by (5.94), that is, by

$$\begin{aligned}
V_1^0 &= L_0 + L_1\alpha_1^2 + L_2\alpha_1^4 + L_3\alpha_2^2\alpha_3^2, \\
V_2^0 &= L_0 + L_1\alpha_2^2 + L_2\alpha_2^4 + L_3\alpha_3^2\alpha_1^2, \\
V_3^0 &= L_0 + L_1\alpha_3^2 + L_2\alpha_3^4 + L_3\alpha_1^2\alpha_2^2, \\
V_4^0 &= M_0\alpha_2\alpha_3 + M_1\alpha_1^2\alpha_2\alpha_3, \\
V_5^0 &= M_0\alpha_3\alpha_1 + M_1\alpha_2^2\alpha_3\alpha_1, \\
V_6^0 &= M_0\alpha_1\alpha_2 + M_1\alpha_3^2\alpha_1\alpha_2.
\end{aligned} \tag{5.116}$$

Thus if equation (5.8) for the total magnetic anisotropy energy density is written in the form

$$V = V^0 + \tfrac{1}{2}V_A^0 E_A^* = (K_0^0 + K_0') + (K_1^0 + K_1')\,S(\alpha_1^2\alpha_2^2)$$
$$+ (K_2^0 + K_2')\,\alpha_1^2\alpha_2^2\alpha_3^2, \tag{5.117}$$

where

$$V^0 = K_0^0 + K_1^0 S(\alpha_1^2\alpha_2^2) + K_2^0\alpha_1^2\alpha_2^2\alpha_3^2, \tag{5.118}$$

then the constants K_0', K_1' and K_2' are given by

$$\begin{aligned}
K_0' &= -\tfrac{1}{2}S_{11}[L_0(3L_0 + 2L_1 + 2L_2) + (L_1 + L_2)^2] \\
&\quad - S_{12}L_0(3L_0 + 2L_1 + 2L_2), \\
K_1' &= S_{11}[L_0(2L_2 - L_3) + L_1(L_1 + 3L_2) + 2L_2^2] \\
&\quad + S_{12}[2L_0(2L_2 - L_3) - L_1(L_1 + L_2 + L_3) - L_2L_3] \\
&\quad - \tfrac{1}{2}S_{44}M_0^2, \\
K_2' &= S_{11}[3L_1(L_2 + L_3) + L_2(4L_2 + L_3)] \\
&\quad + S_{12}[3L_1(L_2 + L_3) + 5L_2L_3 - L_3^2] \\
&\quad - \tfrac{1}{2}S_{44}(6M_0 + M_1)\,M_1.
\end{aligned} \tag{5.119}$$

The quantities K_0', K_1' and K_2' may, alternatively, be expressed in terms of the saturation magnetostriction constants B_0, ... B_5 occurring in the expression for the spontaneous magnetostriction λ, that is in equation (5.96), since the saturation magnetostriction constants are related to the magnetoelastic coupling constants by the equations (5.97). Thus

$$K_0' = -\tfrac{1}{2}C_{11}[B_0(3B_0 + 2B_1 + 2B_4) + (B_1 + B_4)^2]$$
$$- C_{12}B_0(3B_0 + 2B_1 + 2B_4),$$

$$K_1' = C_{11}[B_0(2B_4 - 3B_3) + B_1(B_1 - B_3 + 3B_4) - B_4(B_3 - 2B_4)]$$
$$+ C_{12}[2B_0(2B_4 - 3B_3) - (B_1 + B_4)(B_1 + 2B_3)]$$
$$- \tfrac{1}{2}C_{44}B_2^2, \tag{5.120}$$

$$K_2' = - C_{11}[3B_4(B_1 + B_3) + (B_4 - B_3)(4B_4 - 3B_3)]$$
$$+ C_{12}[3B_4(B_1 + B_3) + B_3(5B_4 - 6B_3)]$$
$$- \tfrac{1}{2}C_{44}(6B_2 + B_5)B_5.$$

For hexagonal crystals the symmetry relations between the elastic compliance moduli simplify the form of $V_A^0 E_A^*$ and

$$V_A^0 E_A^* = - S_{11}(V_1^{0\,2} + V_2^{0\,2} + 2V_6^{0\,2}) - S_{33}V_3^{0\,2}$$
$$- 2S_{12}(V_1^0 V_2^0 - V_6^{0\,2}) - 2S_{13}(V_1^0 + V_2^0)V_3^0$$
$$- S_{44}(V_4^{0\,2} + V_5^{0\,2}), \tag{5.121}$$

whilst the V_A^0 are given by (5.104), that is, to fourth order in the α_i, by

$$V_1^0 = L_0 + L_1\alpha_1^2 + L_2\alpha_2^2,$$
$$V_2^0 = L_0 + L_1\alpha_2^2 + L_2\alpha_1^2,$$
$$V_3^0 = M_0 + M_1(\alpha_1^2 + \alpha_2^2), \tag{5.122}$$
$$V_4^0 = N_0\alpha_2\alpha_3, \qquad V_5^0 = N_0\alpha_3\alpha_1,$$
$$V_6^0 = (L_1 - L_2)\alpha_1\alpha_2.$$

Thus if equation (5.17) for the total magnetic anisotropy energy density is written in the form

$$V = V^0 + \tfrac{1}{2}V_A^0 E_A^* = (K_0^0 + K_0') + (K_1^0 + K_1') \sin^2\theta$$
$$+ (K_2^0 + K_2') \sin^4\theta, \qquad (5.123)$$

where

$$V^0 = K_0^0 + K_1^0 \sin^2\theta + K_2^0 \sin^4\theta, \qquad (5.124)$$

then the constants K_0', K_1' and K_2' are given by

$$K_0' = - (S_{11} + S_{12})L_0^2 - 2S_{13}L_0M_0 - \tfrac{1}{2}S_{33}M_0^2,$$

$$K_1' = - (S_{11} + S_{12})(L_1 + L_2)L_0 - S_{13}[2L_0M_1 + (L_1 + L_2)M_0]$$
$$- S_{33}M_0M_1 - \tfrac{1}{2}S_{44}N_0^2, \qquad (5.125)$$

$$K_2' = - \tfrac{1}{2}S_{11}(L_1^2 + L_2^2) - S_{12}L_1L_2 - S_{13}(L_1 + L_2)M_1$$
$$- \tfrac{1}{2}S_{33}M_1^2 + \tfrac{1}{2}S_{44}N_0^2.$$

The quantities K_0', K_1' and K_2' may, alternatively, be expressed in terms of the saturation magnetostriction constants $R_0, \ldots R_5$ occurring in the expression for the spontaneous magnetostriction λ, that is [vide (5.106)] in the equation

$$\lambda = R_0 + R_1\beta_3^2 + (R_2 + R_3\beta_3^2)(1 - \alpha_3^2)$$
$$+ [R_4\alpha_3\beta_3 + R_5(\alpha_1\beta_1 + \alpha_2\beta_2)](\alpha_1\beta_1 + \alpha_2\beta_2), \qquad (5.126)$$

since the saturation magnetostriction constants are related to the magnetoelastic coupling constants by the equations

$$R_0 = - L_0(S_{11} + S_{12}) - M_0S_{13},$$

$$R_1 = L_0(S_{11} + S_{12}) - (2L_0 - M_0)S_{13} - M_0S_{33},$$

$$R_2 = - L_2S_{11} - L_1S_{12} - M_1S_{13}, \qquad (5.127)$$

$$R_3 = L_2S_{11} + L_1S_{12} - (L_1 + L_2 - M_1)S_{13} - M_1S_{33},$$

$$R_4 = -N_0S_{44}, \qquad R_5 = -(L_1 - L_2)(S_{11} - S_{12}).$$

Thus,

$$K_0' = -(C_{11} + C_{12})R_0^2 - 2C_{13}R_0(R_0 + R_1) - \tfrac{1}{2}C_{33}(R_0 + R_1)^2,$$

$$\begin{aligned}
K_1' = &-(C_{11} + C_{12})\, R_0(2R_2 + R_5) \\
&- C_{13}[2R_0(R_2 + R_3) + (R_0 + R_1)\,(2R_2 + R_5)] \\
&- C_{33}(R_0 + R_1)\,(R_2 + R_3) - \tfrac{1}{2}C_{44}R_4^2,
\end{aligned} \qquad (5.128)$$

$$\begin{aligned}
K_2' = &-\tfrac{1}{2}C_{11}(2R_2^2 + 2R_2R_5 + R_5^2) - C_{12}R_2(R_2 + R_5) \\
&- C_{13}(R_2 + R_3)\,(2R_2 + R_5) - \tfrac{1}{2}C_{33}(R_2 + R_3)^2 \\
&+ \tfrac{1}{2}C_{44}R_4^2.
\end{aligned}$$

In order to obtain estimates of the magnitudes of the quantities K_1' and K_2', it is necessary to know the values of the magneto-striction constants B_0, ... B_5 or R_0, ... R_5. For hexagonal materials the constants R_0, ... R_5 have been measured for cobalt†. For cubic crystals the constants B_1 and B_2 have been measured for a large number of materials, but to obtain an estimate even of K_1' requires the values of the higher-order coefficients B_3 and B_4. The constants B_1, ... B_5 have been evaluated only for nickel, natural and synthetic magnetite and for a 78% nickel–iron alloy. The constant B_0 cannot be measured in a magnetostriction experiment because it is the coefficient of a term of zero order in the α_i and it is therefore associated with the isotropic change in volume that accompanies the appearance of the spontaneous magnetization. The most obvious method of evaluating the constant B_0 is to measure the thermal expansion of the crystal over a temperature range which includes the Curie point. The deformation of the crystal associated with the appearance of the spontaneous magnetization may then be seen superimposed on the normal thermal expansion. Measurements on polycrystals may also be

† These constants have also been measured for gadolinium (BOZORTH and WAKIYAMA [1962]; WAKIYAMA and BOZORTH [1962]). However, the Curie point of gadolinium is very near room temperature and many of the coefficients R_0, ... R_5 are strongly temperature dependent down to very low temperatures.

used in this way for, by a suitable averaging process, it is possible to calculate (BIRSS [1960]) the strain associated with a polycrystal in the ideal demagnetized state in which the magnetic domains are orientated equally in all directions. This quantity may then be identified with the strain, δ, associated with the *appearance* of the spontaneous magnetization. There are at least two indirect methods of estimating B_0. One which involves measuring the rate of change with magnetic field of the saturation magnetization and of the fractional change in volume of a polycrystal (LEE [1955a]) gives values of B_0 which are in general agreement with those obtained from thermal expansion measurements. A second method in which the lattice constant of a binary alloy, one component of which is the ferromagnetic metal under consideration, is measured over a range of composition which includes that of an alloy with the Curie point at room temperature (KÖSTER and SCHMIDT [1934]) gives values of B_0 which are not usually in agreement with the preceding two methods. The reason for this discrepancy is unknown. It is clear, however, from experimental data, that B_0 is usually much larger than the magnetostriction constants B_1, ... B_5 although, owing to the presence of the spontaneous magnetization even in the demagnetized state, the contribution of B_0 to λ is not normally observed and the spontaneous magnetostriction manifests itself as the much smaller anisotropic effect associated with the remaining B_i.

For nickel the elastic stiffness constants and compliance moduli are known from the work of DE KLERK and MUSGRAVE [1955]. Thus,

$$C_{11} = 2.465 \times 10^{12} \text{ dyne cm}^{-2},$$
$$C_{12} = 1.473 \times 10^{12} \text{ dyne cm}^{-2},$$
$$C_{44} = 1.247 \times 10^{12} \text{ dyne cm}^{-2},$$
$$S_{11} = \quad 0.7336 \times 10^{-12} \text{ cm}^2 \text{ dyne}^{-1},$$
$$S_{12} = -0.2744 \times 10^{-12} \text{ cm}^2 \text{ dyne}^{-1},$$
$$S_{44} = \quad 0.8019 \times 10^{-12} \text{ cm}^2 \text{ dyne}^{-1}.$$

$$(5.129)$$

The magnetostriction measurements of BOZORTH and HAMMING [1953] give

$$B_1 = -68.8 \times 10^{-6}, \qquad L_1 = 88.36 \times 10^6 \text{ dyne cm}^{-2},$$

$$B_2 = -73.0 \times 10^{-6}, \qquad L_2 = -12.67 \times 10^6 \text{ dyne cm}^{-2},$$

$$B_3 = -7.8 \times 10^{-6}, \qquad L_3 = 20.11 \times 10^6 \text{ dyne cm}^{-2},$$

$$B_4 = -7.5 \times 10^{-6}, \qquad M_0 = 91.03 \times 10^6 \text{ dyne cm}^{-2},$$

$$B_5 = 15.4 \times 10^{-6}, \qquad M_1 = -19.20 \times 10^6 \text{ dyne cm}^{-2}.$$

$$(5.130)$$

The constant B_0 is related to $\bar{\delta}$, the strain associated with the appearance of the spontaneous magnetization (i.e. the parameter characterizing the polycrystalline thermal expansion anomaly), by means of the equation

$$\bar{\delta} = B_0 + \tfrac{1}{3}B_1 + \tfrac{1}{3}B_3 + \tfrac{1}{9}B_4. \qquad (5.131)$$

Thus,

$$B_0 = \bar{\delta} + 26.367 \times 10^{-6},$$

$$(5.132)$$

$$L_0 \times 10^{-6} = -30.29 - 5.411\bar{\delta} \times 10^6.$$

The most accurate measurement of $\bar{\delta}$ is that of NIX and MACNAIR [1941] who obtained $\bar{\delta} = -3.65 \times 10^{-4}$.

Using the above data, the magnetoelastic contribution to the first anisotropy constant may be found to be

$$K_1' = -13900 \text{ erg cm}^{-3}. \qquad (5.133)$$

The measured value of the first anisotropy constant of nickel is $K_1 = K_1^0 + K_1' = -59000 \text{ erg cm}^{-3}$ (BOZORTH [1951]).

For magnetite the elastic stiffness constants and compliance moduli are known from the work of DORAISWAMI [1947]. Thus,

$$C_{11} = 2.75 \ \times 10^{12} \text{ dyne cm}^{-2},$$

$$C_{12} = 1.04 \ \times 10^{12} \text{ dyne cm}^{-2},$$

$$C_{44} = 0.955 \times 10^{12} \text{ dyne cm}^{-2},$$

$$S_{11} = \ \ \ 0.459 \times 10^{-12} \text{ cm}^2 \text{ dyne}^{-1},$$

$$S_{12} = -0.126 \times 10^{-12} \text{ cm}^2 \text{ dyne}^{-1},$$

$$S_{44} = \ \ \ 1.047 \times 10^{-12} \text{ cm}^2 \text{ dyne}^{-1}.$$

(5.134)

There is a considerable difference between the magnetostrictive behaviour of natural and synthetic magnetite (BICKFORD, PAPPIS and STULL [1955]). For natural crystals of magnetite,

$$B_1 = \ \ \ -15.3 \times 10^{-6}, \quad L_1 = \ \ \ \ \ 82.78 \times 10^6 \text{ dyne cm}^{-2},$$

$$B_2 = \ \ \ 284.8 \times 10^{-6}, \quad L_2 = \ \ -40.04 \times 10^6 \text{ dyne cm}^{-2},$$

$$B_3 = \ \ \ -15.9 \times 10^{-6}, \quad L_3 = \ \ \ \ \ 56.63 \times 10^6 \text{ dyne cm}^{-2},$$

$$B_4 = \ \ \ \ \ -9.7 \times 10^{-6}, \quad M_0 = -272.02 \times 10^6 \text{ dyne cm}^{-2},$$

$$B_5 = \ \ -101.0 \times 10^{-6}, \quad M_1 = \ \ \ \ \ 96.47 \times 10^6 \text{ dyne cm}^{-2},$$

(5.135a)

whilst for synthetic crystals

$$B_1 = \ \ \ -24.5 \times 10^{-6}, \quad L_1 = \ \ \ \ \ 49.22 \times 10^6 \text{ dyne cm}^{-2},$$

$$B_2 = \ \ \ 246.6 \times 10^{-6}, \quad L_2 = \ \ \ \ \ \ 0.80 \times 10^6 \text{ dyne cm}^{-2},$$

$$B_3 = \ \ \ -3.57 \times 10^{-6}, \quad L_3 = \ \ \ \ \ \ 7.34 \times 10^6 \text{ dyne cm}^{-2},$$

$$B_4 = \ \ \ -4.76 \times 10^{-6}, \quad M_0 = -235.53 \times 10^6 \text{ dyne cm}^{-2},$$

$$B_5 = \ \ \ -40.2 \times 10^{-6}, \quad M_1 = \ \ \ \ \ 38.40 \times 10^6 \text{ dyne cm}^{-2}.$$

(5.135b)

The quantity B_0 may be obtained from $\bar{\delta}$, the parameter characterizing the thermal expansion anomaly, in exactly the same way as
for nickel. For natural crystals of magnetite the thermal expansion anomaly has been studied by CHEVENARD [1921a]. Slightly
different curves are obtained for increasing and decreasing temperatures but in both cases $\bar{\delta}$ is approximately -6.0×10^{-4}. For
synthetic crystals the thermal expansion anomaly has been meas-
ured by CHAUDRON and FORESTIER [1924]: four curves are presented which differ significantly between themselves but are all in
general agreement with Chevenard's results on natural single
crystals. Thus for natural crystals

$$B_0 = \bar{\delta} + 11.478 \times 10^{-6},$$
$$L_0 \times 10^{-6} = -29.436 - 4.831\bar{\delta} \times 10^6, \tag{5.136a}$$

whilst for synthetic crystals

$$B_0 = \bar{\delta} + 9.886 \times 10^{-6},$$
$$L_0 \times 10^{-6} = -17.311 - 4.813\bar{\delta} \times 10^6. \tag{5.136b}$$

Using the above data, the magnetoelastic contribution to the
first anisotropy constant may be found to be

$$K_1' = -119100 \text{ erg cm}^{-3} \tag{5.137a}$$

for natural crystals, and

$$K_1' = -31000 \text{ erg cm}^{-3} \tag{5.137b}$$

for synthetic crystals. The measured value of the first anisotropy
constant, $K_1 = K_1^0 + K_1'$, of magnetite may be obtained from the
ferromagnetic resonance measurements of BICKFORD [1949b]. Resonance absorption measurements on synthetic magnetite crystals
at 8923 Mc/sec gave a value for this constant of -112000 erg cm^{-3},
whilst measurements at 23957 Mc/sec gave -111000 erg cm^{-3}.
These measurements, which are accurate to 2%, are in excellent

agreement with the earlier results of BICKFORD [1949a] and SNOEK [1947] on natural crystals of magnetite.

The constants B_1, ... B_5 have been measured for 78% Ni–Fe alloy and, with the exception of B_1 ($= 20.9 \times 10^{-6}$) they are all only a few times 10^{-6}. The thermal expansion anomalies of the nickel–iron alloys have been studied by CHEVENARD [1921b], but estimates of $\bar{\delta}$ are subject to considerable uncertainty near the composition range in which the thermal expansion anomaly changes sign. It would appear that $\bar{\delta}$ changes sign for an alloy with a composition fairly close to 78% nickel–iron: the figure obtained by CHEVENARD [1921b] is 84%, but this is, of necessity, rather approximate. In view of the fact that the measured first anisotropy constant also vanishes at about this composition it is not considered possible to evaluate K_1' with any accuracy. It seems highly probable, however, that K_1' and $K_1 = K_1^0 + K_1'$ both vanish in the region of 78% nickel–iron.

For cobalt the elastic stiffness constants and compliance moduli are known from the work of MCSKIMIN et al. [1954]. Thus

$$C_{11} = 3.071 \times 10^{12} \text{ dyne cm}^{-2},$$

$$C_{12} = 1.650 \times 10^{12} \text{ dyne cm}^{-2},$$

$$C_{13} = 1.027 \times 10^{12} \text{ dyne cm}^{-2},$$

$$C_{33} = 3.581 \times 10^{12} \text{ dyne cm}^{-2},$$

$$C_{44} = 0.755 \times 10^{12} \text{ dyne cm}^{-2},$$

$$\text{(5.138)}$$

$$S_{11} = 0.4731 \times 10^{-12} \text{ cm}^2 \text{ dyne}^{-1},$$

$$S_{12} = -0.2311 \times 10^{-12} \text{ cm}^2 \text{ dyne}^{-1},$$

$$S_{13} = -0.0694 \times 10^{-12} \text{ cm}^2 \text{ dyne}^{-1},$$

$$S_{33} = 0.3191 \times 10^{-12} \text{ cm}^2 \text{ dyne}^{-1},$$

$$S_{44} = 1.3245 \times 10^{-12} \text{ cm}^2 \text{ dyne}^{-1}.$$

The magnetostriction measurements of BOZORTH and SHERWOOD [1954] and BOZORTH [1954] give

$$R_2 = -95 \times 10^{-6}, \quad L_1 = 182.1 \times 10^6 \text{ dyne cm}^{-2},$$
$$R_3 = 205 \times 10^{-6}, \quad L_2 = 253.1 \times 10^6 \text{ dyne cm}^{-2},$$
$$R_4 = -456 \times 10^{-6}, \quad N_0 = 351.1 \times 10^6 \text{ dyne cm}^{-2},$$
$$R_5 = 50 \times 10^{-6}, \quad M_1 = -250.0 \times 10^6 \text{ dyne cm}^{-2}.$$

$$(5.139)$$

The constants R_0 and R_1 are related to $\bar{\delta}$ by means of the equation

$$\bar{\delta} = R_0 + \tfrac{1}{3}R_1. \qquad (5.140)$$

whilst the constants R_0, R_1 and L_0, M_0 are inter-related by means of the equations

$$L_0 \times 10^{-6} = -5.748R_0 \times 10^6 - 1.0269R_1 \times 10^6,$$
$$M_0 \times 10^{-6} = -5.634R_0 \times 10^6 - 3.580R_1 \times 10^6.$$

$$(5.141)$$

However, the relative importance of the two constants R_0 and R_1 is at present unknown and can, of course, only be determined from measurements on single crystals. Further, the quantity $\bar{\delta}$ cannot be estimated directly due to the existence of a phase change between room temperature and the Curie point. The value $\bar{\delta} = -7.7 \times 10^{-3}$ quoted by CARR [1959], obtained by KÖSTER and SCHMIDT [1934], apparently refers to the cubic γ-phase.

Although the calculations given above indicate that the magnetoelastic contribution to the anisotropy energy – defined as the difference between the anisotropy energy at zero stress and at zero strain – is considerable, it should be emphasized that this contribution is large principally because the thermal expansion anomaly, and hence L_0, is large since the state of zero strain has been

arbitrarily chosen to be that in which there are no magnetic interactions to deform the crystal. Thus, for example, if the magnetoelastic contribution to the anisotropy energy density of nickel is
expressed as the sum of $(K_1')_1$, the quantity obtained by setting
$L_0 = 0$ in K_1', and $(K_1')_2 = K_1' - (K_1')_1$, it may readily be shown
that $(K_1')_1 = 2420 \text{ erg cm}^{-3}$ whilst $(K_1')_2 = -16320 \text{ erg cm}^{-3}$.
Taking L_0 to be zero is equivalent to referring strains, not to an
unstrained lattice for which $E_A = 0$, but to a lattice that exhibits
an isotropic volume strain of magnitude

$$E_1 + E_2 + E_3 = -3S_{11}L_0 \simeq 3\bar{\delta}. \qquad (5.142)$$

Since both lattices are cubic it is slightly artificial to regard K_1' as
the magnetoelastic contribution to the anisotropy energy density
rather than, for example, $(K_1')_1$. However, the retention of L_0 in
equation (5.119) is of physical significance for, when the variation
of anisotropy with temperature is considered (§ 3.4), it will be
seen that the temperature dependence of anisotropy may be pro-
foundly modified by the large and rapid variation of L_0 with
temperature near the Curie point.

§ 3.4. *The Temperature Dependence of Magnetostriction and of Magnetocrystalline Anisotropy*

In order to determine the temperature dependence of the magnetoelastic coupling constants by an averaging process similar to that
employed in § 2.4, it is first necessary to ensure that the quantities
to be averaged refer to crystalline lattices which are strained to the
same extent. At temperature T, the magnetic energy is given (for
small strains) by

$$V'(T) = V^0(T) + V_A^0(T)E_A, \qquad (5.143)$$

whilst, for $T = 0$,

$$V'(0) = V^0(0) + V_A^0(0)E_A, \qquad (5.144)$$

the coefficients V^0 and V_A^0 being strain-independent functions of the α_i. Although the state of zero strain has been defined as that in which there are no magnetic interactions to deform the crystal, this state will not be the same for temperature T as for $T = 0$ because of the effect of thermal expansion. If, at all temperatures, values of strain are referred to the state in which the magnetic interactions have been annihilated *at 0°K*, as determined, for example, by extrapolation of the curve of normal (non-magnetic) thermal expansion from above the Curie point to $T = 0$, then the E_A in (5.144) must be replaced by $E_A - \varepsilon_A$ where $\varepsilon_A = \varepsilon_A(T)$ are the strain components which represent the normal (extrapolated) thermal expansion. The existence of thermal expansion also indicates that it is necessary to alter the zero of the elastic energy term so that, at temperature T,

$$U(T, E_A) = \tfrac{1}{2}C_{AB}(E_A - \varepsilon_A)(E_B - \varepsilon_B), \qquad (5.145)$$

$$V'(T, E_A) = V^0(T) + V_A^0(T)(E_A - \varepsilon_A), \qquad (5.146)$$

whilst, for $T = 0$,

$$U(0, E_A) = \tfrac{1}{2}C_{AB}E_AE_B, \qquad (5.147)$$

$$V'(0, E_A) = V^0(0) + V_A^0(0)E_A, \qquad (5.148)$$

as before.

In §§ 3.1 to 3.3 the thermal expansion was ignored, it being assumed that the $\varepsilon_A(T)$ could subsequently be added to the E_A, where necessary. This is justified since minimization of $U(T, E_A) + V'(T, E_A)$ shows that the equilibrium values of strain are given by

$$E_A^{eq} = -S_{AB}V_B^0 + \varepsilon_A = E_A^* + \varepsilon_A, \qquad (5.149)$$

whilst the difference between the anisotropy energy density at zero stress and at zero strain is merely larger by $V_A^0\varepsilon_A$ than that given by (5.114). However, in determining the temperature dependence of the magnetic energy, V', equations (5.146) and (5.148) must be used in comparing crystals which are strained to the same extent at temperatures T and 0. Thus the value of

$$V'(T, E_A) = V^0(T) + V_A^0(T)(E_A - \varepsilon_A) \qquad (5.150)$$

must be equated to the appropriate average value of

$$V'(0, E_A) = V^0(0) + V_A^0(0)E_A. \qquad (5.151)$$

Since such an equation must hold for various fixed values of the E_A including $E_A = 0$, it follows that the average value of $V_A^0(0)$ must be equated to $V_A^0(T)$ whilst the average value of $V^0(0)$ must be equated not to $V^0(T)$ but to $V^0(T) - V_A^0(T)\varepsilon_A(T)$. Thus, if $V^0(T)$ and $V_A^0(T)$ are expressed in the forms

$$V^0(T) = \sum_{n=0}^{\infty} \left[k_{2n,0}^0(T)\, P_{2n}(\cos\theta) + \sum_{m=1}^{2n} (k_{2n,m}^0(T) \cos m\phi \right.$$
$$\left. + k_{2n,-m}^0(T) \sin m\phi)\, P_{2n}^m(\cos\theta) \right], \qquad (5.152)$$
and

$$V_A^0(T) = \sum_{n=0}^{\infty} \left[k_{2n,0}^A(T)\, P_{2n}(\cos\theta) + \sum_{m=1}^{2n} (k_{2n,m}^A(T) \cos m\phi \right.$$
$$\left. + k_{2n,-m}^A(T) \sin m\phi)\, P_{2n}^m(\cos\theta) \right], \qquad (5.153)$$

then an averaging process such as that indicated in equation (5.58) leads to [cf. equation (5.63)]

$$\frac{k_{2n,m}^A(T)}{k_{2n,m}^A(0)} = (\zeta')^{n(2n+1)} \qquad (5.154)$$
and

$$\frac{k_{2n,m}^0(T) - \varepsilon[k_{2n,m}^1(T) + k_{2n,m}^2(T) + k_{2n,m}^3(T)]}{k_{2n,m}^0(0)} = (\zeta')^{n(2n+1)}, \qquad (5.155)$$

the substitution $\varepsilon = \varepsilon_1 = \varepsilon_2 = \varepsilon_3$ having been made since thermal expansion is an isotropic volume strain (of magnitude 3ε).

Equations (5.154) may be used directly to predict the temperature dependence of the magnetoelastic coupling constants. Thus, for example, for cubic crystals the V_A^0 of (5.116) may be written in terms of surface spherical harmonics – that is in terms of the $Y_{n,m}$ of (5.26) – as follows:

$$V_1^0 = \tfrac{1}{15}(15L_0 + 5L_1 + 3L_2 + L_3)Y_{0,0} - \tfrac{1}{21}(7L_1 + 6L_2 - L_3)Y_{2,0}$$
$$+ \tfrac{1}{42}(7L_1 + 6L_2 - L_3)Y_{2,2} + \tfrac{1}{35}(3L_2 - 4L_3)Y_{4,0}$$
$$- \tfrac{1}{105}(L_2 + L_3)Y_{4,2} + \tfrac{1}{840}L_2 Y_{4,4},$$

$$V_2^0 = \tfrac{1}{15}(15L_0 + 5L_1 + 3L_2 + L_3)Y_{0,0} - \tfrac{1}{21}(7L_1 + 6L_2 - L_3)Y_{2,0}$$
$$- \tfrac{1}{42}(7L_1 + 6L_2 - L_3)Y_{2,2} + \tfrac{1}{35}(3L_2 - 4L_3)Y_{4,0}$$
$$+ \tfrac{1}{105}(L_2 + L_3)Y_{4,2} + \tfrac{1}{840}L_2 Y_{4,4},$$

$$V_3^0 = \tfrac{1}{15}(15L_0 + 5L_1 + 3L_2 + L_3)Y_{0,0} \qquad\qquad (5.156)$$
$$+ \tfrac{2}{21}(7L_1 + 6L_2 - L_3)Y_{2,0} + \tfrac{1}{35}(8L_2 + L_3)Y_{4,0}$$
$$- \tfrac{1}{840}L_3 Y_{4,4},$$

$$V_4^0 = \tfrac{1}{21}(7M_0 + M_1)Y_{2,-1} - \tfrac{1}{70}M_1 Y_{4,-1} + \tfrac{1}{420}M_1 Y_{4,-3},$$

$$V_5^0 = \tfrac{1}{21}(7M_0 + M_1)Y_{2,1} - \tfrac{1}{70}M_1 Y_{4,1} - \tfrac{1}{420}M_1 Y_{4,3},$$

$$V_6^0 = \tfrac{1}{42}(7M_0 + M_1)Y_{2,-2} + \tfrac{1}{105}M_1 Y_{4,-2}.$$

It therefore follows from (5.154) that

$$7L_1(T) + 6L_2(T) + L_3(T) = [7L_1(0) + 6L_2(0) + L_3(0)]\,(\zeta')^3,$$
$$L_2(T) = L_2(0)\,(\zeta')^{10},$$
$$L_3(T) = L_3(0)\,(\zeta')^{10}, \qquad\qquad (5.157)$$
$$7M_0(T) + M_1(T) = [7M_0(0) + M_1(0)]\,(\zeta')^3,$$
$$M_1(T) = M_1(0)\,(\zeta')^{10}.$$

(Again, as in § 2.4, the coefficient of $Y_{0,0}$ may not be included in relations of this type.)

Equations (5.157) may be rearranged to give

$$L_1(T) = [L_1(0) + \tfrac{6}{7}L_2(0) + \tfrac{1}{7}L_3(0)](\zeta')^3 - [\tfrac{6}{7}L_2(0) + \tfrac{1}{7}L_3(0)](\zeta')^{10},$$

$$L_2(T) = L_2(0)\,(\zeta')^{10},$$

$$L_3(T) = L_3(0)\,(\zeta')^{10}, \tag{5.158}$$

$$M_0(T) = [M_0(0) + \tfrac{1}{7}M_1(0)]\,(\zeta')^3 - \tfrac{1}{7}M_1(0)\,(\zeta')^{10},$$

$$M_1(T) = M_1(0)\,(\zeta')^{10}.$$

For hexagonal crystals, the V_A^0 of (5.104) may be written (with $N_0 = 2N_0' = 2N_0''$ and $N_1 = 2N_1' = 2N_1''$) in terms of spherical harmonics as follows:

$$
\begin{aligned}
V_1^0 = {}& \tfrac{1}{3}(3L_0 + L_1 + L_2 + 3L_4 + 3L_5)Y_{0,0} \\
& - \tfrac{1}{21}(7L_1 + 7L_2 - L_4 - L_5)Y_{2,0} \\
& + \tfrac{1}{42}(7L_1 - 7L_2 - 6L_3 - L_4 + L_5)Y_{2,2} \\
& - \tfrac{4}{35}(L_4 + L_5)Y_{4,0} + \tfrac{1}{105}(L_3 - L_4 + L_5)Y_{4,2} \\
& - \tfrac{1}{210}L_3 Y_{4,4},
\end{aligned}
$$

$$
\begin{aligned}
V_2^0 = {}& \tfrac{1}{3}(3L_0 + L_1 + L_2 + 3L_4 + 3L_5)Y_{0,0} \\
& - \tfrac{1}{21}(7L_1 + 7L_2 - L_4 - L_5)Y_{2,0} \\
& - \tfrac{1}{42}(7L_1 - 7L_2 - 6L_3 - L_4 + L_5)Y_{2,2} \\
& - \tfrac{4}{35}(L_4 + L_5)Y_{4,0} - \tfrac{1}{105}(L_3 - L_4 + L_5)Y_{4,2} \\
& + \tfrac{1}{210}L_3 Y_{4,4},
\end{aligned}
\tag{5.159}
$$

$$
\begin{aligned}
V_3^0 = {}& \tfrac{1}{15}(15M_0 + 10M_1 + 2M_2)Y_{0,0} - \tfrac{2}{21}(7M_1 - M_2)Y_{2,0} \\
& - \tfrac{8}{35}M_2 Y_{4,0},
\end{aligned}
$$

$$V_4^0 = \tfrac{1}{21}(7N_0 + 3N_1)Y_{2,-1} + \tfrac{2}{35}N_1 Y_{4,-1},$$

$$V_5^0 = \tfrac{1}{21}(7N_0 + 3N_1)Y_{2,1} + \tfrac{2}{35}N_1 Y_{4,1},$$

$$
\begin{aligned}
V_6^0 = {}& \tfrac{1}{42}(7L_1 - 7L_2 - 6L_3 - L_4 + L_5)Y_{2,-2} \\
& + \tfrac{1}{105}(L_3 - L_4 + L_5)Y_{4,-2} + \tfrac{1}{210}L_3 Y_{4,-4}.
\end{aligned}
$$

It therefore follows from (5.154) that

$$7L_1(T) + 7L_2(T) - L_4(T) - L_5(T)$$
$$= [7L_1(0) + 7L_2(0) - L_4(0) - L_5(0)] (\zeta')^3,$$

$$7L_1(T) - 7L_2(T) - 6L_3(T) - L_4(T) + L_5(T)$$
$$= [7L_1(0) - 7L_2(0) - 6L_3(0) - L_4(0) + L_5(0)] (\zeta')^3,$$

$$L_3(T) = L_3(0) (\zeta')^{10},$$

$$L_4(T) = L_4(0) (\zeta')^{10}, \tag{5.160}$$

$$L_5(T) = L_5(0) (\zeta')^{10},$$

$$7M_1(T) - M_2(T) = [7M_1(0) - M_2(0)] (\zeta')^3,$$

$$M_2(T) = M_2(0) (\zeta')^{10},$$

$$7N_0(T) + 3N_1(T) = [7N_0(0) + 3N_1(0)] (\zeta')^3,$$

$$N_1(T) = N_1(0) (\zeta')^{10},$$

which may be rearranged to give

$$L_1(T) = [L_1(0) - \tfrac{3}{7}L_3(0) - \tfrac{1}{7}L_4(0)] (\zeta')^3$$
$$+ \tfrac{3}{7}L_3(0) (\zeta')^{10} + \tfrac{1}{7}L_4(0) (\zeta')^{10},$$

$$L_2(T) = [L_2(0) + \tfrac{3}{7}L_3(0) - \tfrac{1}{7}L_5(0)] (\zeta')^3 - \tfrac{3}{7}L_3(0) (\zeta')^{10}$$
$$+ \tfrac{1}{7}L_5(0) (\zeta')^{10},$$

$$L_3(T) = L_3(0) (\zeta')^{10},$$

$$L_4(T) = L_4(0) (\zeta')^{10}, \tag{5.161}$$

$$L_5(T) = L_5(0) (\zeta')^{10},$$

$$M_1(T) = [M_1(0) - \tfrac{1}{7}M_2(0)] (\zeta')^3 + \tfrac{1}{7}M_2(0) (\zeta')^{10},$$

$$M_2(T) = M_2(0) (\zeta')^{10},$$

$$N_0(T) = [N_0(0) + \tfrac{3}{7}N_1(0)] (\zeta')^3 - \tfrac{3}{7}N_1(0) (\zeta')^{10},$$

$$N_1(T) = N_1(0) (\zeta')^{10}.$$

Equation (5.161) has not been verified by direct experiment but, for nickel, (5.158) appears to be in reasonable agreement with experiment (LEE and BIRSS [1961]; CALLEN and CALLEN [1963]). In addition, CLARK, DESAVAGE, COLEMAN and CALLEN [1963] have shown that an extension of the theory to cover cubic ferrimagnetics is in excellent agreement with measurements on yttrium iron garnet.

The temperature dependence of the anisotropy constants may be obtained from (5.155). For example, for cubic crystals [using (5.30)],

$$\frac{[K_1^0(T) + \frac{1}{11}K_2^0(T)] - [L_3(T) - 2L_2(T)]\varepsilon}{K_1^0(0) + \frac{1}{11}K_2^0(0)} = (\zeta')^{10}, \qquad (5.162)$$

and, neglecting magnetoelastic coupling constants of higher order,

$$\frac{K_2^0(T)}{K_2^0(0)} = (\zeta')^{21}, \qquad (5.163)$$

so that

$$K_1^0(T) - [L_3(T) - 2L_2(T)]\varepsilon$$
$$= [K_1^0(0) + \tfrac{1}{11}K_2^0(0)] (\zeta')^{10} - \tfrac{1}{11}K_2^0(0) (\zeta')^{21}. \qquad (5.164)$$

If $K_2^0(0)$ is neglected in favour of $K_1^0(0)$, (5.164) reduces to the equation

$$K_1^0(T) = K_1^0(0) (\zeta')^{10} + [L_3(T) - 2L_2(T)]\varepsilon, \qquad (5.165)$$

in which the quantity $[L_3(T) - 2L_2(T)]$ may be obtained from measurements of the pressure dependence of the observed anisotropy constant, $K_1(T) = K_1^0(T) + K_1'(T)$, since (BECKER and DÖRING [1939])

$$\frac{\partial K_1(T)}{\partial \varepsilon} = L_3(T) - 2L_2(T). \qquad (5.166)$$

Alternatively, the temperature dependence of $L_2(T)$ and $L_3(T)$ may be obtained from (5.158) and $K_1^0(T)$ written in the form

$$K_1^0(T) = \{[K_1^0(0) + \tfrac{1}{11}K_2^0(0)] + [L_3(0) - 2L_2(0)]\varepsilon\} (\zeta')^{10}$$

$$- \tfrac{1}{11}K_2^0(0) (\zeta')^{21}. \tag{5.167}$$

The observed first anisotropy constant is, of course, not $K_1^0(T)$ but $K_1(T) = K_1^0(T) + K_1'(T)$, where $K_1'(T)$ is given by (5.119). Since this expression for $K_1'(T)$ involves products of pairs of magneto-elastic coupling constants it may be seen, from (5.158), that it may be expressed linearly in terms of $L_0(T)(\zeta')^{10}$, $(\zeta')^6$, $(\zeta')^{13}$ and $(\zeta')^{20}$. However, by far the largest term in $K_1'(T)$ is

$$(K_1')_2 = (S_{11} + 2S_{12})L_0(T) [2L_2(T) - L_3(T)]$$

$$= (S_{11} + 2S_{12})L_0(T) [2L_2(0) - L_3(0)] (\zeta')^{10}. \tag{5.168}$$

It is instructive to consider this equation in relation to the point made in § 3.3 that the size of the magnetoelastic contribution to the anisotropy can be altered by changing the zero to which measurements of strain are referred. If $(S_{11} + 2S_{12})L_0(T)$ were independent of temperature the separation of $K_1(T)$ into two parts, $K_1^0(T)$ and $K_1'(T)$, would have little physical significance, the temperature dependence of both parts being primarily that of $(\zeta')^{10}$. Indeed (5.168) would then be approximately equal to $K_1'(0) (\zeta')^{10}$ and equations (5.165) and (5.168) could be combined to give

$$K_1(T) = K_1^0(T) + K_1'(T)$$

$$= K_1^0(0) (\zeta')^{10} + [L_3(T) - 2L_2(T)]\varepsilon + K_1'(0) (\zeta')^{10}$$

$$= K_1(0) (\zeta')^{10} + \frac{\partial K_1(T)}{\partial \varepsilon} \varepsilon, \tag{5.169}$$

which is exactly analogous to (5.76). At low temperatures, $(S_{11} + 2S_{12})L_0(T)$ is approximately independent of temperature, but near the Curie point L_0 exhibits a large and rapid variation with temperature and the formulation given above is to be preferred.

§ 3.5. *Magnetostriction below Saturation*

In those cases (discussed in § 2.5) in which the detailed distribution of the domains in a crystal is known as a function of the applied magnetic field, it is possible to calculate the magnetostrictive deformation of the crystal by assuming that the resultant strain may be obtained by algebraic addition of the strains within the individual domains after multiplication by weighting factors proportional to their volumes. It is usual to express the magnetostriction, $\lambda = \lambda(\eta)$, as a function of η, the ratio of the intensity of magnetization to its saturation value, and to use the second-order form of equation (5.96), that is

$$\lambda = C_0 + C_1 S(\alpha_1^2 \beta_1^2) + C_2 S(\alpha_1 \alpha_2 \beta_1 \beta_2). \qquad (5.170)$$

The first approach to this problem was made by AKULOV [1931] who evaluated $\lambda(\eta)$ for iron magnetized in the three principal directions. The ternary axis is a particularly simple case since the movement of 90° domain boundaries cannot contribute to the magnetostriction because of the symmetry of the direction of observation. Since equation (5.170) is even in all the α_i, 180° boundary movements give rise to no magnetostriction. Thus $\lambda(\eta) = 0$ below the knee of the magnetization curve at $\eta = 1/\sqrt{3}$. Thereafter magnetization proceeds by domain vector rotation only and $\lambda(\eta)$ is given by the expression displayed in Table 12. In the direction of a binary axis Akulov obtained an expression for λ for the region of domain vector rotation and the calculation was extended to the region of boundary movements by assuming that 90° boundary

TABLE 12

	Quaternary axis	Binary axis	Ternary axis
Region of boundary movements: method of Heisenberg	$\lambda = \frac{3}{4}C_1\left[\sqrt{(1+3\eta^2)}-1\right]$ for $0 \leqq \eta \leqq 1$	$\lambda = \frac{1}{8}C_1\left[2-\sqrt{(4-6\eta^2)}\right]$ for $0 \leqq \eta \leqq 1/\sqrt{2}$	$\lambda = 0$ for $0 \leqq \eta \leqq 1/\sqrt{3}$
Region of boundary movements: method of Akulov	$\lambda = 0$ for $0 \leqq \eta \leqq \frac{1}{3}$, $\lambda = \frac{1}{2}C_1(3\eta-1)$ for $\frac{1}{3} \leqq \eta \leqq 1$	$\lambda = 0$ for $0 \leqq \eta \leqq \frac{1}{3}\sqrt{2}$, $\lambda = C_1(3\eta-\sqrt{2})/3\sqrt{2}$ for $\frac{1}{3}\sqrt{2} \leqq \eta \leqq 1/\sqrt{2}$	$\lambda = 0$ for $0 \leqq \eta \leqq 1/\sqrt{3}$
Region of domain vector rotation	—	$\lambda = \frac{1}{8}C_1 + \frac{1}{4}C_2(2\eta^2-1)$ for $1/\sqrt{2} \leqq \eta \leqq 1$	$\lambda = \frac{1}{6}C_2(3\eta^2-1)$ for $1/\sqrt{3} \leqq \eta \leqq 1$

TABLE 13

	Quaternary axis	Binary axis	Ternary axis
Region of boundary movements: method of Heisenberg	$\lambda = 0$ for $0 \leqq \eta \leqq 1/\sqrt{3}$	$\lambda = \frac{1}{4}C_2\eta^2$ for $0 \leqq \eta \leqq \sqrt{2}/\sqrt{3}$	$\lambda = \frac{1}{3}C_2\eta^2$ for $0 \leqq \eta \leqq 1$
Region of boundary movements: method of Akulov	$\lambda = 0$ for $0 \leqq \eta \leqq 1/\sqrt{3}$	$\lambda = 0$ for $0 \leqq \eta \leqq 1/\sqrt{8}$, $\lambda = C_2 \dfrac{2\sqrt{6}\,\eta - \sqrt{3}}{6(4-\sqrt{3})}$ for $1/\sqrt{8} \leqq \eta \leqq \sqrt{2}/\sqrt{3}$	$\lambda = 0$ for $0 \leqq \eta \leqq \frac{1}{4}$, $\lambda = \frac{1}{18} C_2 (4\eta - 1)$ for $\frac{1}{4} \leqq \eta \leqq \frac{5}{8}$, $\lambda = \frac{1}{3} C_2 (2\eta - 1)$ for $\frac{5}{8} \leqq \eta \leqq 1$
Region of domain vector rotation	$\lambda = \frac{1}{3}C_1 (3\eta^2 - 1)$ for $1/\sqrt{3} \leqq \eta \leqq 1$	$\lambda = \frac{1}{6}C_1 (3\eta^2 - 2) + \frac{1}{4} C_2 \eta^2$ for $\sqrt{2}/\sqrt{3} \leqq \eta \leqq 1$	—

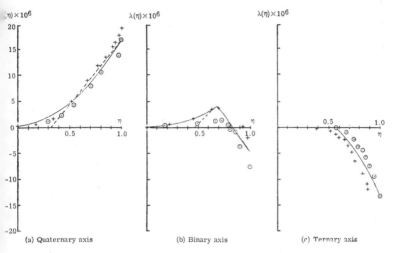

Fig. 5.6. The variation of spontaneous magnetostriction, $\lambda(\eta)$, with reduced magnetization, $\eta = I/I_s$, for single crystals of iron magnetized in the three principal crystallographic directions.

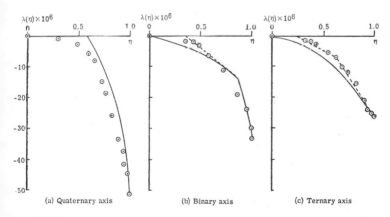

Fig. 5.7. The variation of spontaneous magnetostriction, $\lambda(\eta)$, with reduced magnetization, $\eta = I/I_s$, for single crystals of nickel magnetized in the three principal crystallographic directions.

movements occur only after the movement of 180° boundaries is completed. Thus as the magnetization proceeds, an initial region of zero magnetostriction is followed by a region in which there is a linear variation of λ with η. This method was also employed by Akulov to consider magnetization parallel to a quaternary axis (Table 12), domain vector rotation being entirely absent in this case. A comparison with the experimental data for iron is shown in Fig. 5.6. It may be seen that, in the boundary movement region, the curves of Akulov fit the observed values only approximately. The agreement with experiment is, however, much better in the region of domain vector rotation.

HEISENBERG [1931] developed an alternative approach by assuming that the order in which the boundary movements occur is deducible from a domain configuration which is governed by a statistical distribution. This assumption leads to a smooth curve for $\lambda(\eta)$ in the region of boundary movements which is in somewhat better agreement with the experimental results than the discontinuous curves of Akulov. The two approaches may be held to represent extremes between which the true situation lies. The corresponding curves of $\lambda(\eta)$ versus η are compared with experimental data in Fig. 5.6 (and, for nickel, in Fig. 5.7).

For nickel the easy directions are the ternary axes and the position is slightly more complicated. Once again the form of $\lambda(\eta)$ in the region of domain vector rotation is readily obtained (Table 13). Heisenberg's method was extended to deal with nickel by GANS and VON HARLEM [1933] and a corrected set of their equations has been reproduced by FOWLER [1936]. The corresponding calculation of $\lambda(\eta)$ by Akulov's method has appeared only more recently (AKULOV [1956]), and these expressions, together with those of Fowler, are collected in Table 13. Both sets of equations are in reasonable agreement with experiment (Fig. 5.7), especially in the regions of domain vector rotation. Thus, for both iron and nickel, the agreement between calculated and observed values is as good as can be expected. When the primary and closure domain struc-

tures can both be taken into account (LEE [1955b]) agreement
between theory and experiment is extremely close.

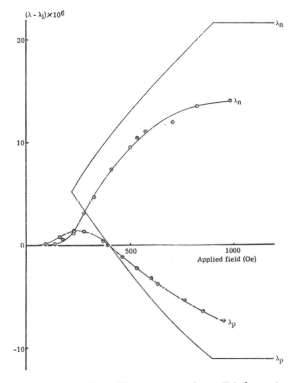

Fig. 5.8. The magnetostriction of iron measured parallel, λ_p, and normal, λ_n,
to the applied field for $\bar{\theta} = 0$ as calculated by BIRSS and LEE [1961] and as
measured by HONDA and MASIYAMA [1926].

For directions of applied magnetic field other than those of the
principal crystallographic axes, few calculations of magnetostriction have been published. This is unfortunate. for the magnetostriction is, in general, much more dependent on the detailed
domain configuration than is the bulk magnetization. BIRSS and

LEE [1961] have dealt with the case of an iron-like single crystal in the form of an oblate spheroid, for which the equatorial plane is a (001) crystallographic plane, with the magnetic field applied in any direction in this plane. They have compared the magnetostriction

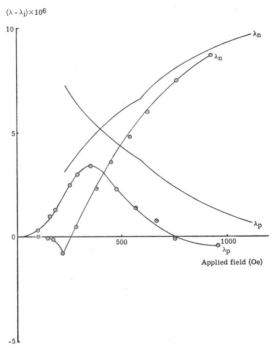

Fig. 5.9. The magnetostriction of iron measured parallel, λ_p, and normal, λ_n, to the applied field for $\bar{\theta} = 15°$ as calculated by BIRSS and LEE [1961] and as measured by HONDA and MASIYAMA [1926].

curves calculated on the basis of Lawton and Stewart's theory of magnetization curves with measurements of HONDA and MASIYAMA [1926] and of themselves. Good agreement is obtained with the latter and such discrepancies as exist can be accounted for satisfactorily. The extent of the agreement with the data of Honda and

Masiyama is shown in Figs. 5.8, 5.9 and 5.10 ($\lambda - \lambda_i$ indicates that the magnetostriction is assumed to be measured from the ideal demagnetized state; $\bar{\theta}$ is again the angle that the applied field makes with a $\langle 110 \rangle$ axis). Part of the disparity between theory

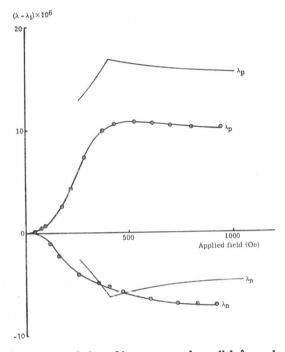

Fig. 5.10. The magnetostriction of iron measured parallel, λ_p, and normal, λ_n, to the applied field for $\bar{\theta} = 30°$ as calculated by BIRSS and LEE [1961] and as measured by HONDA and MASIYAMA [1926].

and experiment revealed by these curves undoubtedly arises because no special precautions were taken to relate measurements to a unique demagnetized state. However, the absence of discontinuous changes in slope in the experimental curves, which was also observed by LEE and BIRSS, must be ascribed to other causes, such as the presence of closure domains (ignored in the calculations) and the departure of the shape of the specimen from that of a perfect oblate spheroid.

§4. GALVANOMAGNETIC EFFECTS:

MAGNETORESISTANCE AND THE HALL EFFECT

The description of galvanomagnetic effects in ferromagnetic or ferrimagnetic crystals provides an example of the application of symmetry considerations to simplify the forms of tensors characterizing transport properties. In the absence of a magnetic field, the relation between electric current density J and electric field E is given by equation (1.2d). When a saturating magnetic field, $H = H\alpha$, with components $H_i = H\alpha_i$, is applied to a crystal, the relationship between E and J is still linear but the resistivity ϱ_{ij} must be replaced in (1.2d) by a tensor $\varrho_{ij}(\alpha)$ which depends on the direction cosines, α_i, of the magnetization vector, so that

$$E_i = \varrho_{ij}(\alpha)J_j. \tag{5.171}$$

The components $\varrho_{ij}(\alpha)$ may (like the V_{ij}^0 of §3) be expressed as series expansions in ascending powers of the α_i: however, terms of odd order in the α_i may not be discarded as in (5.82), for the phenomena under consideration are now transport (i.e. dynamic) properties. Thus,

$$\varrho_{ij}(\alpha) = a_{ij} + a_{kij}\alpha_k + a_{klij}\alpha_k\alpha_l + a_{klmij}\alpha_k\alpha_l\alpha_m$$
$$+ a_{klmnij}\alpha_k\alpha_l\alpha_m\alpha_n + \cdots \tag{5.172}$$

or alternatively

$$E_i = a_{ij}J_j + a_{kij}J_j\alpha_k + a_{klij}J_j\alpha_k\alpha_l + a_{klmij}J_j\alpha_k\alpha_l\alpha_m$$
$$+ a_{klmnij}J_j\alpha_k\alpha_l\alpha_m\alpha_n + \cdots. \tag{5.173}$$

Since the E_i and the J_i are the components of a polar i-vector and a polar c-vector respectively, the galvanomagnetic tensors a_{ij}, a_{klij}, a_{klmnij}, ..., of even rank, are polar c-tensors whilst the galvanomagnetic tensors a_{kij}, a_{klmij}, ..., of odd rank, are axial i-tensors.

Equation (5.173) indicates that the electric field E depends (through the α_i) upon the direction of the saturating magnetic field but not on its magnitude. Such a formulation is appropriate to a true saturation property, such as the spontaneous magneto-striction, but it must be used with caution when dealing with galvanomagnetic phenomena. Even non-magnetic substances exhibit galvanomagnetic effects, and there are two contributions to these effects in a ferromagnetic or ferrimagnetic material – one arising from the presence of the spontaneous magnetization and the other from the magnetic field. The former contribution, which is described by (5.173), is present even in a demagnetized state and is responsible for the anomalous temperature dependence of the resistivity, whilst the latter contribution vanishes in zero magnetic field†.

The tensor $\varrho_{ij}(\alpha)$, being of second rank, may, of course, be divided into its symmetrical and antisymmetrical parts,

$$\varrho_{ij}^s(\alpha) = \tfrac{1}{2}[\varrho_{ij}(\alpha) + \varrho_{ji}(\alpha)] \quad \text{and} \quad \varrho_{ij}^a(\alpha) = \tfrac{1}{2}[\varrho_{ij}(\alpha) - \varrho_{ji}(\alpha)],$$

and it is customary to consider these separately. According to Onsager's theorem (Ch. 2, § 6) as applied to the saturated crystal,

$$\varrho_{ij}(\alpha) = \varrho_{ji}(-\alpha), \tag{5.174}$$

so that the symmetrical part of the tensor $\varrho_{ij}(\alpha)$ must be an even function of the α_i and the antisymmetrical part an odd function. Thus

$$\varrho_{ij}^s(\alpha) = a_{ij} + a_{klij}\alpha_k\alpha_l + a_{klmnij}\alpha_k\alpha_l\alpha_m\alpha_n + \cdots \tag{5.175}$$

† For the Hall effect these two contributions are often referred to as the 'extraordinary' and the 'ordinary' (i.e. non-magnetic) effects respectively.

whilst
$$\varrho_{ij}^{a}(\alpha) = a_{klj}\alpha_k + a_{klmij}\alpha_k\alpha_l\alpha_m + \cdots. \tag{5.176}$$

Similarly, the resultant electric field, E, can be separated into two parts, E^{a} with components $E_i^{a} = \varrho_{ij}^{a}(\alpha)J_j$ and E^{s} with components $E_i^{s} = \varrho_{ij}^{s}(\alpha)J_j$. The physical distinction between the fields E^{a} and E^{s} is that E^{a} changes sign when the saturating magnetic field – and therefore the magnetization – is reversed whilst E^{s} remains unchanged. For *isotropic* media, the $a_{klj}J_j\alpha_k$ of (5.173) constitute the three components of a vector $a_{123}J \times \alpha$: the leading term in E^{a} thus represents an electric field which is perpendicular to both the current density and the magnetic field and E^{a} may therefore be regarded as the electric field associated with a generalized Hall effect. The $a_{klij}J_j\alpha_k\alpha_l$ of (5.173) constitute, for isotropic media, the three components of a vector $a_{1122}J + 2a_{2323}(J \cdot \alpha)\alpha$ which has no component perpendicular to both the current density and the magnetic field – indeed when J and α are perpendicular this vector is parallel to J. E^{s} may therefore be regarded as the electric field associated with a generalized magnetoresistance. For anisotropic media, E^{a} is attributed to a generalized Hall effect and is always perpendicular to the current (but not necessarily to the magnetic field) whilst E^{s} is attributed to a generalized magnetoresistance, although, of course, it is not always parallel to the current.

In experimental investigations of galvanomagnetic effects, a uniform current density is usually obtained by applying a voltage between the opposite ends of a rod-shaped specimen that has been cut so as to be parallel to a known crystallographic direction. It is then possible to measure the potential difference developed in any direction as the saturating magnetic field is applied in various directions. Measurements of the potential difference parallel to the rod-shaped specimen permit the calculation of an effective longitudinal resistivity $\varrho(\alpha, \beta)$ given by

$$\varrho(\alpha, \beta) = \frac{E_i J_i}{J_j J_j} = \varrho_{ij}(\alpha)\,\beta_i\beta_j, \tag{5.177a}$$

where the β_i are the direction cosines of the axis of the rod. However, since $\varrho_{ij}^a(\alpha)\beta_i\beta_j = 0$, the antisymmetrical part of the tensor $\varrho_{ij}(\alpha)$ cannot contribute to $\varrho(\alpha, \beta)$ and

$$\varrho(\alpha, \beta) = \varrho_{ij}^s(\alpha)\beta_i\beta_j. \tag{5.177b}$$

The effective longitudinal resistivity is therefore an even function of the α_i which may be correctly called the magnetoresistivity.

§ 4.1. *Galvanomagnetic Effects in Cubic Crystals*

For the classical crystal class **m3m**, the forms of general polar tensors of second and fourth ranks and axial tensors of third rank may be obtained immediately from Table 4, the columns appropriate to i-tensors being used for this purpose as indicated in Ch. 3, § 3.2. For axial tensors of fifth rank and polar tensors of sixth rank the relations corresponding to (5.3a) and (5.3b) are given (FIESCHI and FUMI [1953]) by

$$xxxyz(20) = -xxxzy = yyyzx = -zzzyx$$
$$= zzzxy = -yyyxz, \tag{5.3d}$$

and by (5.3c). For the galvanomagnetic tensors a_{ij}, a_{klij}, a_{klmnij}, of even rank, the particularization imposed by intrinsic symmetry is the same as for the magnetoelastic tensors c_{ij}, c_{klij}, c_{klmnij} of (5.82b), except that the galvanomagnetic tensors are also necessarily symmetrical in the suffixes i and j since $\varrho_{ij}^s(\alpha)$ is a symmetrical tensor. The forms of the tensors a_{ij}, a_{klij}, a_{klmnij} may therefore be obtained from (5.89), (5.90) and (5.91), and may be displayed by setting out the suffixes of the non-vanishing components in the following schemes:

ij	11	22	33	23	32	31	13	12	21
	11	11	11						

$$(5.178)$$

$\alpha_k\alpha_l$ \\ ij	11	22	33	23	32	31	13	12	21
α_1^2	1111	1122	1122						
α_2^2	1122	1111	1122						
α_3^2	1122	1122	1111						
$\alpha_2\alpha_3$				2323	2323				
$\alpha_3\alpha_1$						2323	2323		
$\alpha_1\alpha_2$								2323	2323

$$(5.179)$$

$\alpha_k\alpha_l\alpha_m\alpha_n$ \\ ij	11	22	33	23	32	31	13	12	21
α_1^4	111111	111122	111122						
α_2^4	111122	111111	111122						
α_3^4	111122	111122	111111						
$\alpha_2^2\alpha_3^2$	112233	112211	112211						
$\alpha_3^2\alpha_1^2$	112211	112233	112211						
$\alpha_1^2\alpha_2^2$	112211	112211	112233						
$\alpha_1^2\alpha_2\alpha_3$				112323	112323				
$\alpha_2^2\alpha_3\alpha_1$						112323	112323		
$\alpha_3^2\alpha_1\alpha_2$								112323	112323
$\alpha_2^3\alpha_3$				111212	111212				
$\alpha_3^3\alpha_1$						111212	111212		
$\alpha_1^3\alpha_2$								111212	111212
$\alpha_3^3\alpha_2$				111212	111212				
$\alpha_1^3\alpha_3$						111212	111212		
$\alpha_2^3\alpha_1$								111212	111212

$$(5.180)$$

The forms of the tensors a_{kij}, a_{klmij}, which are antisymmetrical in the suffixes i and j, may be displayed in a similar way as follows:

α_k \\ ij	11	22	33	23	32	31	13	12	21
α_1				123	−123				
α_2						123	−123		
α_3								123	−123

$$(5.181)$$

$\alpha_k\alpha_l\alpha_m$ \\ ij	11	22	33	23	32	31	13	12	21
α_1^3				11123	− 11123				
α_2^3						11123	− 11123		
α_3^3								11123	− 11123
$\alpha_1\alpha_2^2$				12223	− 12223				
$\alpha_2\alpha_3^2$						12223	− 12223		
$\alpha_3\alpha_1^2$								12223	− 12223
$\alpha_1\alpha_3^2$				12223	− 12223				
$\alpha_2\alpha_1^2$						12223	− 12223		
$\alpha_3\alpha_2^2$								12223	− 12223

$$(5.182)$$

The magnetoresistivity is given by equation (5.177b), that is by

$$
\begin{aligned}
\varrho(\alpha, \beta) = {}& a'_{11} + a'_{1111}S(\alpha_1^2\beta_1^2) + a'_{1122}S(\alpha_1^2\beta_2^2 + \alpha_2^2\beta_1^2) \\
& + 2a'_{2323}S(\alpha_1\alpha_2\beta_1\beta_2) + a'_{111111}S(\alpha_1^4\beta_1^2) \\
& + a'_{111122}S(\alpha_1^4\beta_2^2 + \alpha_2^4\beta_1^2) + a'_{112233}S(\alpha_1^2\alpha_2^2\beta_3^2) \\
& + a'_{112211}S(\alpha_1^2\alpha_2^2\beta_1^2 + \alpha_1^2\alpha_2^2\beta_2^2) + 2a'_{112323}S(\alpha_1\alpha_2\alpha_3^2\beta_1\beta_2) \\
& + 2a'_{111212}S(\alpha_1^3\alpha_2\beta_1\beta_2 + \alpha_1\alpha_2^3\beta_1\beta_2),
\end{aligned} \tag{5.183}
$$

where the primed galvanomagnetic coefficients correspond to the schemes of subscripts set out in (5.178), (5.179) and (5.180) and to the summations implied therein. Equation (5.183) is identical in form to the expression for the spontaneous magnetostriction in cubic crystals, for, by using the relations

$$
\begin{aligned}
S(\alpha_1^2\beta_2^2 + \alpha_2^2\beta_1^2) &= 1 - S(\alpha_1^2\beta_1^2), \\
S(\alpha_1^4\beta_2^2 + \alpha_2^4\beta_1^2) &= 1 - S(\alpha_1^4\beta_1^2) - 2\,S(\alpha_1^2\alpha_2^2), \\
S(\alpha_1^2\alpha_2^2\beta_3^2) &= S(\alpha_1^4\beta_1^2) - S(\alpha_1^2\beta_1^2) + S(\alpha_1^2\alpha_2^2), \\
S(\alpha_1^2\alpha_2^2\beta_1^2 + \alpha_1^2\alpha_2^2\beta_2^2) &= S(\alpha_1^2\beta_1^2) - S(\alpha_1^4\beta_1^2), \\
S(\alpha_1^3\alpha_2\beta_1\beta_2 + \alpha_1\alpha_2^3\beta_1\beta_2) &= S(\alpha_1\alpha_2\beta_1\beta_2) - S(\alpha_1\alpha_2\alpha_3^2\beta_1\beta_2),
\end{aligned} \tag{5.184}
$$

it may be readily verified that the right-hand side of (5.183) is identical to the right-hand side of (5.96) provided that

$$
\begin{aligned}
B_0 &= a'_{11} + a'_{1122} + a'_{111122}, \\
B_1 &= a'_{1111} - a'_{1122} + a'_{112211} - a'_{112233}, \\
B_2 &= 2a'_{2323} + 2a'_{111212}, \\
B_3 &= a'_{112233} - 2a'_{111122}, \\
B_4 &= a'_{111111} - a'_{111122} - a'_{112211} + a'_{112233}, \\
B_5 &= 2a'_{112323} - 2a'_{111212}.
\end{aligned} \tag{5.185}
$$

§ 4.2. *Galvanomagnetic Effects in Hexagonal Crystals*

For the classical crystal class **6/mmm**, the forms of general polar tensors of second and fourth ranks and axial tensors of third rank may again be obtained immediately from Table 4, the columns appropriate to i-tensors being used for this purpose as indicated in Ch. 3, § 3.2. For axial tensors of fifth rank and polar tensors of sixth rank the relations corresponding to (5.10a) and (5.10b) are given (FIESCHI and FUMI [1953]) by

$$xxxyz(xxxy:5) = -xxyxz - xyxxz - yxxxz,$$

$$yyxyz(yyxy:5) = -xxyxz,$$

$$yxyyz(yxyy:5) = -xyxxz,$$

$$xyyyz(xyyy:5) = -yxxxz,$$

$$yyyxz(yyyx:5) = xxyxz + xyxxz + yxxxz,$$

$$yxzzz(20) = -xyzzz,$$

$$(5.10d)$$

and by (5.10c). For the galvanomagnetic tensors a_{ij}, a_{klij}, a_{klmnij}, of even rank, the particularization imposed by intrinsic symmetry is again the same as for the magnetoelastic tensors c_{ij}, c_{klij}, c_{klmnij} of (5.82b), except that the galvanomagnetic tensors are also necessarily symmetrical in the suffixes i and j since $\varrho_{ij}^s(\alpha)$ is a symmetrical tensor. The forms of the tensors a_{ij}, a_{klij}, a_{klmnij} may therefore be obtained from (5.100), (5.101) and (5.102), and may be displayed by setting out the suffixes of the non-vanishing components in the following schemes:

ij	11	22	33	23	32	31	13	12	21
	11	22	33						

(5.186)

$\alpha_k\alpha_l$ \\ ij	11	22	33	23	32	31	13	12	21
α_1^2	1111	1122	1133						
α_2^2	1122	1111	1133						
α_3^2	3311	3311	3333						
$\alpha_2\alpha_3$				2323	2323				
$\alpha_3\alpha_1$						2323	2323		
$\alpha_1\alpha_2$								1212	1212

(5.187a)

$\alpha_k\alpha_l\alpha_m\alpha_n$ \\ ij	11	22	33	23	32	31	13	12	21
α_1^4	111111	111122	111133						
α_2^4	222211	222222	111133						
α_3^4	333311	333311	333333						
$\alpha_2^2\alpha_3^2$	223311	223322	223333						
$\alpha_3^2\alpha_1^2$	223322	223311	223333						
$\alpha_1^2\alpha_2^2$	112211	112222	112233						
$\alpha_1^2\alpha_2\alpha_3$				112323	112323				
$\alpha_2^2\alpha_3\alpha_1$						112323	112323		
$\alpha_3^2\alpha_1\alpha_2$								331212	331212
$\alpha_2^3\alpha_3$				112323	112323				
$\alpha_3^3\alpha_1$						333131	333131		
$\alpha_1^3\alpha_2$								111212	111212
$\alpha_3^3\alpha_2$				333131	333131				
$\alpha_1^3\alpha_3$						112323	112323		
$\alpha_2^3\alpha_1$								222121	222121

(5.188a)

where

$$a'_{1111} = a'_{1122} + a'_{1212} \tag{5.187b}$$

and

$$a'_{111122} = 2a'_{111111} - 3a'_{222222} + a'_{112211},$$

$$a'_{112233} = 2a'_{111133},$$

$$a'_{222211} = 3a'_{111111} - 4a'_{222222} + a'_{112211},$$

$$a'_{223322} = a'_{223311} + a'_{331212}, \tag{5.188b}$$

$$a'_{112222} = 6a'_{111111} - 6a'_{222222} + a'_{112211},$$

$$a'_{111212} = -4a'_{111111} + 6a'_{222222} - a'_{112211},$$

$$a'_{222121} = 2a'_{222222} - a'_{112211}.$$

The forms of the tensors a_{kij}, a_{klmij}, which are antisymmetrical in the suffixes i and j, may be displayed in a similar way as follows:

α_k \ ij	11	22	33	23	32	31	13	12	21
α_1				123	−123				
α_2						123	−123		
α_3								312	−312

$, \quad (5.189)$

$\alpha_k\alpha_l\alpha_m$ \\ ij	11 22 33	23	32	31	13	12	21
α_1^3		11123	-11123				
α_2^3				11123	-11123		
α_3^3						33312	-33312
$\alpha_1\alpha_2^2$		11123	-11123				
$\alpha_2\alpha_3^2$				23313	-23313		
$\alpha_3\alpha_1^2$						11312	-11312
$\alpha_1\alpha_3^2$		23313	-23313				
$\alpha_2\alpha_1^2$				11123	-11123		
$\alpha_3\alpha_2^2$						11312	-11312

$$(5.190)$$

By using these schemes of coefficients and equation (5.177b) it may again be readily verified that the magnetoresistivity, $\varrho(\alpha, \beta)$, can be expressed in the same form as the spontaneous magneto-striction.

CHAPTER 6

CONCLUSION

The aim of this book has been to explain how the symmetry of magnetic and non-magnetic crystals is specified and to survey the various ways in which knowledge of the symmetry of a crystal may be used to simplify the forms of the tensors that represent the various macroscopic physical properties of the crystal. The method adopted throughout to effect this simplification has been successively to impose on to a tensor of the lowest symmetry the condition that it be invariant with respect to the transformations of the appropriate (e.g. crystallographic) point group. This method is applicable, in principle, to tensors of any rank. Moreover, the forms of property tensors of ranks 0, 1, 2, 3 and 4 may be readily obtained from Tables 4 and 7, whilst, for tensors of ranks 5 and 6, Table 7 may be used in conjunction with the results of FIESCHI and FUMI [1953]. It is important, however, that some mention be made of an alternative method of obtaining the forms of property tensors, due mainly to SIROTIN [1960a,b, 1961].

Instead of successively imposing the limitations of crystal symmetry on to a property tensor of the lowest symmetry, it is possible to reverse the procedure by adding, to a tensor of the highest symmetry, terms of lower symmetry until eventually the required property tensor is obtained. The required tensor is therefore plotted in the form of a sum of a few tensors – called basic tensors – the symmetry of which is not less than that of the property tensor itself. To use this method it is necessary to have a sufficient supply of basic tensors available of all possible symmetries, and it is also necessary to be able to determine which of these tensors should be used to plot the required tensor. A method that can readily produce basic tensors of any symmetry is discussed by SIROTIN [1960a]. The number and symmetry of the basic tensors needed for plotting the general form of a tensor of given symmetry are provided by the schemes for the successive expansion of group tensor spaces and by the tables for the dimensions of these spaces given by SIROTIN [1960b]. A later paper (SIROTIN [1961]) illustrates the method actually used for plotting tensors of given intrinsic and crystallographic symmetry. It is to be expected that this method will find increasing application for tensors of higher rank than the sixth, especially in relation to crystals of high symmetry, which are dealt with least efficiently by the conventional methods.

Another interesting development that has not hitherto been mentioned is the extension of the concept of symmetry in space-time to that of double (triple, and so forth) antisymmetry. The operation denoted by R has throughout been taken to be that of time-inversion. In general, however, R might be understood to represent a change in the sign of any attribute that is unaffected by the normal spatial symmetry operations and that can be characterized by associating with it either a plus or a minus sign. When generalized in such a way, the operation represented by R may be referred to as an operation of anti-identity and, in fact, the first concrete manifestation of this concept was the identification of an operation of anti-identity not with time-inversion but with the operation of interchanging black and white motifs in the bi-coloured patterns discussed in the Preface. The generalization of symmetry necessitated by the introduction of an anti-identity operation is often referred to as antisymmetry. Another concrete manifestation of antisymmetry is the identification of an operation of anti-identity with the operation of charge-reversal (NERO-NOVA and BELOV [1959, 1960]): this identification leads to a classification of crystals into 32 'non-electrical' classes and 32 + 58

= 90 'electrical' classes that are analogous to (and, mathematically, isomorphous with) the 32 non-magnetic and 90 magnetic classes. Similarly, if the operation represented by R is assumed to reverse simultaneously the sign of time (and hence magnetic moment) and charge, then $32 + 32 + 58 = 122$ classes of 'magneto-electric symmetry' (SHUVALOV [1962]) are obtained that are again isomorphous with the 122 non-magnetic and magnetic classes.

The objection to these classifications that use other anti-identity operations is, as indicated in Ch. 3, § 4, that they are of little value unless there is some method of ascertaining, a priori, the symmetry of crystals with respect to charge-reversal, simultaneous charge-reversal and time-inversion, and combinations of these operations with spatial symmetry operations. In practice this information would be obtained by studying the property tensors themselves, since neutron diffraction experiments reveal the magnetic, rather than the electrical, structure of a crystal. The advantage of a formulation in terms of time-inversion is that there is an *independent* method by which the symmetry of property tensors can be established. The same objection can be raised to the further generalization of the concept of antisymmetry to double (and higher degrees of) antisymmetry. In double antisymmetry (ZAMORZAEV and SOKOLOV [1957]; SHUVALOV and BELOV [1962]) the plus and minus signs are replaced by ordered pairs of signs, that is by $(+ +)$, $(+ -)$, $(- +)$ or $(- -)$, and two anti-identity operations are allowed, one that reverses the first sign only and the other the second only. There are 116 essentially new classes of double antisymmetry, just as there are 58 essentially new classes of (single) antisymmetry. Further extensions are possible with larger numbers of plus and minus signs and, consequently, anti-identity operations but it seems to the author, for the reasons outlined above, that they are likely to remain of purely formal significance.

Throughout the book the only tensors that have been considered are those that represent steady-state properties, since limitations of space do not permit an extension to more general cases.

It may be noted, however, that cases in which the physical influence or influences vary sinusoidally with time are, in particular, often important. For example, much interest is currently being shown in the propagation of light in crystals subject to external physical influences, e.g. magneto-optical and electro-optical effects (LANDAU and LIFSHITZ [1960]). The description of such effects is complicated even for lossless crystals and a satisfactory tensor formulation that can accommodate such features as nonlinear optical effects (including harmonic generation, mixing and associated attenuation effects) is not yet fully developed. The necessity for such a formulation is emphasized by recent experiments using as light sources pulsed lasers that can produce beams in which the electric field strength exceeds 10^5 volts/cm. Second harmonic generation has been observed in a number of materials (FRANKEN et al. [1961]; BASS et al. [1962]; GIORDMAINE [1962]; MAKER et al. [1962]; LAX et al. [1962]; TERHUNE et al. [1962]) and third harmonic generation has been detected in calcite by TERHUNE et al. [1962]. BASS et al. [1962] have observed the production of a sum frequency in triglycine sulphate by using two ruby lasers operating at different temperatures.

Much of the active research on the optical properties of crystals is at present being carried out in the U.S.S.R. Soviet scientists are currently studying not only optical activity (FEDOROV et al. [1962]), and electro-optical effects (SHAMBUROV [1962]) but also the propagation of light in absorbing crystals (KHAPALYUK [1962a,b]), in absorbing magnetic crystals (TOMILCHIK [1961]) and in crystals that are both magnetically anisotropic and optically active (BOKUT [1961]). It seems likely that, both experimentally and theoretically, the study of optical effects in crystals will provide a fruitful field of research for some time to come.

APPENDIX

A more rigorous proof than that advanced in Ch. 3, § 2 of the fact that it is both a necessary and a sufficient condition for $\mathcal{M}$ to be a group is given below. Consider the set of products of the form $\underline{S}_i^0 S_h$ or $\underline{S}_i^0 S_i$ formed by multiplying a particular member $\underline{S}_i^0$ of the set $R(\mathcal{G} - \mathcal{H})$ with each element of the group $\mathcal{M}$ in turn. Since $\mathcal{M}$ is a finite group, these products are all different and they may be placed in a one-to-one correspondence with the elements of the group $\mathcal{M}$. Products of the form $\underline{S}_i^0 S_h$ cannot be in the sub-group $\mathcal{H}$ (i.e. $\underline{S}_i^0 S_h \notin \mathcal{H}$) since they are expressible in the form RS_g. Further, R commutes with all the S_g and $R^2 = 1$ (as applied to the crystal), so that $\underline{S}_i^0 S_i = S_i^0 S_i$, whence $\underline{S}_i^0 S_i \notin R(\mathcal{G} - \mathcal{H})$. Thus, since the total number of products of both forms is equal to the number of elements in the group $\mathcal{M}$, those of the form $\underline{S}_i^0 S_h$ may be placed in a one-to-one correspondence with members of the set $R(\mathcal{G} - \mathcal{H})$, whilst those of the form $\underline{S}_i^0 S_i$ may be placed in a one-to-one correspondence with the elements of the sub-group $\mathcal{H}$. This can only be done if the number of elements in the sub-group $\mathcal{H}$ is the same as the number of members in the set $R(\mathcal{G} - \mathcal{H})$, from which it follows that the ratio of the order of the group $\mathcal{G}$ to the order of the sub-group $\mathcal{H}$ is 2, i.e. the index of the sub-group is 2. Hence, a *necessary* condition for $M = \mathcal{H} + R(\mathcal{G} - \mathcal{H})$ to be a group is that $\mathcal{H}$ be a sub-group of $\mathcal{G}$ of index 2, and consequently only such sub-groups need be considered.

The requirement that $\mathcal{H}$ be a sub-group of $\mathcal{G}$ of index 2 is also a *sufficient* condition for $\mathcal{M}$ to be a group. This follows directly if the set $M = \mathcal{H} + R(\mathcal{G} - \mathcal{H})$ can be shown to be a closed set, for the associative property is obvious, and it is not necessary to prove the existence of a unit element or an inverse when the number of elements is finite. By considering products of elements of the group $\mathcal{G}$ with a particular element S_h^0 of the sub-group $\mathcal{H}$, it may be seen that products of the form $S_h^0 S_h$ (or $S_{ii} S_h^0$) may be put into a one-to-one correspondence with the elements of the sub-group $\mathcal{H}$, whilst products of the form $S_h^0 S_i$ (or $S_i S_h^0$) may be put into a one-to-one correspondence with members of the set $\mathcal{G} - \mathcal{H}$. Further, since the index of the sub-group $\mathcal{H}$ is 2, the number of products of the form $S_i^0 S_h$ (or $S_h S_i^0$) is equal to the number of products of the form $S_i^0 S_i$ (or $S_i S_i^0$); whence the latter must belong to the sub-group $\mathcal{H}$ since the former belong to the set $\mathcal{G} - \mathcal{H}$. Hence, of the possible products of two members of the set M (sic), all products of two S_h's are elements of the sub-group $\mathcal{H}$, and all products of an S_h and an $\underline{S}_i$ are members of the set $R(\mathcal{G} - \mathcal{H})$. The remaining products – those of two $\underline{S}_i$'s – are elements of the sub-group $\mathcal{H}$, since any product of two $\underline{S}_i$'s is identical to the product of the two corresponding S_i's. It has thus been shown that any product of two members of the set M is itself a member of the set, so that the set M must constitute a group.

REFERENCES

Akulov N.S., 1929, Z. Phys. **57** 249.

Akulov, N.S., 1931, Z. Phys. **69** 78.

Akulov, N.S., 1956, Dokl. Akad. Nauk S.S.S.R. **106** 31.

Astrov, D.N., 1960, J. Exp. Theor. Phys. U.S.S.R. **38** 984 [translation: Soviet Physics – JETP **11** (1960) 708].

Barnier, Y., R. Pauthenet and G. Rimet, 1961, C.R. Acad. Sci. (Paris) **252** 2839.

Bass, M., P.A. Franken, A.E. Hill, C.W. Peters and G. Weinreich, 1962, Phys. Rev. Letters **8** 18.

Becker, R., and W. Döring, 1939, Ferromagnetismus (Berlin, Springer-Verlag) [Photo-lithoprint reproduction, 1943, Ann Arbor, Michigan, Edwards Bros.].

Bickford, L.R., 1949a, Phys. Rev. **75** 1298.

Bickford, L.R., 1949b, Phys. Rev. **76** 137.

Bickford, L.R., J. Pappis and J.L. Stull, 1955, Phys. Rev. **99** 121.

Birss, R.R., 1960, Proc. Phys. Soc. **75** 8.

Birss, R.R., 1962, Proc. Phys. Soc. **79** 946.

Birss, R.R., and E.W. Lee, 1961, Proc. Roy. Soc. A **263** 387.

Bokut, B.V., 1961, Kristallografiya **6** 671 [translation: Soviet Physics – Crystallography **6** (1962) 540].

Borovik–Romanov, A.S., 1959, J. Exp. Theor. Phys. U.S.S.R. **36** 1954 [translation: Soviet Physics – JETP **9** (1959) 1390].

Borovik–Romanov, A.S., 1960, J. Exp. Theor. Phys. U.S.S.R. **38** 1088 [translation: Soviet Physics – JETP **11** (1960) 786].

Borovik–Romanov, A.S., G.G. Aleksanjan and E.G. Rudashevskij, 1962, International Conference on Magnetism and Crystallography, Kyoto, Japan, paper 155.

Borovik–Romanov, A.S., and M.P. Orlova, 1956, J. Exp. Theor. Phys. U.S.S.R. **31** 579 [translation: Soviet Physics – JETP **4** (1956) 531].

Bozorth, R.M., 1951, Ferromagnetism (New York, Van Nostrand).

Bozorth, R.M., 1954, Phys. Rev. **96** 311.

Bozorth, R.M., and R.W. Hamming, 1953, Phys. Rev. **89** 865.

Bozorth, R.M., and R.C. Sherwood, 1954, Phys. Rev. **94** 1439.

Bozorth, R.M., and T. Wakiyama, 1962, J. Phys. Soc. Japan **17** 1669.

Buerger, M.J., 1956, Elementary Crystallography (New York, Wiley).

Callen, E.R., and H.B. Callen, 1960, J. Phys. Chem. Solids 16 310.

Callen, E.R., and H.B. Callen, 1963, Phys. Rev. 129 578.

Carr, W.J., 1959, Magnetic Properties of Metals and Alloys (Cleveland, Ohio, Amer. Soc. for Metals).

Chaudron, G., and H. Forestier, 1924, C.R. Acad. Sci. (Paris) 179 763.

Chevenard, P., 1921a, C.R. Acad. Sci. (Paris) 172 320.

Chevenard, P., 1921b, C.R. Acad. Sci. (Paris) 172 594.

Clark, A.E., B. DeSavage, W. Coleman and E.R. Callen, 1963, J. appl. Phys. 34S 1296.

Corner, W.D., W.C. Roe and K.N.R. Taylor, 1962, Proc. Phys. Soc. 80 927.

Corson, E.M., 1953, Introduction to Tensors, Spinors and Relativistic Wave-Equations (London, Blackie).

Curie, P., 1908, Œuvres de Pierre Curie (Paris, Société Française de Physique).

De Groot, S.R., 1951, Thermodynamics of Irreversible Processes (Amsterdam, North-Holland).

De Klerk, J., and M.J.P. Musgrave, 1955, Proc. Phys. Soc. B 68 81.

Doraiswami, M.S., 1947, Proc. Indian Acad. Sci. A 25 413.

Dzialoshinskii, I.E., 1957, J. Exp. Theor. Phys. U.S.S.R. 32 1547 [translation: Soviet Physics – JETP 5 (1957) 1259].

Fedorov, F.I., B.V. Bokut and A.F. Konstantinova, 1962, Kristallografiya 7 910 [translation: Soviet Physics – Crystallography 7 (1963) 738].

Fieschi, R., 1957, Physica 24 972.

Fieschi, R., and F.G. Fumi, 1953, Nuovo Cim. 10 865.

Folen, V.J., G.T. Rado and E.W. Stalder, 1961, Phys. Rev. Letters 6 607.

Fowler, R.H., 1936, Statistical Mechanics (Cambridge, University Press).

Franken, P.A., A.E. Hill, C.W. Peters and G. Weinreich, 1961, Phys. Rev. Letters 7 118.

Fumi, F.G., 1952, Nuovo Cim. 9 739.

Gans, R., and E. Czerlinski, 1932, Schr. Königsb. gelehrt. Ges. Naturw. Kl. 9 1.

Gans, R., and J. von Harlem, 1933, Ann. Phys. (Leipzig) 16 162.

Giordmaine, J.A., 1962, Phys. Rev. Letters 8 19.

Graham, C.D., 1958, Phys. Rev. 112 1117.

Graham, C.D., 1962, J. Phys. Soc. Japan 17 1310.

Heisenberg, W., 1931, Z. Phys. 69 287.

Honda, K., and S. Kaya, 1926, Sci. Rep. Tôhoku Univ. 15 721.

Honda, K., and Y. Masiyama, 1926, Sci. Rep. Tôhoku Univ. 15 755.

Jeffreys, H., and B.S. Jeffreys, 1950, Methods of Mathematical Physics, second edition (Cambridge, University Press).

Joel, N., and W.A. Wooster, 1958, Nature (London) 182 1079.

Kaya, S., 1933, Z. Phys. 84 705.

Khapalyuk, A.P., 1962a, Kristallografiya **7** 581 [translation: Soviet Physics – Crystallography **7** (1963) 468].

Khapalyuk, A.P., 1962b, Kristallografiya **7** 724 [translation: Soviet Physics – Crystallography **7** (1963) 588].

Köster, W., and W.Schmidt, 1934, Arch. Eisenhüttenw. **8** 25.

Landau, L.D., and E.M.Lifshitz, 1960, Electrodynamics of Continuous Media (Oxford, Pergamon).

Laval, J., 1951a, C.R.Acad. Sci. (Paris) **232** 1947.

Laval, J., 1951b, Inst. Inter. Phys. Solvay, Conseil Phys. 9th Conseil, Brussels 273.

Laval, J., 1954a, C.R.Acad. Sci. (Paris) **238** 1773.

Laval, J., 1954b, Bull. Soc. franç. Minéral. Crist. **77** 219.

Lawton, H., 1949, Proc. Camb. Phil. Soc. **45** 145.

Lawton, H., and K.H.Stewart, 1948, Proc. Roy. Soc. A **193** 72.

Lax, B., J.G.Mavroides and D.F.Edwards, 1962, Phys. Rev. Letters **8** 166.

Le Corre, Y., 1953a, Thesis, University of Paris.

Le Corre, Y., 1953b, C.R.Acad. Sci. (Paris) **236** 1903.

Le Corre, Y., 1953c, Bull. Soc. franç. Minéral. Crist. **76** 464.

Le Corre, Y., 1954a, Bull. Soc. franç. Minéral. Crist. **77** 1363.

Le Corre, Y., 1954b, Bull. Soc. franç. Minéral. Crist. **77** 1393.

Le Corre. Y., 1955, Bull. Soc. franç. Minéral. Crist. **78** 33.

Lee, E.W., 1955a, Rep. Prog. Phys. **18** 184.

Lee, E.W., 1955b, Proc. Phys. Soc. A **68** 65.

Lee, E.W., and R.R.Birss, 1961, Proc. Phys. Soc. **78** 391.

Lomer, W.M., 1963, private communication.

Love, A.E.H., 1944, A Treatise on the Mathematical Theory of Elasticity, fourth edition (Cambridge, University Press).

McLachlan, N.W., 1955, Bessel Functions for Engineers, second edition (Oxford, Clarendon Press).

MacRobert, T.M., 1927, Spherical Harmonics (London, Methuen).

McSkimin, H.J., A.J.Williams and R.M.Bozorth, 1954, Phys. Rev. **95** 616.

Maker, P.D., R.W.Terhune, M.Nisenoff and C.M.Savage, 1962, Phys. Rev. Letters **8** 21.

Morse, P.M., and H.Feshbach, 1953, Methods of Theoretical Physics (New York, McGraw-Hill).

Mueller, H., 1940, Phys. Rev. **58** 805.

Neronova, N.N., and N.V.Belov, 1959, Dokl. Akad. Nauk S.S.S.R. **129** 556 [translation: Soviet Physics – Doklady **4** (1959) 1179].

Neronova, N.N., and N.V.Belov, 1960, Kristallografiya **4** 805 [translation: Soviet Physics – Crystallography **4** (1960) 769].

Niggli, A., 1955, Z.Krist. **106** 401.

Nix, F.C., and D.MacNair, 1941, Phys. Rev. **60** 597.

Nye, J.F., 1960, Physical Properties of Crystals (Oxford, University Press).

Onsager, L., 1931a, Phys. Rev. **37** 405.

Onsager, L., 1931b, Phys. Rev. **38** 2265.

Rado, G.T., and V.J.Folen, 1962, J. appl. Phys. **33**S 1126.

Raman, C.V., and K.S.Viswanathan, 1955, Proc. Indian Acad. Sci. A **42** 1.

Rodbell, D.S., 1962, J. appl. Phys. **33**S 1126.

Seitz, F., 1940, The Modern Theory of Solids (New York, McGraw-Hill).

Shamburov, V.A., 1962, Kristallografiya **7** 730 [translation: Soviet Physics – Crystallography **7** (1963) 592].

Shuvalov, L.A., 1962, Kristallografiya **7** 520 [translation: Soviet Physics – Crystallography **7** (1963) 418].

Shuvalov, L.A., and N.V.Belov, 1962, Kristallografiya **7** 192 [translation: Soviet Physics – Crystallography **7** (1962) 150].

Sirotin, Yu.I., 1960a, Dokl. Akad. Nauk S.S.S.R. **133** 321 [translation: Soviet Physics – Doklady **5** (1960) 774].

Sirotin, Yu.I., 1960b, Kristallografiya **5** 171 [translation: Soviet Physics – Crystallography **5** (1960) 157].

Sirotin, Yu.I., 1961, Kristallografiya **6** 331 [translation: Soviet Physics – Crystallography **6** (1961) 263].

Sizoo, G.J., 1929, Z. Phys. **56** 649.

Snoek, J.L., 1947, New Developments in Ferromagnetic Materials (Amsterdam, Elsevier).

Stewart, K.H., 1954, Ferromagnetic Domains (Cambridge, University Press).

Stoner, E.C., 1950, Rep. Prog. Phys. **13** 83.

Stratton, J.A., 1941, Electromagnetic Theory (New York, McGraw-Hill).

Terhune, R.W., P.D.Maker and C.M.Savage, 1962, Phys. Rev. Letters **8** 404.

Tomilchik, L.M., 1961, Kristallografiya **6** 61 [translation: Soviet Physics – Crystallography **6** (1961) 50].

Voigt, W., 1928, Lehrbuch der Kristallphysik (Leipzig, Teubner).

Wakiyama, T., and R.M.Bozorth, 1962, J. Phys. Soc. Japan **17** 1670.

Zamorzaev, A.M., and E.I.Sokolov, 1957, Kristallografiya **2** 9 [translation: Soviet Physics – Crystallography **2** (1957) 5].

Zener, C., 1954, Phys. Rev. **96** 1335.

Zocher, H., and C.Török, 1953, Proc. Nat. Acad. Sci. **39** 681.

AUTHOR INDEX

247

SUBJECT INDEX